LEVEL
3

HEALTH & SOCIAL CARE DIPLOMA

Caroline Morris
Maria Ferreiro Peteiro

HODDER
EDUCATION
AN HACHETTE UK COMPANY

Orders: please contact Bookpoint Ltd, 130 Milton Park, Abingdon, Oxon OX14 4SB. Telephone: (44) 01235 827720. Fax: (44) 01235 400454. Lines are open from 9.00–5.00, Monday to Saturday, with a 24-hour message answering service. You can also order through our website, www.hoddereducation.co.uk.

British Library Cataloguing in Publication Data

A catalogue record for this title is available from the British Library

ISBN 978 1 4718 0662 9

First Published 2015

Impression number   10 9 8 7 6 5 4 3 2 1

Year   2018 2017 2016 2015

Hachette UK's policy is to use papers that are natural, renewable and recyclable products and made from wood grown in sustainable forests. The logging and manufacturing processes are expected to conform to the environmental regulations of the country of origin.

Cover photo © Vikram Raghuvanshi/iStockphoto.com

Typeset by Palatino LT Std Roman 10.5/13.5 by Integra Software Services Pvt. Ltd., Pondicherry, India

Printed in Slovenia for Hodder Education, an Hachette UK company.

Contents

Additional resources

Go to **www.hoddereducation.co.uk/HSCDiploma** to access a range of additional resources to support you through your study of the Level 3 Health and Social Care Diploma!

HEALTH & SOCIAL CARE LEGISLATION UPDATES

Keep up to date with all the important information on Health & Social Care assessment, regulation and legislation.

Watch this space - stay informed...

Legislation is always changing. To make sure that you are up to date with the latest changes and developments, simply click on the Legislation updates link which will guide you through all you need to know.

LEVEL 3 SAMPLE MATERIAL

Preview a chapter from the Level 3 Health & Social Care Diploma textbook, Unit HSC 3047 Support use of medication in social care settings

Access the additional HSC 3047 Support use of medication in social care settings unit.

DOWNLOAD

E-UPDATES

Keep up to date with new publishing, curriculum info and special offers.

SIGN UP

Sign up to e-updates for all the latest news on the curriculum as well as our new publishing.

Also available:

A comprehensive glossary, grids to clarify the different qualifications unit names, additional activities and a range of other resources to guide you through the Diploma!

Author biographies

Caroline Morris has a background in health and social care, having worked as a nurse, Registered Care Manager and, more recently, a teacher and lecturer, delivering qualifications in Health and Social Care since 1992. Caroline has worked with Edexcel, OU and Pearson as an external verifier in Public Services since 1997 and has been involved in writing materials and specifications for publishers and awarding organisations. Caroline is carrying out post-graduate research in education to achieve a PhD, and also undertakes inspections on behalf of awarding organisations and BAC.

Maria Ferreiro Peteiro commenced her career in health and social care in 1990 living and working in a lay community in France alongside individuals with a range of disabilities and health conditions. Maria's journey continued through a range of services and settings in the UK that included working within and leading provision for young and older adults who have learning disabilities, physical disabilities, dementia, mental health needs, challenging needs and sensory impairments. Having achieved her BA (Hons) in Health and Social Care Maria embarked on delivering a range of health and social care programmes and qualifications in both college and work based settings. Navigation round work and academic based settings led Maria to become a qualified assessor, internal and external quality assurer. Maria continues to practice in the social care field with adults, children and young people and currently holds the Chief Verifier and Chief Co-ordinator roles with awarding body OCR for a number of vocational based qualifications in Health and Social Care and Children and Young People services.

How to use this book

This book is your constant companion and covers all the mandatory and 10 optional units you need to master the knowledge and skills for the Level 3 Diploma in Health and Social Care. An additional optional unit is available online.

Key features of the book

What are you finding out?

This unit is about identifying ways you can communicate with individuals on difficult, complex and sensitive issues.

A summary of what will be covered in the unit.

SHC 31 Assessment Criteria	Unit PWCS31
AC 1.1	AC 1.1
AC 1.2	AC 1.2

Some learners may be working towards their L3 Diploma in Health and Social Care after achieving units from the L3 Certificate in Preparing to Work in Adult Social Care. The units across both qualifications share some of the same knowledge content. The table at the beginning of each mandatory unit identifies the assessment criteria that are shared between both qualifications.

LO1 Understand why effective communication is important in the work setting

AC 1.1 Identify the different reasons people communicate

Understand all the requirements of the new qualification fully with clearly stated learning outcomes and assessment criteria fully mapped to the specification.

Key terms

Acronyms are words formed from the first letters of the words in a name, e.g. NHS is an acronym for the National Health Service.

Understand important terms.

Time to think

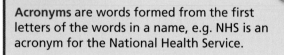

1.1 Reasons for communication

1 Think about all the people you communicate with. Reflect on your day, or think about

Learn to reflect on your own skills and experiences.

Research and investigate

1.2 Communication methods

Investigate the range of communication methods used in a specific setting, e.g. nursery or learning

Enhance your understanding of topics with research-led activities encouraging you to explore an area in more detail.

Case study

1.3 Confidentiality

Ms Smith lives with her two children in a small market town. She is to have a minor operation

See how concepts are applied in settings with real life scenarios.

Evidence activity

3.4 Ineffective communication

Give two examples of how ineffective communication may affect individuals. Think

Test your knowledge and skills with questions linked to assessment criteria to help you generate evidence as well as short tasks to help enhance your understanding of assessment criteria, and apply your knowledge in the work setting.

Useful resources

Websites
Community Care
www.community-care.co.uk

Includes references to websites, books and other various sources for further reading and research.

Acknowledgements and photo credits

Caroline Morris

The author would like to thank Stephen Halder, Publisher, Sundus Pasha, Development Editor and Sebastian Rydberg, Desk Editor at Hodder Education for all their support with the book.

Maria Ferreiro Peteiro

This book would not have been possible without the support and understanding of my husband Chris for all those long nights sitting in front of the PC. I'd also like to thank my family and friends for their encouragement and my loyal Simba for being my companion on all those long walks. A BIG thank you to the Hodder team – Stephen, Sebastian and Sundus you kept me going and knew how to get the best out of me.

Photo credits

People appearing in the following photographs are models. Any statements attributed to them are for illustrative purposes only.

Mandatory
Group A Units

Unit SHC 31

Promote communication in health, social care or children's and young people's settings

This unit is worth 3 credits

What are you finding out?

This unit is about identifying ways you can communicate with individuals on difficult, complex and sensitive issues. The unit also explores the importance of communication in health and social care settings, and looks at ways of overcoming barriers to meet individual needs and preferences in communication.

You will also learn about difficult, complex and sensitive aspects of communication which include issues of a personal nature and distressing situations. Finally, the unit looks at the importance

of confidentiality and the impact it has on your daily practice at work.

By the end of this unit you will:

1 Understand why effective communication is important in the work setting.
2 Be able to meet the communication and language needs, wishes and preferences of individuals.
3 Be able to overcome barriers to communication.
4 Be able to apply principles and practices to confidentiality.

Links to Level 3 Certificate in Preparing to Work in Adult Social Care

SHC 31 Assessment Criteria	Unit PWCS31
AC 1.1	AC 1.1
AC 1.2	AC 1.2
AC 2.2	AC 2.2
AC 3.1	AC 3.1
AC 3.2	AC 3.2
AC 3.5	AC 3.5
AC 4.1	AC 4.1
AC 4.3	AC 1.3

LO1 Understand why effective communication is important in the work setting

AC 1.1 Identify the different reasons people communicate

Communication between workers and individuals

Communication is about conveying information. This can be both verbal and non-verbal, and can range from talking to facial expressions, gestures as well as written communication. As a worker you can provide a range of information to individuals who use services so that they can understand the support that is available to meet their needs. You may need to communicate with individuals for a number of reasons, for example to find out about the activities they can access or the medication they have been prescribed. You can ask for their opinions about the service provision available and encourage them to make choices according to their needs and preferences.

Exchanging information is important in understanding the needs of an individual, so that you can provide the support they require and improve the quality of service provision. If the information exchanged is inaccurate, mistakes can be made; for example, an individual could be prescribed the wrong medication if the GP did not know they were allergic to it. If information is not exchanged, individuals may not feel supported and workers will not be able to carry out their job roles effectively.

Developing and promoting relationships

You will establish many different relationships across the sector, some of which will be formal and others more informal. For example, you will liaise with other professionals, carers, friends and family of the person you are supporting. Two-way communication is required to form relationships and establish the boundaries, and it will help to

Figure 1.1 How do you use communication to form relationships?

ensure that everyone concerned understands the purpose of the relationship and what they are aiming to achieve. See Figure 1.1.

The relationships between workers and individuals (and also between colleagues) have a significant impact on the worker's ability to provide effective care and support. Respect for each other can be developed through communication. Getting to know people by talking and listening to them will enable you to develop an understanding and awareness which will lead to stronger relationships in the long term.

Relationships are developed between workers and individuals when they communicate effectively and appropriately, and trust is established. In order to maintain effective support and achieve success, each person involved in a relationship should know their responsibilities and the other person's expectations. The target for effective communication is to form a good working relationship or partnership where each contributor is valued. This involves:

- respecting individuals' rights
- maintaining confidentiality
- considering the person's beliefs and cultural views and opinions
- supporting individuals in expressing their views and opinions
- respecting **diversity** when individuals do not behave in the same way or have the same views as you.

Key term

Diversity means variety, particularly in relation to people. You must understand that each individual is unique or one of a kind.

Time to think

1.1 Reasons for communication

1 Think about all the people you communicate with. Reflect on your day, or think about yesterday. How many people did you talk to? Why did you communicate with them?
2 Consider the different reasons we communicate. Make a list of the different people you communicate with and why you communicate with them.

Evidence activity

1.1 Communication

List the reasons why people communicate. Think about your setting. Who communicates with who and why?

AC 1.2 Explain how communication affects relationships in the work setting

Formal and informal interactions

Conversations are such common, everyday events that people often think they do not need any specific or specialist skills to carry them out. This is partly true as some interactions will be informal, such as speaking with friends or family members. Other conversations will be more formal, such as having a conversation with a health specialist, colleague or employer, and this is where more specialist skills and knowledge are needed.

Key term

Interaction if you talk, look, share or engage in any kind of action that involves at least two people, you can be said to have *interacted* with that person.

Building trust

Communication in work settings may have several purposes. As a worker, you will need to be aware that each individual has their own way of interpreting or understanding what is said. Effective communication means more than just passing on information: it means involving or engaging the other person or people with whom you are interacting and making sure they understand, that you can share their views and ultimately build trust with the individuals and the people with whom you work. See Figure 1.2.

Communication as a two-way process

Communicating has to be a two-way process where each person is attempting to understand and interpret (make sense of) what the other person is saying. Often it is easier to understand people who are similar to us, such as a person who has the same accent as us, or is in a similar situation. When we communicate, the decoding equipment in our brain tunes in, breaks down the message, analyses the message, understands it and interprets its meaning, and then creates a response or answer. When a practitioner is speaking with an individual they are forming a mental picture of what they are being told.

Supporting communication with individuals

See AC 2.2 for information on factors to consider when promoting effective communication.

Research and investigate

1.2 Communication methods

Investigate the range of communication methods used in a specific setting, e.g. nursery or learning disability provision, and list the benefits of each method.

Evidence activity

1.2 Ineffective communication

Two friends are talking to each other but both are very excited, so they are talking at the same time.

Think about the above example and describe two examples of how poor communication may affect individuals.

Your communication experience

Think about a time when you wanted to make a comment or complain about a service you received. How did you do this? How did you feel? What was the outcome? Did you need someone to help you?

How does communication affect relationships in your setting?

Figure 1.2 Positive interaction supports communication

LO2 Be able to meet the communication and language needs, wishes and preferences of individuals

AC 2.1 Demonstrate how to establish the communication and language needs, wishes and preferences of individuals

Active listening

You will need to be able to communicate well so that you can understand the verbal and non-verbal communication needs of individuals. In your role you are encouraged to use active listening techniques so that you can encourage effective communication and make the best use of the communication process.

Active listeners focus on:

- what is being said verbally, i.e. content
- how the person is saying it, i.e. the tone of voice
- what is being communicated non-verbally, i.e. body language.

Questioning

Only about 10 per cent of our communication is actually spoken. It is very important that you make the most of your conversations with individuals and their families, as this will allow you to establish relationships and accurately identify their needs and feelings. Much of this information can be collected through careful questioning, and it is important that you consider the different techniques that might be used to

Evidence activity

2.1 Establish communication needs

Ask three different people how they like to be spoken to. For example, English may not be their first language so how can you make the communication effective? Compare their different requirements and reflect on the support you or they may need.

Your supervisor will need to observe and assess while you are doing this.

collect information without creating too much distress. For example, you might use:

- *Closed questions* – e.g. 'Would you like an extra pillow, Mr Smith?' The breathless person need only reply 'Yes' or 'No'. A more complex question would need a longer answer, and cause further breathlessness and discomfort.
- *Open questions* – e.g. 'Tell me about your family, Mr Smith.' This will enable you to start up a conversation.
- *Process questions* – e.g. 'What did you think the doctor was saying, Mr Smith?' This type of questioning can give you an indication of how the individual understands his or her situation.
- *Clarification* – e.g. 'I think you said that this made you feel worse. Is that right, Mr Smith?' This is a useful way of checking or summarising the outcomes of a conversation, and shows that you are listening.

See AC 2.2 for more information on factors to consider when communicating, such as body language and gestures. Also see AC 2.3 for communication methods.

AC 2.2 Describe the factors to consider when promoting effective communication

Eye contact – focus on the individual

Eye contact is a way of showing that the person who is listening is interested in the conversation. Eye contact will help the person you are communicating with realise that you are concentrating on what they are saying rather than on other conversations or activities that may be going on around you. Eye-to-eye contact can also help you to know how the other person is feeling. If either the individual or the practitioner is angry or upset, they might have a fixed stare that can send out that message; if they are excited or interested in someone, then their eyes will get wider. This means that when you are talking to an individual, the person can tell whether you like what you are hearing or not.

Good eye contact can encourage individuals to talk more openly. It indicates that you understand their situation; you can put yourself in the person's position and can see things from their viewpoint, making it easier to provide support for them.

As a practitioner, you need to understand that eye contact has different meanings for people from different cultures. For example, direct eye contact is considered to be rude in some cultures and should be avoided. It is important to understand what is and what is not acceptable for the people with whom you are working. Also, some individuals may be unable or unwilling to make and/or maintain eye contact because of a disability.

Listen attentively and respond

Active listening helps to make communication effective. It is important to show that you are listening to the individual, and that you have heard and understood what they have said. By responding to what has been said, you will reassure the individual and encourage them to speak more openly. Responses can include nodding, smiling, or reflecting back what has been said. Making encouraging sounds can also show interest and can be used to gain further information. The person who is talking is encouraged by signals which show that the listener wants to know more.

Look interested

Using smiles and eye contact ensures that people know that you are interested in what is being said. You should display open body language and use gestures which can also be helpful. Showing interest also helps to develop a trusting relationship which, over a period of time, can help improve communication.

Be aware of personal space and positioning

This involves being aware of your own and others' personal space, the room around them. There may be reasons why a person does not like others to be too close to them, for example they feel closed in or threatened.

Also be aware of talking down to someone. This can be intimidating and impact on the level and effectiveness of communication. So try to be at eye level with the person. If information is to be communicated to a large audience then a lecture theatre layout would be more appropriate, as the speaker could be seen and heard by all.

Awareness of individuals' body language

Being aware of an individual's **body language** can help to support communication. When the individual is displaying open and positive body language it indicates that they are actively involved in the communication and are not feeling uncomfortable. If there is evidence of closed or negative body language this can indicate that there is tension, and the individual is less likely to communicate or listen to what is being said. Acknowledging body language in this way will help to improve the communication – for example, when there is tense, closed body language it may be time to have a short break or give the individual the opportunity to ask questions. This could refocus the communication and improve the situation.

See AC 2.3 for more information on body language.

Timing

Communication should never be rushed, as this may make an individual feel that they are not important, or that you lack respect for them. Also, taking too much time can be seen as dragging out

Key term

Body language is communication through movements, positioning or attitudes of the body that you are aware and unaware of.

the conversation and can make people feel uneasy. Timing should be appropriate for the purpose of the communication and take into account the needs of the individuals involved. It is important to give individuals time to say what they want to; this ensures that they feel respected and that their personal interests have been considered fully. Individuals should not be interrupted when they are speaking, as this may make them feel that they are not being listened to properly.

Place

Choose the right moment and the right place. If you need to discuss something in private with a person, make sure that the choice of venue is private and that you do not feel uncomfortable about the possibility of being overheard. On the other hand, if you need to make your point before a group of people, choose your location so that your discussion will be audible to all who are present, to ensure that you engage everyone in the group.

Dress and appearance

The way an individual dresses, the clothes they wear and their physical appearance can play an important role in the way they are perceived by others and creates a definite impact on the communication process. When working in the health and social care sectors, clothing should be appropriate for the task, and for the group of people you are working with. For example, when attending a community meeting you should dress in a way that shows respect for the people who are involved in the interaction – their culture, age, gender, etc. – while leaving a positive impression on them. See Figure 1.3.

People's appearance may make a statement about their gender, age, economic class, and often their intentions before you even speak to them. Individuals begin to recognise the important cultural clues for this at an early age. Wearing certain types of clothing can change an individual's behaviour and the behaviour of others towards them. For example, when an individual is approached by a police officer in **uniform** they may feel scared even though they know they have not done anything wrong. Their behaviour

would be different if they were approached by a plainclothes police officer.

A uniform is a symbol of status or position, and clearly identifies an individual as belonging to a particular organisation so that individuals can approach them with some level of confidence. Confusion can occur where there are several different uniforms worn by workers. For example, the variety of uniforms and name badges within the NHS can be very confusing.

Figure 1.3 How do you ensure you dress appropriately for work?

Key term

A **uniform** is clothing of a distinctive design worn by members of a particular group or organisation to identify themselves.

Evidence activity

2.2 Helping an individual

Alice is a new member of staff and speaks very quietly and slowly. Not all individuals are able to understand her. How can you help Alice to communicate more effectively? Think about the factors you should consider.

AC 2.3 Demonstrate a range of communication methods and styles to meet individual needs

When communicating with individuals, you will need to consider a range of methods and styles to meet their communication needs. As well as the different methods, you will need to consider:

- The right vocabulary and think about the person who you are speaking to. Is it the right type and level for the person you are addressing?
- What is the context for the conversation? Is it a formal or informal conversation? Think about the tone and pitch that you use when address the individual. Will you need to address the person in a lower pitch if it is a particularly sensitive subject that you are discussing?
- Take into account people with hearing/visual difficulties and how you will need to adjust your communication to suit their needs.

Non-verbal communication includes:

- eye contact, see AC 2.2
- touch – the use of touch can help you to gain someone's attention or make them feel that you are listening fully to what they are saying.
- physical gestures, see AC 2.3
- body language, see ACs 2.2 and 2.3
- behaviour – includes how we stand or how we show someone we are listening to them or giving them our full attention, for example not playing with a mobile phone while communicating with them.

Verbal communication includes:

- vocabulary – too much jargon or difficult terminology can confuse people.
- linguistic tone
- pitch – the tone and pitch can for example indicate urgency or be of a happier nature.

Body language

The non-verbal signals you use when talking to people, such as gestures, facial expressions, body positioning and movement of the body, are known as 'body language'. Body language is a way of giving messages to those we are speaking to, for example, smiling will convey friendliness.

First impressions are often made from observing an individual's body language. A person can convey confidence or lack of confidence through their body language, which can have an impact on how effectively they communicate.

There are subtle, and sometimes less subtle, movements, gestures, facial expressions and even shifts in individuals' whole bodies that suggest something is going on. The way they talk, walk, sit and stand all say something, and whatever is happening on the inside can be reflected on the outside. There are also times when mixed messages are sent – a person says one thing but their body language displays something different. This can be confusing, so it is important to understand the messages being sent to others as well as those being received.

Take care not to assume meanings, particularly when communicating with individuals from other cultures. For example, not making eye contact may be read as 'having something to hide' for some people, while others may see it as a mark of respect.

Gestures

Gestures are hand or arm movements that can pass a message to another person, and help us to understand what a person is saying. Usually gestures are used to enhance the understanding of what is being said verbally, but some gestures carry their own meaning and can be **misinterpreted** by others (see page 10 for definition).

People who cannot use sign language may be able to communicate a message to, or understand a message from, a person with speech impairments by using or watching gestures. Gestures can be used to convey both positive and negative responses. For example, 'thumbs up' can mean 'OK', 'success' or even 'yes please'. Putting a hand up with the palm facing a person gives the meaning of 'stop that'. Shrugging shoulders can mean 'not sure'. However, you should be aware that these gestures can mean different things to people from different cultural groups; for example, in some cultures it can be very rude to give the thumbs-up sign.

Facial expressions

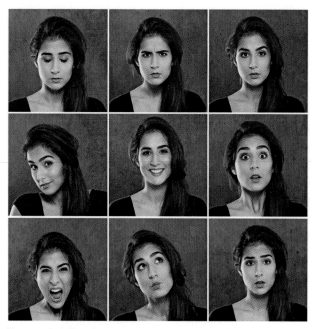

Figure 1.4 Our faces can convey many different meanings

Faces are used to convey meaning in communication (see Figure 1.4). They can indicate the emotional state of the person communicating. Facial expressions include smiling, frowning, raising an eyebrow or pulling the mouth into particular shapes. A quizzical expression can show that a person has misunderstood or wants to ask a question. A sad expression can indicate that something is wrong. Facial expressions can also show pain or surprise.

Written communication

In many health and social care settings, written communication is used to record personal information on a day-to-day basis. In all sectors, accuracy of the written word is very important. If **inaccuracies** occur when keeping formal records, a person using the services could have the wrong treatment or be given incorrect information, with disastrous results. False, inaccurate or misleading written records could result in wrong or inappropriate actions, failure to carry out the required actions or even complaints and litigation.

When writing down information, make sure it is clear, accurate and legible.

Evidence activity

2.3 Written communication
Review some of the daily reports you have written in your setting. Do they make sense? Have you used lots of initials or **acronyms** that others may not understand?

Key terms

Acronyms are words formed from the first letters of the words in a name, e.g. NHS is an acronym for the National Health Service.

Inaccuracies contain mistakes/errors.

Misinterpretation means to wrongly understand something.

Using written communication when working with others

Communicating in writing helps services to maintain contact with other professionals within and across the sectors. Written communication is a means of giving information to others, obtaining information from others and exchanging ideas relating to a variety of aspects of the sectors involved. Some services also require that certain information is confirmed in writing; for example, when making a referral to a social services department regarding concerns about the well-being of a child, the initial referral may be taken over the phone but must be confirmed in writing. In many settings the communication policy will state that all written communication must be shown to the manager before it is passed on.

Storing written records

Copies of written communication should be stored securely so that they are accessible if required for future reference. In some roles written notes and records may be required for use in hearings or court cases, for example in care proceedings regarding children. It is essential that all copies of information regarding children are kept, including jotted notes, typed-up notes, letters and records of phone calls, emails, faxes, etc. and stored according to the guidelines and procedures of the organisation. Documentation that is no longer required should be destroyed using the correct procedures to ensure that confidentiality is maintained – it should not be retained or kept unsecured.

The writer needs to clearly establish the purpose of writing, for example:

- Who will be reading the written information?
- What points are to be made?
- What does the writer hope to achieve?

Clear, concise writing cannot be done in a hurry. You will need to learn how to express yourself clearly and effectively in writing.

Using technology/ICT

In recent years the development of electronic mail (email) has proved to be a significant form of communication. Emails can be formal or informal, depending on their purpose. The internet is also being used increasingly as a source of information for a variety of purposes.

An advantage of emails is that they provide a very quick way of interacting with other people or organisations, as answers can be received in a matter of minutes, rather than having to wait several days for a letter.

Confidentiality

Care needs to be taken to ensure that confidentiality is maintained. 'Secure' systems are necessary before personal confidential information can be exchanged.

Electronic forms of communication such as email and text messaging are now a well-established way of everyday life. In health and social care settings, computers can be used for networking between one organisation and another. A GP surgery could use the computer to send information about a patient to a consultant at a hospital or to send a prescription to a pharmacy. Similarly, an internal system can enable employees within one setting to be linked with others to share information. In all situations, care must be taken to ensure that the requirements of the Data Protection Act 1998 are followed so that personal data is safeguarded and kept **confidential**.

Emails are a common form of communication, but there are risks with these too as email accounts

> **Key term**
>
> **Confidential** information is given in private and intended to be kept secret.

can be hacked or viewed by others. See LO4 for more information on confidentiality.

Technological aids

These can be used to enhance communication with people who may otherwise have difficulties. Some people may use word or symbol boards to support their speech so that a picture enables the listener to understand. Others may use speech synthesisers, which replace speech either by producing a visual display of written text or by producing synthesised speech that expresses the information verbally. Hearing aids, hearing loops, text phones, text messaging on mobile phones and magnifiers are also forms of technological communication devices. Voice recognition software can be purchased for a computer that supports the communication of individuals who find writing difficult. Computers can also be used to present information with graphics and sound.

Use of technology such as JAWS

JAWS is a computer program that reads information on the screen and speaks it aloud through a speech synthesiser. It works with any PC to provide access to software applications and the internet. It also gives refreshable **Braille** displays, providing Braille support for screen readers. Where a person prefers to use technology to assist with communication, this should be encouraged so that everyone feels actively involved, can understand what others are saying and presents their own ideas or opinions.

Sign language

The British Sign Language (BSL) is used by nearly 70,000 people within the UK. The government officially recognised the BSL in March 2003. It is a language that has developed over hundreds of years and enables interaction between people who have hearing difficulties and might otherwise experience problems. It may be the first language of those using it.

Makaton

Makaton is a large collection of symbols that can help people who have a hearing impairment, or who have a learning difficulty, to communicate with others. It is a system that uses signs, speech and symbols (see Figure 1.5). Those using Makaton may use all three methods to help them communicate with others. Makaton uses an established set of hand movements to convey meaning. It is usually taught to children when they are young, as soon as it is realised that they have a need.

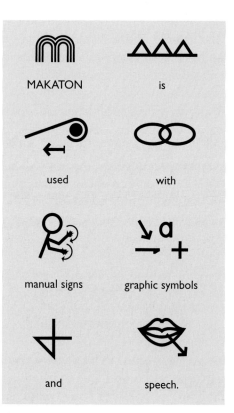

Figure 1.5 Makaton uses signs, symbols and speech

Braille

The communication system known as Braille was introduced in 1829, by a blind man called Richard Braille. The system is one of raised dots that can be felt with a finger. For people who have limited vision or who are blind the system provides the opportunity for independent reading and writing as it is based on 'touch'. It is possible, with the correct computer software, to change the printed word into Braille and to print out using special printers.

Use of advocates

An **advocate** is a person who tries to understand the needs and **preferences** of an individual and then speaks on their behalf. Advocates are often needed when someone has a disability which makes it difficult for them to speak for themselves. An advocate should try to get to know the individual and develop an understanding of their culture and background, so that they can represent them accurately. The advocate should understand the person's needs and communicate these to practitioners or professionals involved with them. To ensure that they are unbiased, advocates are independent of the professional carers who work with the individual.

Interpreters and translators

Interpreters can help people for whom English is not their preferred or first language. In the past interpreters may have been family members of the person in question, but this is now discouraged as much as possible for confidentiality reasons. For example, a mother whose daughter is interpreting for her may not want her daughter to know that she has cancer.

Interpreters communicate meaning of one spoken language to another, while **translators** change written material from one language to another.

Key terms

Braille is a system of writing and printing for blind or visually impaired people. Varied arrangements of raised dots representing letters and numerals are identified by touch.

Advocates enable a person to express their views, access information and promote their rights.

Preferences means a greater liking for one thing over another.

Interpreter is a person who translates speech orally or into sign language.

Translator is a person who converts one language into another.

There are drawbacks to using translators and interpreters, as it may sometimes be difficult to grasp the exact meaning of a message or to express the meaning in the other language. Where an interpreter is used, it is important to remember to communicate with the individual rather than the interpreter, to ensure that the individual is empowered and feels valued.

Communicating information

In many services, leaflets concerning health topics or health facilities are produced in several other languages in addition to English, so that people from ethnic minorities can access the information. If information is not readily available in the relevant language it will need to be translated.

AC 2.4 Demonstrate how to respond to an individual's reactions when communicating

How you respond to a person's reactions indicates how you have accepted or interpreted the information conveyed. You can use body language to speak your thoughts, a smile, a nod of the head, a facial expression of understanding. You must be careful not to show shock or upset at what you are being told as this could further distress the person.

LO3 Be able to overcome barriers to communication

AC 3.1 Explain how people from different backgrounds may use and/or interpret communication methods in different ways

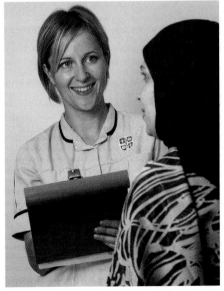

Figure 1.6 Working with people from different backgrounds

Respect cultural preferences and differences

It is important to respect people's different cultural preferences, values and priorities (see Figure 1.6).

Body language can be interpreted differently by different cultures. Certain cultures use gestures or touch much more than others, and gestures can mean different things in different cultures. For example, in some cultures, touching someone shows understanding and empathy (see page 15 for definition) but in British culture it might be considered unacceptable in a work situation. Making direct eye contact when communicating may be considered acceptable and even desirable in one culture (e.g. British), but rude and totally unacceptable in another (e.g. Greek). In order to avoid causing any offence or misunderstanding, it is worth taking time to find out about an individual's cultural background.

It is important to develop your knowledge and understanding of different cultures. You will need to consider a range of aspects – the language they use to communicate, whether they have a learning disability, a visual or hearing impairment or any other illness.

For example, you should know that in some cultures, young women can only receive medical attention if they are accompanied by an older family member. Also, decisions about whether to have treatment or care are often made collectively by the senior members of the family rather than by the individual. These considerations may not at first seem to be directly linked to communicating with service users, but they do have an impact on the way people communicate and with whom.

Tips for communicating with people from different cultures include:

1 Understand that people from other cultures might have entirely **different value systems** from yours. It is useful to check the person's records for information, or speak to a member of their family or a friend if appropriate or possible. Ask someone else from the same culture, either another worker or an advocate. Use reference books and/or the internet if necessary.

2 Different cultures have different norms regarding a person's **personal or public space** (in which others can stand and speak with you) and their private space (reserved only for people who are close to you). For example, people from Arab countries do not share the British concept of 'personal space' – for them it is considered offensive to step or lean away while talking to someone. Make sure you leave the correct amount of space between yourself and others when you talk to them. If you are unsure, you can always ask what the other person prefers.

3 **Physical gestures** that are acceptable when communicating vary widely between different cultures. When people visit other countries they often miss subtle cultural cues, which leads them to misinterpret others. For example, the use of irony or the implication of a laugh may be shown only in a squinting of the eyes or a shaking of the hand, which a cultural outsider might miss.

4 **Learn about their culture**: greetings, goodbye rituals, before-meal ceremonies, food and clothes.

Use language appropriate to the individual's understanding

It is important to avoid using language that individuals do not understand, such as using adult language when working with a child. Likewise, using sophisticated language when communicating with an adult with learning difficulties is inappropriate. If acronyms or technical terminology are used these should always be explained, to ensure that the person understands what has been said. You should always assess the individual you are communicating with before progressing with your communication, so that the interaction is as effective as possible.

Ask questions to clarify points and aid understanding

Asking the right questions without being too intrusive is an important skill to develop. It will help you to clarify the important points and understand the communication. Questions should be short and to the point. Using language and vocabulary that is easy to understand will help to avoid confusion. You should avoid asking multiple questions, as these may be difficult for the individual to answer.

Closed questions (with 'yes' and 'no' answers) should be used to gather factual information when you need to know about specific points, such as date of birth, allergies or medication being taken. See AC 2.1 for more information.

Open questions should be used where more detailed information is required, as these give the individual the opportunity to offer longer answers. These questions give more of an insight into how the individual is feeling or about their views and opinions.

AC 3.2 Identify barriers to effective communication

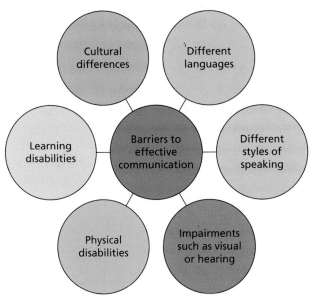

Figure 1.7 How many of these barriers have you come across?

Attitude of the worker

Your attitude can affect the way others communicate with you. When a worker is abrupt towards an individual, that person could feel intimidated or scared and not want to communicate. They may feel that the worker is not interested in them and does not want to help. An insincere approach or lack of empathy may make an individual feel that they are wasting their time, and could make them unwilling to disclose personal information. A sincere and polite attitude is likely to promote more open communication from the individual.

Limited technology

Some individuals need technological aids to support their communication. When there is limited availability of a technology, communication may be more difficult. For example, the absence of a **hearing loop** could be a barrier to an individual who uses a hearing aid. Workers who have limited experience of using technology (e.g. computers, fax machines or other technological devices) might not be able to communicate effectively; for example, they may not be able to communicate via email or use a fax machine. This could delay messages being received and responded to, and could undermine someone's authority if they need to ask for help.

Sitting too far away or invading personal space

Sitting too far away from a person may make them feel that they are not important or that the practitioner is not interested in what they have to say. It may also mean that they need to speak more loudly, which could compromise confidentiality or make them feel uncomfortable about communicating. Invasion of personal space (getting too close) can also make people feel uncomfortable. Most people prefer to get to know someone first, and often only allow those who are close to them into their 'intimate zone'.

Emotional distress

Emotional issues, especially those that cause worry or distress, can make people behave unpredictably (see Figure 1.8). When individuals have serious emotional needs they can be afraid or depressed because of the stress they are experiencing. They may lack self-awareness or appear to be shy or aggressive, which has an impact on their ability to

Figure 1.8 Communication is difficult in times of distress so it is important to reassure the individual

communicate. Listening involves learning about frightening and depressing situations, which can mean that workers sometimes avoid listening properly to avoid feeling unpleasant emotions. Workers can become emotionally distressed by the needs of the individual and can also make assumptions, or label or stereotype others.

Workers may have their own emotional issues that can create barriers, and may not be able to focus or may be tired due to worrying and lack of sleep. Listening and empathising takes mental energy, which may not be available if the worker has their own concerns. Workers who believe they do not have sufficient time to communicate properly can become stressed and so create a barrier.

When individuals are depressed, angry or upset, these emotions will influence their ability to understand what is being communicated to them, and to be able to communicate their own needs. Additionally, individuals who do not trust service providers or practitioners are less likely to share information with them.

Not giving individuals time to say what they want

Some individuals need more time than others to express themselves. This may be due to a lack of confidence or because they have communication difficulties. When individuals are not given the time they need to express themselves, they may feel that they are being rushed. They get annoyed when, for example, someone else finishes their sentences for them, or they may 'clam up' and not talk at all.

Poor or unwelcoming body language

A worker who displays negative body language in the form of crossed arms or legs, using inappropriate gestures, poor facial expressions, poor body positioning or constant fidgeting creates barriers to communication.

Poor interpersonal skills

A worker who has poor **interpersonal skills** does not make an individual feel welcome. They may use inappropriate language or rely too heavily on technical terminology. Their manner and demeanour may be off-putting, which can create a barrier to successful communication. If the worker is not paying attention to the individual or is not listening properly, they may miss important information. It is inappropriate to then ask for this to be repeated, as it will make the individual feel that they are not being valued.

Lack of privacy

Conversations should not be held in a public place where others can overhear what is being said, as this lack of privacy can feel disrespectful. Interruptions by other people may make the individual feel intimidated and unimportant. A person is likely to communicate much more freely if they feel that what they are saying is being taken seriously and kept private.

Stereotyping

Stereotyping means describing everyone in a particular category as being the same, or describing aspects of their behaviour or characteristics as the same. It is an easy way of grouping people together. For example, it is stereotyping to believe that everyone over 70 years old is less mentally able or needs a walking aid, or that all children below the age of four are unable to make decisions for themselves. Sometimes individuals are stereotyped because of their language or race. For example, some people may assume that anyone who is not white cannot speak English, so they speak in 'broken English' to the individual without first finding out if they can speak English or if English is their preferred language.

Lack of respect

An individual is unlikely to communicate if they feel that they are not being respected. Addressing someone as 'dear' or 'lovie', or invading their personal space, shows a lack of respect. Any action that is going to be taken should be clearly explained before actually carrying it out and the opinions and choices of the individual should be respected.

AC 3.3 Demonstrate ways to overcome barriers to communication

Respect cultural preferences and differences

Cultural differences can influence communication. Culture is much more than just the language that is spoken; it includes the way people live, think and how they relate to each other. In some cultures children are not allowed to speak if certain adults are present. Other cultures do not allow women to speak to men they do not know. Cultural differences can sometimes make relationships difficult; therefore workers across the sectors need to make sure they prepare well for this.

It is important across the sectors for information to be made available in a person's chosen language. It may also be appropriate to employ interpreters to support individuals so that they can be actively involved in any communication and understand the support available or the procedures being carried out.

When communicating it is important to remember the following points:

- Do not make assumptions when meeting a person. They could appear to be demanding simply because they feel insecure or because they are not familiar with their surroundings.
- Treat a person with a same-sex partner accompanying them in the same manner as everyone else.
- Show respect for the values of individuals.
- Do not invade personal space. Often people feel uncomfortable with this until they develop trust.
- Acknowledge the beliefs and differences of individuals from other cultures.

- Develop knowledge and understanding of different cultures in order to avoid making mistakes or causing offence.

See AC 3.1 for more information.

Ask questions

- Ask an individual to summarise their understanding of the situation so that further explanation can be given if necessary. Consider Figure 1.9.
- Always ask if there is anything that is not understood: this can prevent mistakes being made or something being interpreted in the wrong way.
- Ask questions relating to timing, place and procedures to enhance understanding.

There is more information on this in AC 3.1.

Use level appropriate to individual's understanding

- If possible, check the approximate age of the individual before communicating with them.
- Read through their records to find out what level of understanding they are likely to have.
- Never use technical terminology that has not been explained to the individual.
- Never use acronyms without explaining what they mean.
- Do not assume that an individual will understand what you have said, or that they must have understood because they did not state otherwise. See AC 3.1 for more information.

Figure 1.9 How do you ensure that you are understood?

Create a comfortable, safe environment

- Make sure that the environment is at the right temperature: not too hot and not too cold.
- Check the environment for any hazards and take precautions to reduce these risks before the communication takes place.
- Make sure the layout of the room is appropriate for the communication to take place.
- Make sure the environment has adequate ventilation: not too draughty or too stuffy.
- Check suitability of seating arrangements: some people prefer chairs with arms so that they can push up to get out of them, some may prefer softer seating, and others may prefer lower or higher chairs.

Respect dignity and privacy

- Ask what name the individual prefers to be called by.
- Do not speak to the pusher of a wheelchair and by-pass the wheelchair user.
- Involve children in conversation: do not presume they do not understand the discussions.
- Talk to the child and ask their opinions.
- Offer choices wherever possible.
- Allow preferences to be expressed.
- Use a private room where appropriate.
- Do not discuss personal issues where others can overhear.
- Use passwords on the computer.
- Never disclose information over the telephone unless the identity of the caller can be established.
- Ask people to leave the room when appropriate to respect the privacy of the individual.
- Ask permission from the individual before sharing information with others.
- Explain who will have access to personal information.

For more information on sensory loss see AC 3.4. See AC 2.3 for information on sign language and British Sign Language. For information on other barriers such as physical disability, learning disability and impairments see units LD 201 and HSC 2028.

3.3 Integration

Hamid is a new service user. He speaks little English but is keen to get to know people. How can the service, and you, help Hamid to integrate? Think of a time when you have demonstrated a way to overcome barriers to communication.

AC 3.4 Demonstrate strategies that can be used to clarify misunderstandings

However you choose to send a message, you must try to ensure that those who are receiving it are aware that it is genuine and purposeful. However, there may be occasions when a message is misinterpreted because potential barriers to the communication process have not been duly considered. These might include:

- language barriers
- environmental barriers
- barriers due to sensory loss
- barriers due to physical disability
- cultural barriers
- barriers due to prejudice and discrimination.

Barriers and strategies to overcome them
Language barriers
Successful communication hinges on how well you listen and respond to others. Here are some language behaviours that may hinder the communication process:

- Do not be dominating – if someone dominates the communication process, communicating becomes a one-way process and responses from individuals are hindered.
- Be aware of inappropriate self-disclosure – if someone talks too much about themselves, the topic or focus of the communication changes.
- Self-protection – individuals often protect themselves from meaningful contact by: talking only about safe topics; avoiding uncomfortable issues; emotionally detaching themselves from the topic of conversation.

- Do not swear – such language may be powerful, but it usually turns others off.
- Be clear. Don't use jargon – people often use words that belong exclusively to their area of expertise.
- Do not judge others – as a health and social care worker it is important that you do not impose your own value judgements on others. Avoid telling others that their ideas or opinions are bad or wrong. Simply say, 'I disagree.'
- Do not patronise – acting like you are superior, or using condescending words, tone or behaviour, will make individuals and their families feel angry and defensive.
- Do not pressurise – or use threats, implied or explicit, to persuade someone.
- Be sensitive – do not be callous or unaware of your own feelings and the feelings of others.

All of the approaches discussed can help you to have a very clear understanding of what someone has said. This avoids confusion and upset for the person involved.

Environmental barriers
A health and social care environment can be noisy, distracting and confusing at times. It is important that members of staff recognise this and reduce any background noise to a minimum. For example, how often have you seen individuals placed next to a noisy television that no one is watching? What effect do you think this will have on their ability to concentrate or to converse with others? It is also important to ensure that the environment is freely accessible, and that the placement of furniture encourages individuals to interact with each other. Notices to inform individuals of activities and events should also be placed in freely accessible locations. This will not only encourage conversation between carers and individuals, but will also encourage individuals to plan for the event, and to participate and socialise with other individuals and their families.

Sensory loss
Some older people may have difficulty communicating because of poor eyesight or hearing. You can assist individuals who have

visual impairment by making sure that their eyesight is tested regularly, that their spectacles are clean and worn properly, and that their possessions are kept in the same, familiar place. You could also learn the correct way to guide and assist a partially sighted person while they are walking, and find out what visual aids are available in your nursing home, such as large-print books and newspapers or talking books. When communicating with visually impaired individuals, it is important that you:

- let them know you are nearby in a quiet and unhurried manner
- introduce yourself by name
- use appropriate forms of touch to initiate and then sustain the conversation
- ask the individual what form of communication suits them best
- allow the individual to take your arm before you lead them around
- treat the person as an individual, and never assume that all visually impaired people have the same communication needs.

You can support individuals with hearing impairment by making sure that their hearing is tested regularly, that a hearing aid, if they wear one, is clean and worn properly, and that the battery is not flat. You can also learn the correct way to replace a hearing aid battery, or talk to colleagues about how the hearing impaired use sign language. You can also find out what aids are available, such as flashing lights instead of telephone bells or door bells.

When communicating with hearing-impaired individuals, it is important that you:

- speak clearly, listen carefully and respond to what is said to you
- minimise any distractions, e.g. noisy television
- make sure any aids to hearing are working
- use written forms of communication that are appropriate
- use signing, where appropriate, by involving a properly trained interpreter.

Evidence activity

3.4 Ineffective communication

Give two examples of how ineffective communication may affect individuals. Think about some of the strategies we have discussed such as:

- clarification
- repeat what has been said
- ask questions
- asking for feedback
- allowing sufficient time
- adapting your approach to communication.

AC 3.5 Explain how to access extra support or services to enable individuals to communicate effectively

If problems with communication are identified, a range of services can be accessed. Never presume that you or anyone else can be heard, understood and responded to without first thinking about the person involved. Ensure that you are supporting someone to communicate as effectively as possible by working with them to overcome challenges and barriers to communication. It may be necessary to access additional support or services to help make communication better, or clearer. People may have problems in communicating with others due to:

- intellectual impairment leading to problems comprehending and processing information
- sensory difficulties (hearing, vision)
- problems in understanding social interaction (e.g. autism)
- speech problems (e.g. articulation problems)
- others not listening or not valuing what they are trying to communicate.

Many different professionals may be involved in this, but a person's motivation and efforts are equally important. Key experts likely to be encountered include advocates, translators, interpreters (see AC 2.3) and speech and language therapists to help with communication problems, and clinical psychologists to help with problems affecting mental processes and emotions.

Speech and language services assess people's communication abilities and needs, to enable them to communicate better. This service is generally accessed through a referral system but there are private providers too.

Health professionals need to:

- take time and have patience
- value what is being communicated
- recognise non-verbal cues
- find out about the person's alternative communication strategies if verbal communication is difficult (e.g. their typical non-verbal cues, use symbols, sign language)
- explain things clearly in an appropriate way (verbally and with pictures, etc.)
- be prepared to meet the person several times to build up rapport and trust
- use the knowledge and support of people's carers.

Evidence activity

3.5 Support mechanisms

Think about the support services available. Carry out research into two of these and identify their key features. How could you access these to enable individuals to communicate more effectively?

LO4 Be able to apply principles and practices relating to confidentiality

AC 4.1 Explain the meaning of the term confidentiality

What is confidentiality?

Information given to a worker should not be disclosed without the person's informed permission. Confidentiality means that personal and private information obtained from or about an individual must only be shared with others on a 'need-to-know' basis. If you tell people something

Case study

4.1 Confidentiality

Ms Smith lives with her two children in a small market town. She is to have a minor operation and arrangements need to be made for the care of her children while she is in hospital and convalescing.

Arrangements for the care of the children are being discussed at a case conference by Ms Smith and the family's GP, social worker and health visitor. The elder child's school will be informed of the final arrangements.

Various pieces of information are known to the four people at the case conference, although no one has every piece of information. The privacy of interests of Ms Smith, her children and their absent father may be different.

Here are some criteria that can influence whether or not information is disclosed or shared:

- confidence that the recipient of the data will handle it responsibly
- the need for consent to disclosure and respect for refusals to **consent**
- the accuracy, relevance and pertinence of the data.

1 Can you think of any other considerations?
2 It is not always easy to decide which pieces of information should be shared. Consider the following:

The GP knows that the absent father is HIV positive. To the best of the GP's knowledge, neither the social worker nor the health visitor is aware of this. It is also possible that Ms Smith is unaware.
In these particular circumstances, should the GP share this information with the following people, and why?

(a) Ms Smith
(b) the health visitor
(c) the social worker.

3 As a health or social care professional it is vital that you apply the principles of confidentiality. Inappropriate disclosure of information can have a significant negative impact on people's lives. What could be the impact of disclosure in this situation?

Key term

Consent is giving permission or agreeing to do something.

Figure 1.10 Confidentiality is vital in record-keeping

on a need-to-know basis, it means you only tell them the facts they need to know at the time they need to know them, and no more. It is an important principle in health and social care because it provides guidance on the amount of personal information and data that can be disclosed without **consent**. A person disclosing personal information in a relationship of trust reasonably expects his or her privacy to be protected, i.e. they expect the information to remain confidential. The relationship between health and social care professionals and their patients/clients centres on trust, and trust is dependent on the patient/client being confident that personal information they disclose is treated confidentially.

However, confidentiality can be countered when there is a public interest in others being protected from harm.

See AC 4.2 for more information on the Data Protection Act and unit HSC 038 for more information on good practice in handling information.

AC 4.2 Demonstrate ways to maintain confidentiality in day-to-day communication

Importance of maintaining confidentiality
Maintaining confidentiality is a very important aspect of building trust between a client and a worker (see Figure 1.10). Without trust, communication is less likely to progress between two or more people. This involves honouring commitments and declaring conflicts of interest. It also means making sure that the policy that relates to ways of communicating with people is followed.

The right to confidentiality means that a person's notes must not be left lying around or stored insecurely (e.g. left in a car). Computerised information relating to the person should only be accessed by those who have the authority to do so, so it should be password-protected and the password given only to authorised staff. Conversations with clients should not be so loud that others can hear and, if the content of the conversation is personal, the interaction should be in a room where others are not present and the door is closed. People have the right not to be spoken about in such a way that they can be identified.

There are occasions when a worker may have to break confidentiality. Such situations arise when:

- a person is likely to harm themselves
- a person is likely to harm others
- a child or vulnerable adult has suffered, or is at risk of suffering, significant harm
- a person has been, or is likely to be, involved in a serious crime.

You should also remember that other professional workers will require specific information on a need-to-know basis, and in these circumstances information may have to be passed to others.

Ways to maintain confidentiality

- Store information safely so that people who should not see the information cannot gain access to it.
- Use passwords for logging onto computers.
- Only give information on a need-to-know basis.
- Do not pass on information without the relevant permission.

- Only use the information for the intended and agreed purpose.
- Follow relevant legislation relating to data protection and accessing personal files.

The most common ways in which confidentiality can be breached

- Notes left in an unattended area.
- Failure to ask whether information may be disclosed to others.
- Discussions in public areas about individuals.
- Failure to log off the computer system.
- Allowing others to know and use your password.
- Leaving information on a VDU screen which can be seen by the public.
- Failure to establish a person's identity before giving them information.
- Holding conversations, including on the telephone, in a public area.
- Leaving personal and private information in a car.

Legal requirements

The approach of courts of law to record-keeping tends to be that 'if it is not recorded, it has not been done'. Health and social care workers have a professional and a legal duty of care to their clients, so their record-keeping should be able to demonstrate:

- a full account of their assessment and the care that has been planned and provided
- relevant information about the condition of the person at any given time
- the measures taken by the worker to respond to their needs
- a record of any arrangements that have been made for the continuing care of a patient/client
- confidentiality has been maintained at all times.

Organisational policies

All organisations have their own policies and procedures regarding recording and reporting of information to make sure that all practitioners observe the regulations that apply to them. Confidentiality is an essential component of an accessible service. Some users of services bring issues with them and provide personal

details in order for practitioners to help them. By being assured that their information is going to be recorded, stored and shared appropriately, individuals feel more able to disclose information that they may not have been previously happy to discuss. Some people feel intimidated or reluctant to talk about their issues. Young people, refugees and offenders, for example, may feel especially vulnerable. Users of services need reassurance that they will not be judged, and that anything they tell workers will not be shared with others without the client's knowledge and consent. The few exceptions to this are usually outlined in the policies followed by the organisation. In order for policies to operate successfully, there needs to be commitment from all the staff.

Many different organisational policies refer to responsibility in relation to recording and reporting of information, including:

- confidentiality policies
- health and Well-being policies
- information Governance policies
- health and Safety policies
- child Protection policies
- assessment, Recording and Reporting policies
- codes of Conduct and National Standards Frameworks relating to practitioners across the sectors, which also apply within organisations.

Meet the needs of individuals

Only information required to meet the individual's specific needs should be recorded and reported. Information that is not relevant should not be recorded at all. For example, financial information would not be relevant to a patient who has been admitted to hospital for an operation; however, it may be needed to determine an individual's ability to pay for adult social care services. Information describing personal characteristics such as age, gender, disability, ethnicity, religion and sexual orientation should only be used to support the provision of high-quality care to meet individual needs. This information can be used to meet the requirements of legislation, regulations and policies and to demonstrate good practice.

The Caldicott Principles

The Caldicott Principles were developed for the NHS in relation to the recording and sharing of personal information. These principles can easily be applied to any organisation or setting. The Caldicott Standards are based on the Data Protection Act 1998 principles. Caldicott Guardians are senior staff in the NHS and social services appointed to protect patient information to make sure that it is only used for the purposes intended. For more information on the Caldicott Principles, go to https://www.gov.uk/government/uploads/system/uploads/attachment_data/file/192572/2900774_InfoGovernance_accv2.pdf

Procedures and practices

Across the sectors there are different procedures and practices that may be expected to be followed within each organisation.

Every organisation must have a policy that explains the procedures to be followed for sharing information. The policy should clearly state:

- which senior managers have the responsibility to decide about disclosing information
- what to do when action is required urgently
- how to make sure that information will only be used for the purpose for which it is required
- procedures to be followed to obtain manual records
- procedures to be followed to access computer records
- arrangements for reviewing the procedures.

Relevant legislation relating to data protection, accessing personal files and medical records

Data Protection Act 1998

Data Protection Act 1998 governs access to the health records of living people. It became effective from 1 March 2000, and superseded the Data Protection Act 1984 and the Access to Health Records Act 1990, though the Access to Health Records Act 1990 still governs access to the health records of deceased people. The Data Protection Act 1998 gives every living person the right to apply for access to their health records.

The Data Protection Act protects people's rights to confidentiality and covers both paper and electronic records. The act provides individuals with a range of rights, including:

- the right to know what information is held on them and to see and correct this information
- the right to refuse to provide information
- the right that data held should be accurate and up to date
- the right that data held should not be kept for longer than is necessary
- the right to confidentiality: information should not be accessible to unauthorised people.

The Data Protection Act 1998 is not confined to health records held for the purposes of the NHS. It applies equally to the private health sector and to health professionals' private practice records.

Access to Medical Reports Act 1988

This Act gives guidelines covering requests from employers or insurance companies wanting medical reports on individuals. For example, the individual's specific consent has to be given before a medical report can be written for employment or insurance purposes. The individual also has the right to see the report before it is passed to the employer or insurance company; they can then request alterations to be made and refuse permission for the report to be sent. For example, a GP could not give information about an individual's medical history to an insurance company without a consent form signed by the individual stating that they agree to their personal information being given. The consent form would include a statement saying that the individual did or did not want to see the report before it was sent to the insurance company.

See the legislation section at the end of the unit for other relevant legislation.

4.1 and 4.2 Maintaining confidentiality

A client's cousin has telephoned from Australia asking for an update on their family member's health. They say that due to the distance, they will not be able to get over to visit for a long time so they should be given the information.

Think about what you understand by the term 'confidentiality'. What action do you take and why?

How do you ensure confidentiality in your role on a day-to-day basis? Your supervisor will need to observe you demonstrating this.

AC 4.3 Describe the potential tension between maintaining an individual's confidentiality and disclosing concerns

Workers have a duty to protect the confidentiality and privacy of service users, but must also protect their safety and well-being as well as that of the public. For example, an individual may have disclosed information in confidence, but as a worker you may need to inform your manager of this to protect both the individual and others. There is therefore a potential conflict between protecting the privacy and confidentiality of individuals, protecting the public, and disclosing concerns.

Confidentiality can be breached in the following instances:

- To protect children at risk of significant harm as defined by the Children Act 1989.
- To protect the public from acts of terrorism as defined in the Prevention of Terrorism Act 2005.
- As a duty to the courts.
- Under the Drug Trafficking Offences Act 1986.
- Section 115 of the Crime and Disorder Act 1998 gives public bodies the power, but not a duty, to disclose information for the prevention or detection of crime.

- To ensure that the service provides a duty of care in a life-threatening situation, for example serious illness or injury, suicide and self-harming behaviour. This includes when an individual continues to drive against medical advice when unfit to do so. In such circumstances relevant information should be disclosed to the medical advisor of the Driver and Vehicle Licensing Agency, without delay.
- To protect the service provider in a life-threatening situation, for example calls to police regarding a violent individual. There is government guidance about the issue of violence against staff, which can be accessed via the Department of Health website: https://www.gov.uk/government/organisations/department-of-health

Risks involved in information-sharing

Whenever and wherever information is shared, there are always **risks** involved, whether the information is shared verbally or in written format.

Risks to individuals

Information could be passed on to people who should not have access to it. If unauthorised people gained access to the personal details, medical or financial information this could be used fraudulently or illegally by others. The identity of the individual could be used by someone else to take money from them or to pretend they are the individual for a variety of reasons. The individual could be put at risk themselves. The information may not be passed on accurately and this could result in their welfare or care needs not being met.

Key term

Risks, in this context, are things that may cause loss of or damage to information.

Evidence activity

4.3 Maintaining confidentiality

Have you come across a situation where there has been a tension between maintaining an individual's confidentiality and disclosing concerns? List things you may need to pass on to your manager which cause you worry or concern.

Explain the boundaries of own responsibility in relation to confidentiality and disclosure

When to disclose confidential information, what to disclose and to who

When information is shared, the full details surrounding the collection of the information may not be obvious. Workers receiving the information may not fully understand the individual's circumstances. There could be confusion over when it is appropriate to share confidential information, how much of the information can be shared and who the information should be shared with. Ethical dilemmas can create issues in this way, for example when a 15-year-old girl goes to see her GP because she is pregnant, should the girl's parents be informed? Services should include guidance in their confidentiality policy to ensure that all workers are following the same procedures and are absolutely clear about these issues.

Risks to workers

Practitioners may not understand the information that has been shared and could make mistakes. The accuracy of the information shared may lead to misinterpretation by the practitioner which could mean they cannot carry out their role effectively, such as when and where to provide the care required. Practitioners may, inadvertently, break confidentiality without realising what they have done by including too much detail in the information they share or, when receiving information, sharing it with others who did not need to know.

Record-keeping and the importance of accuracy of records

All records that are kept must be accurate, as others may need to use them and mistakes can be made as a result of the wrong information being recorded. Workers should always read through the information they have recorded to check that it is accurate. There are a number of reasons why accuracy is particularly important.

It may be a legal document

A legal document may be required to be used as evidence in a court of law. If the information is not accurate the evidence recorded could cause many issues. For example, if it were to be used for criminal proceedings, the person may not be able to be prosecuted or, if there was a claim that malpractice had been carried out in the care provided to an individual, the records may not support the evidence given and a worker could be sued, when in fact they had not done anything wrong.

If it is a medical record

Medical records have to be accurate to ensure that the needs of the individual are met. When an individual sees a care professional regarding their medical care, the records of their previous treatment and care may need to be referred to in order to ensure that any changes or progression of their care meet their needs. This may not be possible if there are any inaccuracies in the records that have been made. It is also important to remember that individuals have the right to see their medical records under the Access to Medical Records Act and may be annoyed if the information is not accurate or includes insensitive or judgemental comments.

Misinterpretation of illegible drug dosage could be fatal

On drugs charts used in hospitals and nursing homes the dosage of a prescription must be accurate and legible. If this is not the case, individuals could easily be given too much of the medication which could have fatal consequences.

Too little of the medication could result in their health deteriorating and their needs not being met.

Currency, accuracy, validity and reliability

All records that are kept should be current (up to date), accurate, valid and reliable.

Accuracy of information is essential to ensure that mistakes are not made and the needs of individuals are met. In health, up-to-date information about a patient's condition is crucial. In children's and young people's care settings, accurate details of children's allergies might be essential. In adult social care, accurate contact information for next of kin may be necessary, and any care plan changes must be recorded clearly. See unit SHC 32 for more information on accuracy and reliability.

Useful resources

Websites
Community Care
www.community-care.co.uk

Royal National Institute for the Deaf
www.rnid.org.uk

Royal National Institute of the Blind
www.rnib.org.uk

Social Care Sector Skills Council
www.skillsforcare.org.uk

Health Care Sector Skills Council
www.skillsforhealth.org.uk

Skills for Justice Sector Skills Council
www.skillsforjustice.com

Legislation

- Data Protection Act 1998
- Crime and Disorder Act 1998
- Criminal Procedures and Investigations Act 1996
- Human Rights Act 1998
- Freedom of Information Act 2000
- The Computer Misuse Act 1990
- The Children Act 1989
- Prevention of Terrorism Act 2005
- Drug Trafficking Offences Act 1986
- Crime and Disorder Act 1998

Engage in personal development in health, social care or children's and young people's settings

This unit is worth 3 credits

What are you finding out?

Engaging in personal development involves not only finding out what influences your practice but also listening to and being open to how your working practices have affected others. In this unit you will learn about how to carry out your job role, duties and responsibilities to a consistently high standard. Having the ability to take a step back and reflect on your working practices can help you to develop your knowledge and understanding further as well as your skills.

You will also learn more about the different types of support that are available to you, both within and outside of the setting where you work, and how you can make use of these to develop personally and

professionally. Personal development will not only increase your understanding about your strengths, weaknesses and needs but will also make you more aware of the impact that your practice has on individuals and others you work with.

By the end of this unit you will:

1 Understand what is required for competence in your work role.
2 Be able to reflect on your practice.
3 Be able to evaluate your performance.
4 Be able to agree a personal development plan.
5 Be able to use learning opportunities and reflective practice to contribute to personal development.

Links to Level 3 Certificate in Preparing to Work in Adult Social Care

SHC32 Assessment criteria	Unit PWCS32
AC 1.2	AC 1.3
AC 2.1	AC 1.2
AC 2.3	AC 1.4
AC 4.1	AC 3.2

LO1 Understand what is required for competence in own work role

AC 1.1 Describe the duties and responsibilities of own work role

When you first start working in the health or social care sector, or for a different organisation or in a new role, your employer will provide information about how the organisation is structured, including who you will work with and be supported by, and the principles, rules and standards that you must follow. This initial introduction to your job role is often referred to as an **induction** and provides you with a greater insight into your work colleagues and day-to-day duties and responsibilities.

What are duties?

Duties are the work activities that you will be expected to carry out as part of the job. Your job description will set out clearly the purpose of your work role as well as the details about the day-to-day work activities that your employer will expect you to carry out. Your duties will also reflect the level and type of job role that you have been employed to do.

Senior care workers in residential settings and senior support workers in supported living and community-based services may have the following **duties**:

- **d**eveloping work rotas
- **u**pdating individuals' person-centred **plans** and attending reviews

Key terms

Competence means putting into practice the knowledge and skills required to carry out your job role to a high standard and in line with your job description.

Induction is the introduction to your job role and responsibilities conducted by your employer when you start a new job.

Plans may be known by other names, e.g. support plans, individual plans. A plan is the document in which day-to-day requirements and preferences for care and support are detailed.

Personal development is a process used to increase your self-awareness and achieve your goals.

- training and supporting new care and support workers
- increasing the independence of individuals
- ensuring partnership working with other professionals and agencies
- supporting individuals to access their local communities.

What are responsibilities?

Responsibilities relate to the way that you carry out your work duties, including the way you approach your role and the duties you are contracted to carry out.

Senior care workers in residential settings and senior support workers in supported living and community-based services may have the following **responsibilities**:

- role modelling
- encouraging positive relationships with individuals
- supporting care and support workers' development
- promoting safe working practices
- organising activities
- non-judgemental working
- supporting individuals' needs and preferences
- involving individuals' advocates
- being flexible
- inspiring care and support workers
- listening actively to individuals and others
- inspiring good quality services
- treating individuals and others with respect
- inspiring working practices that are responsive to individuals' needs
- encouraging positive communications
- supporting good working relationships.

Duties and responsibilities go together: you cannot have one without the other. Being competent in your job role means carrying out your duties and responsibilities to a consistently high standard.

Research and investigate

AC 1.1 National occupational standards

Find out more about the Health and Social Care NOS on the National Occupational Standards database.

Case study

1.1 Ben

Ben is an experienced senior support worker and has worked at the project at Dawes Road for over three years. Ben has called an urgent team meeting as he is concerned over the impact that Mr J (who has recently moved into the project) is having on the other three individuals who live there.

Ben expresses his concerns about Mr J to the rest of the team. He is concerned about Mr J's use of the kitchen at nights when everyone else is asleep, and the different friends he invites to stay overnight at the house.

One support worker present in the meeting agrees with Ben as she feels that this is unfair to the rest of the individuals who live at the project. The other support worker disagrees with Ben as he feels that the other individuals like him living at the house and have never complained about him using the kitchen at nights or about his friends.

1 Do you think Ben is right to have concerns?
2 Do you think anyone is letting their own values and beliefs affect the situation?

Evidence activity

1.1 Duties and responsibilities

Find a copy of your job description and read through your duties and responsibilities.

In your own words detail what each of these mean and how you carry these out in your working practices.

AC 1.2 Explain expectations about own work role as expressed in relevant standards

Being competent also involves complying with the requirements and associated standards and codes of practice that are set out by **regulators** (see page 31 for definition) in the UK for every health and social care profession. These standards exist to ensure that the individuals for whom you provide care and support are safeguarded from any danger, harm or abuse, have their rights respected and receive a high standard of care and support.

Standards vary according to the UK country in which you work. In England, the Care Quality Commission (CQC) regulates all health and social care adult services including services provided by local authorities, the NHS, private and voluntary organisations.

National Occupational Standards

The Health and Social Care **National Occupational Standards** (NOS) describe the skills and knowledge that health and social care professionals must have to carry out their jobs well. Evidencing that you understand the reasons behind your work practice and that you have the ability to apply these skills and knowledge will determine your level of **competence** in your job role (see page 29 for definition).

The Health and Social Care NOS have been developed by Skills for Care and Skills for Health, the two **sector skills councils** responsible for supporting adult social care workers and healthcare workers deliver high-quality care in England.

The Health and Social Care NOS set out the skills, knowledge and understanding required of health and social care professionals working in a range of settings and are made up of both knowledge-based and competence-based units. Some of the units are mandatory and must be completed by all those who work in health and social care. There is also a large range of optional units which allows you to demonstrate your skills, knowledge and understanding in specialist areas such as dementia care or learning disabilities. The optional units provide you with an opportunity to reflect the areas of specialism you have and the current activities you carry out as part of your job role.

National minimum standards

The Care Standards Act 2000 requires that national minimum standards are set for different care services through the provision of regulations. National minimum standards guide providers and inspectors of care services in relation to making judgements about the standard of services provided and the areas that require improvement.

Key terms

Regulators are organisations responsible for monitoring health and social care professionals.

Standards are the principles that are required to attain a high-quality service.

National Occupational Standards are the skills and knowledge that are required for professionals to carry out their jobs to a high standard.

Sector skills councils are employer-led, independent organisations that aim to improve people's skills at work.

National Minimum Standards are the standards that must be met by a service.

Regulations are laws and principles designed to guide the conduct of professionals.

Essential Standards of Quality and Safety are the standards that individuals who require care or support can expect to receive from a provider.

Codes of practice are written guidelines provided by a professional body to enable workers in that profession to work in a way that complies with its values and ethics.

Regulations

The Health and Social Care Act 2008 (Regulated Activities) **Regulations** 2010 and the Care Quality Commission (Registration) Regulations 2009 describe the **essential standards of quality and safety**. Sixteen of these standards focus on the quality and safety of care that all individuals who require care and support can expect to receive; these standards include respect for individuals' dignity and protection of their rights. The outcomes expected of care providers associated to these are identified in Figure 2.1.

Codes of Practice

Sector Skills Councils, Skills for Care and Skills for Health have also developed a Code of Practice for Healthcare Support Workers and Adult Social Care Workers in England.

This describes the professional conduct expected from workers in relation to their conduct, behaviour and attitudes when providing healthcare, care and support.

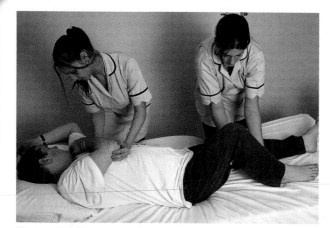

Figure 2.1 Care providers are expected to produce the outcomes discussed

Time to think

1.2 How well do you carry out your work?

- How do I approach my work tasks?
- Why do I approach my work tasks in this way?
- How does this affect others?
- Why does this affect others in this way?
- What can I do differently next time?

Evidence activity

1.2 Expectations of your work role

Read through the different standards that are relevant to health and social care professionals.

Choose three different standards and for each detail how and why these link to your job role, duties and responsibilities.

Time to think

LO1 Are you competent in your work role?

- Are you carrying out your duties and responsibilities well?
- How do the requirements of the standards compare to the requirements of your job role?
- Think about a time when you or someone else you know let their personal attitudes or beliefs get in the way of their job role. What were the consequences?

LO2 Be able to reflect on practice

AC 2.1 Explain the importance of reflective practice in continuously improving the quality of service provided

Key term

Reflective practice is an approach used to think about and improve your knowledge, understanding and skills.

Reflective practice impacts not only on you and others but also on the overall quality and standard of the service provided, because it encourages different ways of working and the development of problem-solving skills.

Sources of information

The media is a useful way to keep up to date with what is happening in the health and social care sector; the internet, reading newspaper articles, listening to news stories on the radio and watching television documentaries can all raise your awareness about changes in legislation that have occurred, new ways of working as well as serious failures that can occur when the principles that underpin health and social care are not complied with.

For example, there are a number of reports and reviews that have highlighted concerns about the quality of care experienced by individuals accessing hospitals and care services. In 2013 the Care Quality Commission published a report based on a set of inspections that focused on the dignity and nutrition of older people in hospital. 100 hospitals were inspected with respect to whether older people are treated with respect and whether they get food and drink that meets their needs – 45 hospitals met both standards, 35 hospitals needed to make further improvements to either one or both standards and 20 hospitals did not meet one or both standards. In 2014 the findings of a Serious Case Review were published following an inquest into the deaths of 19 older people who lived in Orchid View, a West Sussex care home run by Southern Cross; 34 recommendations were made to help prevent this abuse from happening again.

Attending training sessions, updates and conferences are good ways of receiving information about health and social care topics such as safeguarding, infection control and moving and handling as well as sharing ideas, ways of working and resources with others who also work in the sector. Contacts you make with other professionals and organisations that attend these events can prove to be valuable sources of information and support when issues arise in your work setting. Having others to talk to can also help you to learn about new ways of practising and to reflect on how you use this information to manage different issues that may arise.

Your own workplace setting is also a valuable source of information. Meeting your manager or supervisor, your colleagues and other professionals you may have contact with can be helpful for your development, as they can provide you with information and guidance on specific areas of your work practices as well as share with you their experiences of working in the sector. They could advise you on updates to documentation that you may be required to complete, changes to the workplace's policies and procedures and how these changes will impact on your own and others' ways of working, and training courses. All of these are good opportunities for you to update and reflect on your current and future knowledge and skills.

Much of the information that you will discuss and share with others is based on research that has been completed in the health and social care sector. Research in the sector is important as it informs both policy and work practice developments. It can help you to reflect on and increase your knowledge and understanding of current issues in the sector. Research can also help you to develop your knowledge and skills in line with current trends and approaches, and make improvements to the quality of care and support you and others provide.

The importance of research

There are three different approaches to carrying out research that are important for you to understand more about: basic, strategic and applied. Basic research helps you to develop your knowledge and understanding of the theory that underpins practices. Strategic research builds on findings from basic research by testing whether theories that are developed are reliable and valid and can be applied in practice. Applied research is research that is carried out for a specific reason such as the development of a new way of working, or testing a new approach to an issue that has arisen and proved difficult to address.

Quantitative methods

The research information you will read about and collect will fall under two types: quantitative and qualitative. Quantitative methods of research gather information in numerical and factual form which can then be measured and used for developing and improving services, for example, and can include surveys and questionnaires such as about the number of individuals living in their own homes and in residential care or the numbers of individuals living with dementia.

Qualitative methods

Qualitative methods of research gather information that is not in numerical or factual form but is descriptive and based on people's experiences, thoughts and feelings about the quality of an aspect of care or service. Examples of qualitative research can include case studies, reflective diary accounts, observations of community-based projects and initiatives, interview-led questionnaires and workshops and can be focused around how people experience living with a health condition, or the experience of caring for a relative.

Making use of all these available sources of information and support will not only enable you to build on your existing knowledge and skills and improve the quality of the service you provide but will also provide a framework for you to use when

Figure 2.2 What are the methods you use to research?

reflecting on what you have learned and how this is relevant to your practice.

Reliability and Validity

It is important to question the reliability and validity of these sources of information to ensure that the information is accurate, fair and true and has the capability to measure what we want to measure. Both reliability and validity are critical for the quality of the information collected.

AC 2.2 Demonstrate the ability to reflect on practice

As you read in the previous section, your workplace is a valuable source of information and learning. Putting into practice your knowledge and skills on a day-to-day basis while carrying out your job role and duties is another important method of learning new information.

Working in the health and social care sector means that no two days are the same; similarly every activity you carry out as part of your job will be a different experience each time, depending on who you carry it out with, when and how. It is also important not to forget about the experience and knowledge held by the people that you work with. A colleague with

more experience than you can provide you with a useful insight into the specific techniques that have been developed and used to communicate with an individual. It is also important that you see your manager or supervisor as someone you can confide in and share honestly with them what you are thinking and how you are feeling. It is only by using formal supervision sessions and discussing issues with your manager or supervisor that you can begin to reflect on what has worked well and why, the reasons why some approaches used have not been as effective as others, and the improvements you need to make to your working practices. In this way you can learn from both your mistakes and your successes and use these to further your understanding and knowledge of how to improve working practices.

Continuously looking back over the work that you do on a day-to-day basis and considering how to improve is an integral part of being a reflective practitioner (see Figure 2.2). When you choose to reflect on your work practices will depend on how much experience you have had in dealing with different types of work activities and situations. It will also depend on your individual preferences for learning, i.e. whether you prefer to learn and develop your practices as and when activities and situations unfold (this is known as reflection in action), or do so after the activity or situation has happened so that you can think about it and discuss it with work colleagues and your manager (this is known as reflection on action).

Time to think

AC 2.1, 2.2 How do you reflect?
- Do you use all stages of the reflective cycle? Why?
- Why is reflective practice important?
- Do you reflect during or after activities and situations?

AC 2.3 Describe how own values, belief systems and experiences may affect working practice

We are all individuals with different personalities, views, ways of thinking and feeling. Who we are depends on our personal characteristics, as well as who and what influence us socially; this is called our identity.

Our identity is made up of unique and diverse characteristics such as our physical appearance, our likes, dislikes, preferences, what we believe to be of value and important in life. Our identity is also based on characteristics that are similar to those of others. This is referred to as our social identity and includes factors such as:

- age (the years you have lived)
- gender (the characteristics associated with being a male or a female)
- race (the history and nationality you share with others)
- class (your socio-economic status)
- religion (your faith)
- ability (your skills and capability)
- sexuality (your sexual preference).

Values, beliefs and experiences

We are all different as a result of our personal characteristics, backgrounds and life experiences. Our values and beliefs are what we think, feel and hold as important in life. These can be moral, religious, cultural or political and could be the same as or different from those of others. Values

and beliefs are formed and developed by our life experiences and interactions with others, and can change over time with new experiences and meeting different people. Sometimes attitudes can be formed about individuals that are not based on the individual's characteristics but rather on assumptions about their social identity such as their age or religion; this can result in stereotyping and discriminating against individuals. It is important that we do not make assumptions about individuals, but rather make time to ask them about themselves and find out more about who they are.

Health and social care professionals come from a wide range of backgrounds, cultures and life experiences and these are some of the factors that influence the development of personal attitudes and beliefs. As part of your job role you will work alongside individuals and others who may have similar or different backgrounds, cultures and life experiences.

Figure 2.3 below identifies some of the key factors that can influence personal attitudes and beliefs.

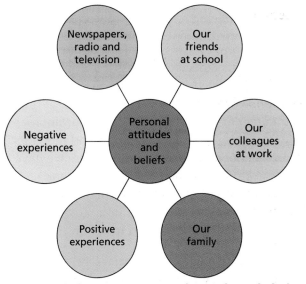

Figure 2.3 Influences on personal attitudes or beliefs

If we think about each of these factors in more detail we can begin to see how they can affect our personal attitudes and beliefs. Our relationships and activities with friends at school can shape our thinking and ideas from a young age and we may carry these through with us to our teenage years.

Similarly, later on in life our colleagues can be good sources of advice and support and also good people to observe when we are making decisions at work and interacting with others on a daily basis.

Our families can be a source of personal and emotional support or a source of conflict and so can have an impact on what we value as being important in life and how we develop as individuals.

Positive experiences in life can make us feel more confident and help to develop a sense of achievement. Negative experiences may make us feel resentful and develop negative personal attitudes or even more determined to ensure we use these in positive ways. What we read and hear about in the media can affect our views on a range of topics. Published reports and inquiries can make us more informed but will also shape our views about the sector.

Ensuring that personal attitudes or beliefs do not obstruct the quality of the care and support provided to others requires having sufficient awareness of your own and others' beliefs and attitudes and being respectful of these particularly when they are different to your own.

As part of this reflective process it is important that we acknowledge that we are all different and therefore what we think and feel will also at times be different to others. It is equally important for us to recognise that our viewpoints and thoughts will affect how we behave and therefore we have to be aware of this when providing care and support to others, otherwise this may get in the way of practising competently and providing high standards of care and support to others.

A useful way for health and social care professionals to reflect on how their personal attitudes or beliefs are affecting the quality of the care and support they provide to others is by asking themselves the following five questions:

1 How did I approach my work task?
2 Why did I approach my work task in this way?
3 How did this affect others?
4 Why did this affect others in this way?
5 What can I do differently next time?

Evidence activity

2.3 Values, beliefs and experiences
Think about your personal attitudes or beliefs.

Identify three of these and for each one detail how they may affect your working practices. How do you ensure that you do not let these affect the quality of your work?

Research and investigate

LO2 Models of reflection
Research other models of reflection. What models do you find useful? Why?

LO3 Be able to evaluate own performance

AC 3.1 Evaluate own knowledge, performance and understanding against relevant standards

Once you have understood the importance of reflecting on your practice and how to do so, the next step is to consider how you can determine how effective you are in your work role. This is an integral part of being a **reflective practitioner**.

Self-evaluation
Self-evaluation involves health and social care professionals assessing and making honest judgements about whether their knowledge, understanding and skills are up to date, reflect good practice and require any further improvements.

Self-evaluation is a continuous process that you repeat over and over again and how you do this will depend on your learning preferences both as an individual and as a practitioner.

Peter Honey and Alan Mumford (1982) developed a **model** to explain the process of learning from experience; it involved four key stages and these included Having an experience (Stage 1), Reviewing the experience (Stage 2), Concluding from the experience (Stage 3) and Planning the

Key terms

A **reflective practitioner** is someone who looks back over the work they do on a regular basis and spends time thinking about and making improvements to their working practices.

Self-evaluation is a process that involves assessing your progress, development and learning to determine what has improved and what areas still need improvement.

A **model** is a simplified way of understanding a concept.

Evaluation is a process used to assess the effectiveness of an activity or piece of work.

Professional development refers to the skills and knowledge necessary to develop your work practices and understanding.

next steps (Stage 4). It was these four stages that led to them to developing their theory around learning styles, i.e. that people had different preferences for the way they learned. The four key learning styles they developed were linked to each stage of their model: Activists (Stage 1), Reflectors (Stage 2), Theorists (Stage 3) and Pragmatists (Stage 4). See AC 5.3.

How do you evaluate yourself against relevant standards?

When you **evaluate** yourself you are:

- **assessing** the knowledge, understanding and skills **you have**
- **assessing** the knowledge, understanding and skills **you do not have**
- **assessing** the knowledge, understanding and skills that **you would like to have**.

Standards as we considered in AC 1.2 are ways of measuring health and social care professionals' levels of knowledge, understanding and performance at work both within specific work settings and nationally across the sector as a whole.

Evaluating what you do and how you do it requires you to be in control of your **professional development**. You need to take the lead in actively monitoring yourself and determining how

effective you are as a practitioner. To do this you first need to be clear about:

- what you want to do
- how you are going to do it
- why and how you are going to know when you have achieved it.

Second, you need to be prepared to be an explorer and find out the learning options available to you.

Third, you need to be a decision maker and decide on the most suitable and relevant learning options, including their availability.

Finally, you need to put your plan to develop yourself into practice. Remember you can only do this with the support and feedback from all those important others you work with.

Figure 2.4 details some of the different ways that you can evaluate yourself.

Going through the self-evaluation process will help you begin to take notice and become familiar with your strengths and areas for development with respect to your knowledge, understanding and skills against relevant standards. You can then begin to think about how you plan to gain additional knowledge, understanding and skills and set yourself some targets to aim for. This will usually be in the form of a personal development plan and can include training you would like to undertake, skills you would like to improve such as being able to make decisions, manage your time better, problem solve and/or liaise with others in the team.

AC 3.2 Demonstrate use of feedback to evaluate own performance and inform development

As with self-evaluation, feedback from others is an important way of helping us to understand our strengths and areas for development. Feedback can occur in a one-to-one situation or in a group, i.e. when meeting with your manager or when sitting in on a residents' house meeting. It can be informal or formal, i.e. verbally through a day-to-day

Finding out what you know about the standards, how much you understand, how they relate to your job role and the working practices that you follow and are good practice examples.

Finding out what standards you don't know about, aspects of the standards that you are unsure about, how they relate to your job role and the working practices that you follow that require improvement.

Planning how to build on and further develop your current levels of knowledge, understanding and working practices. Thinking into the future and deciding what kind of professional you would like to be.

Figure 2.4 Self-evaluation

conversation with a colleague or in writing through a completed complaint or suggestion form. Feedback can be open and transparent or anonymous, i.e. through a telephone discussion with an individual's relative or through an unnamed questionnaire received in the post.

Constructive criticism

Constructive criticism involves others sharing with us their views, thoughts and feelings about how our knowledge, understanding and skills have affected them, the aspects they liked and they thought worked well (positive feedback), the aspects they did not like and why they thought they did not work as well (negative feedback).

Receiving feedback

As you may have already experienced, feedback from others can be critical, constructive or negative. Receiving feedback from others and hearing what the person is trying to say through the words they use can be an important way for you to assess how effective you are as a practitioner. Giving critical feedback is a two-way process (see Figure 2.5). This involves the person giving the feedback objectively identifying the areas that require improvement as well as the person receiving the feedback having the ability to welcome the feedback received and not view it as a personal attack on them. This will help you to develop as a reflective practitioner.

When feedback is constructive it often involves using a positive tone and praising the person on their strengths and what they have done well. Very often this also involves providing clear examples of what was said or done, the

feedback received and why this worked well. When feedback is negative a positive tone can still be used when identifying the areas that require improvement. Although it is much easier to welcome feedback about what you have done well than what you have not done well it is important to be aware that some people may find this embarrassing or difficult to believe as being genuine. Other reactions to negative feedback can include being defensive and dismissive about what is being said.

Being able to accept and value both positive and negative feedback will enable you to develop and put into practice new knowledge gained and new ways of working. Ultimately it will also improve the overall quality of the service being provided, and will ensure that it meets individuals' varied and changing needs.

Figure 2.5 People who can provide you with feedback

Key term

Performance means how you carry out your job role and duties.

Case study

3.2 Marco

Marco is not sure about whether he can work with his new manager. Having recently been supervised by him, Marco found him quite critical of his working practices and always finding fault with what he is doing. Marco knows that his working practices are good because the individuals he supports and their families are always telling him what a good senior care worker he is. His previous manager also used him as a good role model for other new staff who would shadow him for their first week's shift.

1 What would you say to Marco?
2 How could Marco use the feedback he has received from his new manager?

Research and investigate

LO3 Feedback

Find out how others you work with use feedback.

Time to think

LO3 How do you evaluate your work performance?

- On a scale of 1–10 (with 10 being the highest), how do you rate your knowledge, skills and understanding? Why?
- What feedback do you receive from others? How do you use this?

Evidence activity

3.1, 3.2 Evaluating your knowledge, understanding and performance

Read through the different standards (see AC 1.2) that are relevant to health and social care professionals.

Choose three different standards and for each one assess whether your knowledge, understanding and skills match the requirements of the standards, and whether there are gaps that you need to address.

You will need to be observed by your assessor evaluating your knowledge, understanding and **performance** against relevant standards as well as using feedback from others to do so.

You will also need to explain how people might react and respond to constructive feedback, the importance of seeking feedback in improving your practice and informing your development, as well as the importance of using feedback in improving your practice.

LO4 Be able to agree a personal development plan

AC 4.1 Identify sources of support for planning and reviewing own development

Once you have understood the importance of engaging in a range of learning activities, the next step is to consider how to agree a **personal development plan** with others.

Sources of support

There are many sources of support within the workplace and externally, which will enable you to plan and review your personal and professional development in relation to your learning and

Key terms

A **personal development plan (PDP)** is a way of recording your past achievements and future learning objectives.

Development opportunities refer to any learning or practice-based opportunities for achieving your personal and career goals.

Action learning means working with others in small groups or sets to discuss and resolve issues and difficulties.

working practices. Figure 2.6 identifies some useful sources of support that can be used by health and social care professionals.

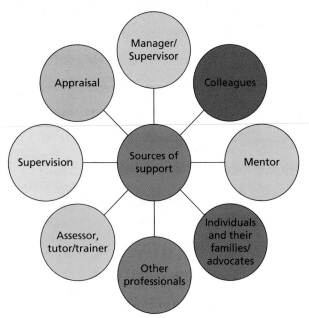

Figure 2.6 Sources of support

Planning and reviewing your development

Talking to your **manager** or **supervisor** is a good starting point for planning how you want to progress in your current work role and career, as your manager/supervisor is responsible for your performance at work. Their roles will also involve monitoring and reviewing your past and current performance.

Your **colleagues**, **individuals** and their **families/advocates** can help you to plan for areas of knowledge or skills that you need to update to meet the unique and changing needs and expectations of the people you care for, and can be valuable sources of informal support. You may do this by sharing ideas and discussing different situations that have arisen and the different ways of dealing with these in small groups or sets as part of **action learning** (see page 39 for definition). Feedback can indicate how effective your care and support have been.

When used as a source of support, **mentors** can be very effective in providing encouragement, support, guidance and feedback on your **personal development** needs, including training and

development opportunities you have accessed (see page 39 for definition and AC 4.2 for more information).

Supervision is a formal process (see Figure 2.7) used to further develop your knowledge and skills on an ongoing basis and can involve one-to-one supervision with your manager or supervisor, supervision with experienced colleagues (known as peer supervision) and/or supervision as a team (known as group supervision). Supervision can be a useful way of reflecting on practice and planning for improvements. Supervision from others can be useful for discussing and sharing your ideas about your personal development, i.e. your roles and responsibilities, what you learned and/or achieved, to what extent this improved your practice, any gaps in your knowledge and skills and how to plan to address these.

Appraisal is a formal process that involves reflection and making plans for how to address any learning and performance needs that may have been identified; usually this involves planning for the year ahead. Your personal development plan is usually the outcome of this process.

Externally, other **professionals**, your **assessor, tutor or trainer** can be additional sources of support for planning and reviewing your personal development. They can guide you on how to evidence and improve your knowledge and skills.

Figure 2.7 Formal supervision

AC 4.2 Demonstrate how to work with others to review and prioritise own learning needs, professional interests and development opportunities

It is important for health and social care professionals to be able to review and prioritise their learning needs. You will have to agree these with your manager or supervisor; considering the benefits of these to you, your employer and the service overall can help you both to decide and agree on your learning needs that take priority.

Professional interests

Your professional interests are closely linked to your job role and your career plans. How you **review** and **prioritise** your professional interests will depend primarily on the knowledge and skills that are required for your job role, and the areas

that you are required to develop by your employer to ensure that you carry out your job role duties and responsibilities well. Your manager or supervisor and other professionals will play a key role in providing you with guidance in this area.

Your professional interests will also be closely linked to your plans for your career and the knowledge and skills you require to progress towards achieving your career goals. Mentors, career advisors and all those who know you well will be central to supporting you with realising your career plans.

Development opportunities

The development opportunities you undertake and prioritise will depend on the training you have already undertaken, as well as how experienced you are. Future training and other qualifications will depend on whether they are required as part of your job role and the resources available. Development opportunities may also be prioritised where a service requires this, e.g. expertise around dementia care or end-of-life care.

Development opportunities will be reviewed and prioritised by working alongside your manager or supervisor, your colleagues, other professionals as well as individuals, carers and advocates. You can only do this effectively by working closely with others as 'no man is an island'.

AC 4.3 Demonstrate how to work with others to agree own personal development plan

When agreeing your personal development plan with others it is important to remember that your personal development plan is organic; in other words, it grows, changes and develops with you as you progress through your career and life. It is a continuous progress of learning and development as well as a plan for your career.

Agreeing your personal development plan involves working with others such as your manager or supervisor, your colleagues, other professionals and individuals to:

1 Decide on what you want to achieve (goals).
2 Identify the areas you need to improve on (targets).

3 Identify the methods you will use to make improvements.

4 Put together a plan of action.

5 Put your plan of action into practice.

6 Evidence the results.

7 Evaluate and review your development activities.

Whatever form your personal development plan takes, it is important to remember that you cannot agree and develop it by working on your own. You need to work closely with the relevant people to clearly identify, access and review suitable training and development opportunities within realistic timescales.

SMART objectives

You will need to be able to develop a series of manageable steps to enable you to achieve the knowledge and skills you require by working with others in SMARTER ways, i.e. by developing goals that are:

- Specific
- Measurable
- Achievable
- Realistic
- Time-bound
- Evaluating them regularly
- Re-doing or repeating them.

A personal development plan is not just a record of your development, it is part of a process that you will change and will move forward with you in your life and work.

Evidence activity

4.2, 4.3 Working with others

Read through your personal development plan.

Identify three people who provide you with support and feedback in relation to your personal development.

For each person, consider and explain how you work with them to:

- review and prioritise your learning needs, professional interests and development opportunities
- agree your personal development plan.

Explain the benefits of using a personal development plan to identify ongoing improvements in knowledge and understanding.

Research and investigate

LO4 Personal development opportunities

Find out what personal development opportunities are available across the organisation you work for.

Time to think

LO4 Personal development plan

- Who supports you at work? How?
- Who support you outside of work? How?
- What roles do others play in your personal development plan?

LO5 Be able to use learning opportunities and reflective practice to contribute to personal development

AC 5.1 Evaluate how learning activities have affected practice

Once you have understood the importance of evaluating your practice and how to do so by using feedback from others, the next step is to consider how you can use learning opportunities and reflective practice to contribute to your personal and professional development.

Learning opportunities can take place in both your personal and professional working life. They often involve experiencing something new or different that can be useful for your development both as a person and a professional.

For example, completing a work-related course requires good organisation and time management skills; it can also bring with it a great sense of achievement and can open our minds to new ideas and knowledge. Managing our time effectively and being organised are useful skills to have for day-to-day activities, and when we are feeling confident and proud of our achievements at work it is very often the case that we can bring some of that newfound confidence to our personal lives and relationships.

Assessing the extent that learning opportunities affect working practices requires health and social care professionals to think about the reasons why they completed learning opportunities. They also need to reflect on whether their needs and expectations were met, as well as why this may not have happened. Health and social care professionals can also measure the effectiveness of learning activities by giving careful consideration to what they have learned from both their achievements and their mistakes. This process involves health and social care professionals assessing themselves, a process known as self-assessment.

How do we learn?

There are many different theories about the processes we follow when learning. A useful theory for understanding how we learn and a model often used by professionals for reflection is David Kolb's experiential learning cycle as shown in Figure 2.8.

Figure 2.8 David Kolb's experiential learning cycle

David Kolb's experiential learning cycle emphasises how important experience is as part of the learning process and involves four key stages.

Meaning of stages of Kolb's experiential learning cycle

Stage 1: Concrete Experience – This stage of the learning cycle is the action of having an experience such as completing a task you are familiar with, a new situation or a different activity.

Stage 2: Reflective Observation – This stage of the learning cycle is the review of the experience that has taken place. It involves thinking about what has occurred and why.

Stage 3: Abstract Conceptualisation – This stage of the learning cycle is the learning that takes place following your reflections of the experience that has taken place. It involves understanding and bringing together all your thoughts and ideas.

Stage 4: Active Experimentation – This stage of the learning cycle is the trialling and checking of the thoughts and ideas you have suggested. It involves putting into practice what you have learned.

As David Kolb's learning cycle suggests, although stage 4 is the final stage to go through you may find that you need to repeat all four stages several times before you can make sense of your learning. Whether you choose to do this as an experience unfolds or afterwards will depend on whether you prefer to reflect in or on action, a concept you read about in AC 2.3.

How we learn will also be determined by our learning preferences and the more aware that we are of our own and others' preferred ways of learning the more effective reflectors and practitioners we will become. Learning styles must also form the basis of any development opportunities that are identified, i.e. to get the most learning from a development activity you should choose one that reflects your learning style.

> ### Time to think
>
> **5.1** **Honey and Mumford**
>
> Peter Honey and Alan Mumford developed a theory that linked people's learning styles to each stage of Kolb's experiential learning cycle. They identified four different learning styles or preferences: Activist, Theorist, Pragmatist and Reflector – see Figure 2.9.
>
> Research the different styles and preferences.

Figure 2.9 Different learning styles – how do you learn best?

Whatever your learning style is, it is very important that you use the information that you find out about yourself in relation to the way you prefer to learn to help you to take part in learning activities that are going to help you fully achieve your personal development plan.

AC 5.2 Demonstrate how reflective practice has led to improved ways of working

Reflective practice involves health and social care professionals taking time out to think about and assess their experiences, knowledge and skills with the aim of improving working practices. This also involves thinking about the impact that your personal and professional development has on others such as the individuals, colleagues and professionals you work with as part of your job role; an integral part of being a reflective practitioner as you will have read about in section 2.2.

Reflective practice can lead to improved ways of working by:

- **developing your knowledge and skills**: gaining new and additional knowledge and skills will mean that you are up to date with current best practice
- **developing new approaches**: putting into practice different and more effective ways of meeting individuals' and others' needs
- **raising your awareness about your strengths and areas for development**: increased self-awareness will mean you having a greater

Evidence activity

5.1, 5.2 Learning activities and reflective practice

Identify three learning activities you have undertaken and assess how each has affected your practice.

Think about how reflective practice has contributed to improving working practices.

You will also need to be observed by your assessor evaluating how learning activities and reflective practice have impacted on ways of working.

insight into your knowledge, skills and gaps which can help you plan for future learning and development

- **making you more aware of how your actions affect others**: increased insight into the impact your actions have on others can make you more attentive and empathetic to others' feelings and views. You will have a better understanding of them and be able to provide a better service as a result
- **improving your working relationships with others**: listening to and sharing views and ideas with others can improve the way you interact and work with others.

Being a reflective practitioner therefore involves very many different elements, including wanting to learn, knowing how to do so, being able to make use of development tools such as learning cycles and styles and being prepared to find out as much as you can about yourself, both personally and professionally.

AC 5.3 Show how to record progress in relation to personal development

Once you have completed all the learning and development you can it is important to be able to evidence this so that you can reflect on your achievements and make plans for the future.

Personal development plans (PDPs), also known as **Personal learning plans (PLPs)** and **Personal development reviews (PDRs)**, are a formal way of recording how health and social care professionals plan and review their development in their job roles, i.e. the learning and development activities they have achieved over the past year as well as their planned activities for the year ahead such as new skills, training or courses. PDPs are also often used as the basis for developing five-year career plans as they are regularly updated and reflected on by health and social care professionals and their managers.

Creating your PDP

How your PDP is put together will depend on where you work, as this varies from one work setting to another. It may include some or all of the following:

- **Your Details** – details about your name, job role, where you work, the name of your manager or supervisor
- **Your Areas of Strength and Development** – details about your strengths and how you can make the most of these, details about areas that you are aware of that need further development and ways to address these
- **Your Goals** – details about what you would like to achieve, how these link to your personal goals but also to your job role and workplace's requirements
- **Actions** – details about specific actions for achieving your goals including realistic timescales, i.e. next 3 months, 6 months, 12 months, 1 year, 2 years, 3 years, 4 years, 5 years
- **Barriers** – details about potential barriers that may stop you from achieving your goals including how to minimise or remove these
- **Sources of Support** – details about who will support you and how, other resources that are available to you
- **Monitoring Progress** – details about how to keep track of your progress including details

about activities undertaken, what you have achieved and what you have not yet achieved.

Monitoring progress

The Monitoring Progress section is often shown as the final section in your personal development plan and is one of the most important as keeping this section up to date will help you and others who are supporting you to see how you are continuing to develop with your personal and professional plans and goals. Keeping a close check on how you are progressing with your planned learning will ensure that you give yourself the best possible chance of achieving your goals. Reaching this final section in your personal development plan will not be the end of the process but rather a good way to review and re-plan your learning cycle.

Figure 2.10 shows other ways of recording your personal development. How many of these have you used?

Recording and reviewing your progress in relation to your personal and professional development with others such as your manager and supervisor will enable you to be clear about you want to achieve, how and by when. Moving forward with your learning and development is a journey you will make not on your own but with the support from others.

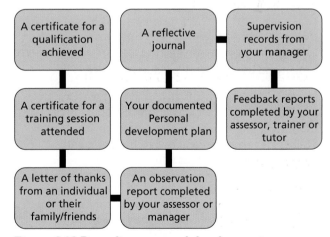

Figure 2.10 Recording personal development

Key terms

PDP is an action plan for planning and goal setting that is used for both personal and professional development.

PLP is an action plan for achieving short, medium and long-term learning goals.

PDR is the process of discussing achievements, as well as improvements that are required.

Case study

5.3 David

David, a community-based senior support worker, has recently achieved his L3 Diploma in Health and Social Care (Adults). He has noticed that his knowledge around health and safety risk assessments and person-centred practices has improved. David also feels that his colleagues seem to turn to him more for support and advice, and that he has developed better working relationships with them.

1 Why do you think this is?
2 How can David evidence his achievements?

Evidence activity

5.3 Personal development plan

Read through a copy of your personal development plan and use it as work product evidence.

You will need to be able to detail what each part of your personal development plan is about.

You will also need to be observed by your assessor recording and reviewing personal development activities you undertake.

Research and investigate

LO5 Recording your personal development

Research different ways of recording your personal development. Ask your manager or supervisor for advice.

Time to think

LO5 How do you use reflective practice?

- Think about a learning activity you completed and enjoyed. How did it affect your practice? Why?
- Think about a learning activity you would like to complete. How do you think it will affect your practice?
- What improvements have you made to your and others' working practices?
- What records do you keep of your personal development?

Legislation

- The Care Standards Act 2000
- The Health and Social Care Act 2008

Useful resources

Websites

Care Quality Commission:

cqc.org.uk

Honey and Mumford:

peterhoney.com

National Occupational Standards database:

nos.ukces.org.uk

Skills for Health:

skillsforhealth.org.uk

Skills for Care and Development:

skillsforcareanddevelopment.org.uk

Publications

Bloom, B.S. (1956) *Taxonomy of Educational Objectives. Handbook I: The Cognitive Domain*, New York: David McKay Co Inc.

Honey, P. (2007), *Continuing Personal Development*, Maidenhead: Peter Honey Publications.

Knapman, J. and Morrison, T. (1998), *Making the Most of Supervision in Health and Social Care*, Brighton: Pavilion Publishers.

Schön, D. (1983), *The Reflective Practitioner. How professionals think in action*, London: Temple Smith.

Promote equality and inclusion in health, social care or children's and young people's settings

This unit is worth 2 credits

What are you finding out?

Equality and inclusion are fundamental principles in our society not just ideals to be considered in the context of health and social care. The principles of equality and inclusion are, for example, embedded in legislation like the Human Rights Act, 1998, which legislates that people should be protected from discrimination and the Equality Act 2010 which addresses social and economic inequalities.

Britain is now a multi-cultural society which is reflected in the wide spectrum of people who use health and social care. As workers we must be both aware of and sensitive to the differences in culture, beliefs and preferences of our service users. Inequality and exclusion have no place in those services which often deal with the most vulnerable and unwell members of our society.

We continue to be a society marked by extremes – consider the current anti-Islamic movements, or the

anti-abortion lobby. It can be argued that in a free society we have the right of freedom of expression to voice these opinions. However, as health and social care workers we also have a responsibility not to collude with extreme views which can lead to activities like hate crime. In this unit you will find out how discriminatory practice (treating someone unfairly because of their race, age or ethnicity) can affect the individual, and how positive inclusive practice counteracts this. You will be able to demonstrate ways of working which promote diversity, equality and inclusion as positive concepts applied in everyday practice.

The reading and activities in this unit will help you to:

1 Understand the importance of diversity, equality and inclusion.
2 Be able to work in an inclusive way.
3 Be able to promote diversity, equality and inclusion.

Links to Level 3 Certificate in Preparing to Work in Adult Social Care

SHC33 Assessment criteria	Unit PWCS33
AC 1.1	AC1.1 (diversity, equality, inclusion)
AC 1.2	AC1.2
AC 3.3	AC3.1

LO1 Understand the importance of diversity, equality and inclusion

AC 1.1 What is meant by diversity, equality and inclusion?

Diversity

Diversity describes a wide range of people. The concept assumes that we accept, respect and celebrate the cultural, sexual, social and economic differences between us.

Types of diversity

In our work in health and social care – whether in collective care settings or in the person's own home, we will encounter a diverse range of people. Our work in health and social care reflects the wider society. Diversity means variety. The dance group 'Diversity' is a good example. It comprises boys and young men of different ages, backgrounds and styles who perform a wide variety of dance routines. 'Diversity' also implies pride in their differences and celebrates the way these differences are a positive force.

The people you encounter in your work setting will also come from a variety of cultures and social groups and will have different attitudes and preferences. This also includes your colleagues. We are all shaped by our history, education and the social norms we grew up with. We all respond to these in different ways, and we must avoid using stereotypes to describe a particular social or ethnic group – for example, people from the Roma community are often denied access to education or jobs because it is assumed they are unreliable, or not willing to engage.

People differ in many ways, not only because of their cultural, social or political background age and sexual orientation. Other differences includes:

- Language and communication. Communication is not just talking and listening. We know that a significant part of communication is through body language which varies in different cultures. For example, in some cultures it is considered impolite to make eye contact. People from many cultures find it uncomfortable if their '**personal space**' (see page 49 for definition) is invaded and certainly, when supporting the individual with personal care you must take into account their preferences and wishes, which may include a woman preferring female care support workers helping them.
- We also use body language to communicate emotions and preferences. There are some types of body language like signing that are used for a specific purpose and in this example it is in place of the spoken word. As health and care support workers it is important to be able to both understand and use body language effectively. For example, be wary of using 'defensive' body language like crossing your arms or intrusive language like leaning over an individual.
- Religious belief. We know that we must be sensitive to the practices of different faiths, for example fasting during Ramadan, or attending Mass. However, we should also not make assumptions – people of the Muslim faith will have different views as will those of the Catholic faith. It is a principle of person centred care that

Key term

Culture refers to the characteristics of particular group or society.

Figure 3.1 What does diversity mean to you?

we find out how each individual views their faith – one size does not fit all.

- Social norms. These are formed by the way you were brought up by your parents, the education you received and the situations and experiences you were exposed to. This helps to shape your attitude to your place in society and defines how you behave within society. For example, there will be particular social norms observed in a care home – an expectation that staff and residents behave or conform in particular ways.

Stereotypes and prejudice

We have used the term 'stereotypes' in the example of the Roma people earlier. When we use a stereotype when we believe unfairly that all people or things with a particular characteristic are the same and will behave in a particular way. It negates the idea of diversity because by stereotyping people we categorise and isolate them. If we

believe that all Roma people behave in a particular way and need the same things we ignore their individuality and cannot meet individual needs.

Prejudice can go hand in hand with the concept of stereotypes because it describes the unjustified or incorrect attitude (usually negative) towards an individual based solely on the individual's membership of a social group. There are many examples of prejudice throughout history, from racial hatred to the punishment of gay men and women in the early 20th Century (**homophobia**).

Labelling

Labelling is an inherent aspect of stereotyping – so all old people are 'frail' or all looked after children must be 'difficult' or come from 'unstable or dysfunctional backgrounds'. This is clearly not the case and to think in this way damages our ability to support the individual in a person centred way because it clouds our ability to see the person as an individual.

Key terms

Homophobia is the hatred, intolerance, and fear of lesbian, gay and bisexual (LGB) people. These negative feelings support myths, stereotypes, and discrimination.

Prejudice does not celebrate diversity, rather it fears or punishes it.

Personal space is the area surrounding a person that they regard as psychologically theirs.

Time to think

1.1 What are you learning about?

Now think about the people that use your service. They may seem the same in that they all belong to a particular service user group; for example, they are all children, older people, people with a disability or people with a similar health condition. What did you assume about them when you first met them? How has your opinion changed once you got to know the individual?

Figure 3.2 Labels and stereotypes should not inform your interaction with individuals

By acknowledging the diversity of others, you are a step closer to recognising the differences in people and to celebrate those differences. Being 'different' is a problem when it prevents the individual from accessing services and the person's individuality is not considered important. For example, you may always wear red clothes – that makes you different but may not be the issue – the issue may be that you use a wheelchair and the local cinema is not recognising that difference because it is not providing you equal access by providing a ramp.

Equality

Equality means that we ensure individuals or groups of individuals are treated fairly and equally or not less favourably, including in areas of:

- Sex discrimination
- Pay and conditions

- Racial equality
- Disability and rights of access to public places.

The Equality Act of 2010 replaces anti-discrimination laws like The Sex Discrimination Act 1975, The Race Relations Act 1976, and The Disability Discrimination Act 1995.

The Equality Act Codes of Practice 2011 provide guidance about how to implement anti-discriminatory practice.

There are new headings including gender reassignment, religion or belief, marriage and civil partnership, and pregnancy which are now known as 'protected characteristics'. This means that individuals who may have one or more of these characteristics, for example, have legal protection against discrimination.

There is also a new 'equality duty' which requires public authorities to pay attention to:

- Eliminating discrimination
- Advancing equal opportunities
- Fostering (encouraging) good relations and promoting understanding.

Promoting equality is also a personal ideology – a standard by which, as an individual, you try to live your life. For example; you may have decided to be an Equality and Diversity Champion in your place of work. It is also a legal requirement – as we can see from the legislation described. This means that a legal responsibility is placed on statutory, independent and voluntary organisations to behave within

Research and investigate

1.1 Equal opportunities

Select a service user group (such as children with learning difficulties) and find out what support services are available to prevent individuals being disadvantaged or treated less fairly than anyone else.

Think about the legislation we have described. What principle of the legislation does this fall under? (For example, advancing equal opportunities).

the spirit of the law. Your own organisation will have policies which promote equality of access to services and opportunities. As a member of that organisation you also have a responsibility to uphold the promotion of equality and diversity – to respect the right for people to have the same opportunities to access health and social care services and not to be treated unfairly or in a discriminatory manner because of their gender, faith, social group, disability etc.

Inequality

Inequality implies a lack of opportunity and of being disadvantaged because of particular traits which include:

- Race, for example, people from particular ethnic backgrounds may not be considered for housing in certain areas – this is called social exclusion
- Appearance, for example, being considered for a job may be precluded because of your appearance, despite you having the appropriate abilities, qualifications and experience
- Disability, for example being excluded from a social group because you live with dementia and no adjustments are made to accommodate this
- Age, for example, not being able to continue working after a certain age.

There are also social inequalities like:

- **Health inequality** – when people from certain groups may be disadvantaged or unable to access the care they need. People with mental health needs do are an example of this because they may be reluctant to access mainstream services or are reluctant to talk about their mental health.
- **Economic inequality** – when people are trapped within a standard of living that is sometimes called 'the poverty trap', for example working age people with disabilities are more likely to be unable to earn enough money to change their situation and are dependent on benefits.
- **Social mobility** – a combination of low income, poor access to education or employment can lead to inequality of opportunities – people become 'stuck' in a low income job with little prospect of moving on or improving their social situation.

Case study

1.1 Inequality and disadvantage

Anna is six years old and uses a wheelchair. She has cerebral palsy, misses a lot of school and has frequent appointments at hospital, many of which she is unable to attend. She lives with her mother, Jane, who is single and unable to work due to her caring commitments. Jane finds caring for Anna and getting her to school and hospital quite exhausting. She does not drive and receives no help other than social security benefit payments.

In which ways are Anna and Jane being disadvantaged?

Describe the inequalities both Anna and Jane are experiencing.

Key term

Cerebral palsy is a general term used for a number of neurological conditions that affect movement and co-ordination. It is typically caused by damage to the brain before or at birth.

Inclusion

Inclusion describes being part of something, and more importantly, being accepted as a part of the whole. Social inclusion refers to how society and groups within society accept people into their social group. Social inclusion is incorporated into social policy, and addresses how people are disadvantaged when they are not accepted and included in particular groups because of their particular characteristics. Think about the incidence of gay men in football or rugby. Very few gay men have 'come out' and this is probably because it has historically been seen as unacceptable for gay men to be included in this social group.

We all have to accept that discrimination and exclusion (opposed to inclusion) is present both in society and in our own workplace. Any worker should challenge this because such practices will always disadvantage the individuals they are there to support. It is also important to take a critical look at our values and attitudes to others. As health and social care workers you have a responsibility and duty to act in a non-discriminatory way to help those we support to experience a level of social inclusion enjoyed by less disadvantaged people. See AC 1.2 for more information on discrimination.

Evidence activity

1.1 Diversity

Think about three health and social care settings, such as a youth club, a mother and baby clinic and a day care centre for people with learning disabilities.

- In what ways might the individuals attending each setting be different from one another?
- Why is it important that each setting has a diverse range of service users?

Equality

Think about Anna and Jane's situation in the case study above. Explain why it is important that they are not disadvantaged, that they are treated fairly.

Inclusion

Think about the health and care services that you identified above as aiming to reduce social exclusion. Explain how an individual would benefit from using each service. Can you give examples of other ways of ensuring social inclusion which do not involve age or disability related services. For example, real social inclusion might be just being able to go to the pub!

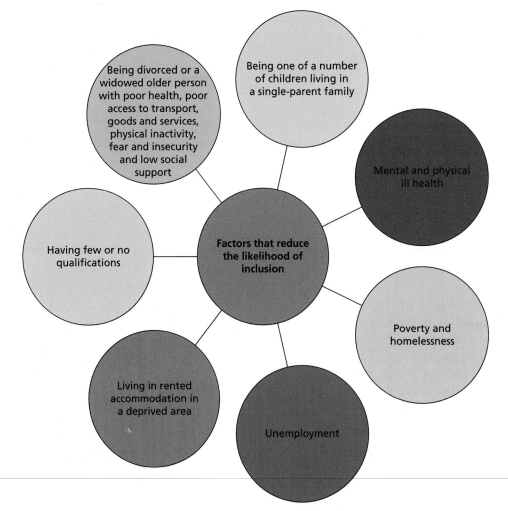

Figure 3.3 Factors that reduce the likelihood of inclusion

AC 1.2 Describe the potential effects of discrimination on individuals

What is discrimination?

Discrimination occurs when we judge people on their differences and use these differences to create disadvantage or oppression. This can prevent opportunities to access employment or services. In the workplace, discrimination can occur because we make assumptions about people.

There are two types of discrimination – direct and indirect:

Direct or deliberate discrimination describes a situation when an individual is treated unfairly intentionally, based on their differences. Examples include discrimination because of their sexual orientation, skin colour or age – i.e. sexism, racism or ageism.

Indirect or inadvertent (accidental) discrimination can be just as damaging but you may not even be aware of it. This applies to ways of working which may be aimed at the majority but do not take into account the differences between people. For example, the information leaflet about your service – might be aimed at the majority of your service users and there may even be several translations, but there may be no acknowledgement that some service users are not be able to read at all. They are therefore discriminated against because this has not been acknowledged and their needs have been (unintentionally) ignored.

Who is affected?

When we discriminate we ignore that which makes the person an individual. We make assumptions based on prejudice and this affects the way in which we can deliver services. We might discriminate based on:

● Ethnic background, or religion – we still discriminate against people from different cultures and faiths – consider the current 'Islamophobia' – do you think that some

employers, for example, may now think twice before employing a devout Muslim?

● Age – despite being an ageing society there are still myths about older people being frail or confused and not being able to contribute to society. As in other cases we tend to look at what the person can't do rather than what they can do.

● Gender – as a society we still assume there are hetero sexual, lesbian and gay people, but in fact, gender is far more complex and we continue to discriminate against people who are undergoing gender reassignment, for example.

● Financial status – people living on a low income or benefits are less likely to be considered for some rented accommodation.

● Hate crime against people with a disability is a known phenomenon.

What are the effects of discrimination?

There can be long and short term effects of discrimination, on the individual, their social group and society. There can also be social, political and economic consequences. For the individual – discrimination can be very personal and as a result leaves them feeling marginalised, victimised and despondent. It can have an adverse effect on mental well-being.

Social groups who are discriminated against will sometimes 'turn in' on themselves and retreat from the wider society – they are then accused of not integrating, this can be seen, for example in some ethnic groups.

Discrimination should not to be tolerated in society as a whole and certainly not in your area of work. If discriminatory behaviour is ignored or colluded with it leads to institutional racism, abuse, hate crime and many other expressions of intolerance.

There are many organisations that are politically active in fighting discriminatory practice, one of the most famous being www.amnesty.org/en/discrimination.

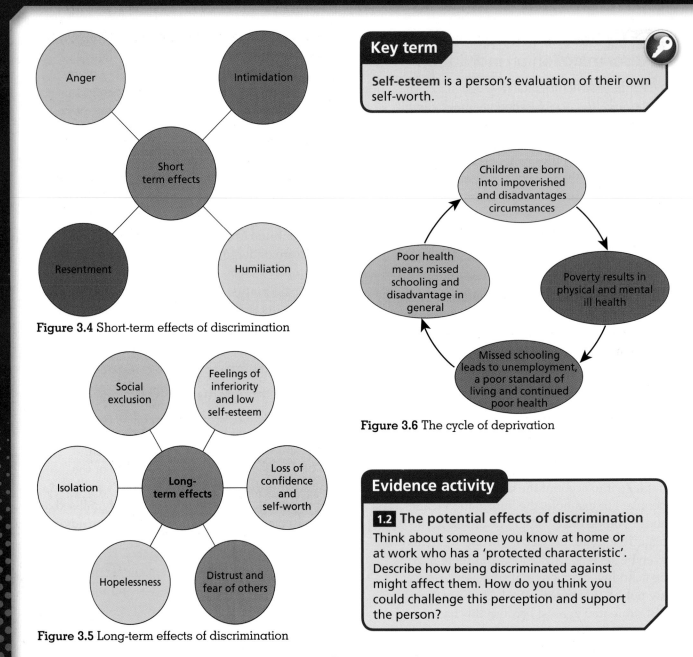

Figure 3.4 Short-term effects of discrimination

Figure 3.5 Long-term effects of discrimination

Figure 3.6 The cycle of deprivation

Key term

Self-esteem is a person's evaluation of their own self-worth.

Evidence activity

1.2 The potential effects of discrimination

Think about someone you know at home or at work who has a 'protected characteristic'. Describe how being discriminated against might affect them. How do you think you could challenge this perception and support the person?

Case study

1.2 Direct and indirect discrimination

The manager of a local care home for older people has ruled that staff cannot wear anything on their heads as the residents are having difficulty recognising each staff member. What sort of discrimination does this situation illustrate?

How do you think it could be challenged?

Can you think of any solutions to this problem?

Positive discrimination

The Equality Act 2010 builds on current legislation and extends it to include 'protected characteristics' such as age and disability. It allows, but does not require, action to be taken to support those with a protected characteristic, as long as it is proportionate (reasonable, given the circumstances). Examples of this include training to enable individuals to gain employment, or specific health services to address their needs.

AC 1.3 Explain how inclusive practice promotes equality and supports diversity

Inclusive practice means that in your work you should promote social inclusion, and integration. This includes:

- building on the strengths and achievements of individuals
- providing support in times of vulnerability.

In doing so you are acknowledging the personhood of the individual and the impact that discrimination can potentially have on their life.

You also have a responsibility to challenge discriminatory practice and respect the values of equal opportunities. You can also lead by example and demonstrate good practice.

Adult social and health care is changing, to ensure that the people who use services are at the heart of their own care and support. 'Our Health, Our Care, Our Say' (2006) and 'Putting People First' (2007), described greater choice and control for individuals and better support for carers and families. The most recent legislation, The Care Act 2014 aims to achieve:

- clearer, fairer care and support
- people being in control of their care.

These are examples of inclusive practice at a national level which should be implemented by health and social care practitioners with their service users. The diversity of people is recognised by equality of access to support. People will have a greater sense of belonging and well-being and feel that their differences are being acknowledged and not discriminated against.

Figure 3.7 A sense of belonging and well-being

Evidence activity

1.3 Inclusive work practice

Think about a particular individual you support. Can you demonstrate inclusive practice in the way that supports them – does their care plan reflect inclusivity?

LO2 Be able to work in an inclusive way

AC 2.1 Explain how legislation and codes of practice relating to equality, diversity and discrimination apply to your work role

Legislation

There has been a series of laws (legislation) over the past twenty years which govern the way in which we ensure and treat minority and disadvantaged members of society in a non-discriminatory way. They include:

- Human Rights Act 1998
- The Equality Act 2010
- Disability Discrimination Act 1995
- The Sex Discrimination Act 1975 (amended 1986).
- Race Relations Act 1976 (amended 2000).

Some legislation and codes of practice may directly affect your work, like the Human Rights Act. This Act prohibits discrimination on a wide range of grounds including 'sex, race, colour, language, religion, political or other opinion, national or social origin, association with a national minority, birth or other status'.

In your work this means that you should never judge, or give preferential treatment to one person over another based on their background, age or disability. Care and support is offered based on assessed need.

There are other laws which are aimed at legislating policies in the health and social care sector. These include:

- The Residential Care and Nursing Homes Regulations 2002, which outlines standards for care homes
- The Children Act 1989 put a responsibility on Local Authorities to meet children's needs in a more tailored way and placed the needs of the child as 'paramount'
- The NHS and Community Care Act 1980 put an emphasis on choice, and living and receiving care in the community. This legislation puts a statutory responsibility on Local Authorities and NHS Providers to ensure services are delivered in a fair and impartial way
- The most recent pieces of legislation which have a bearing on this are: The Equality Act 2010 and The Care Act 2014.

The Equality Act 2010

This has replaced other laws like the Disability Discrimination Act and The Race Relations Act. The Act is aimed at removing inequalities. It defines 'protected characteristics' like age or race, and outlines prohibited conduct like direct and indirect discrimination.

The Act is aimed at all public services, like education, health and social care. Public authorities have a duty to promote equality, prevent discriminatory practice and encourage equal opportunities.

The current UK legislation (Equality Act 2010) places a duty on all public sector organisations to:

- eliminate discrimination, harassment and victimisation in the workplace
- advance equality of opportunity between people from different groups
- foster good relations between people of different groups.

The Care Act 2014

This Act aims to promote equality and diversity in the provision of services.

'Local authority responsibilities ... tend to focus on what service should be provided, rather than on what the person actually needs or wants. We want a care and support system built around the individual. We therefore need change, so that assessments focus on what the person wants to achieve.'

(Department of Health Feb 2015)

Figure 3.8 How do you ensure you follow legislation and codes of practice?

Research and investigate

2.1a Legislation

Look at two pieces of the legislation listed previously. Consider how they relate to equality, diversity and discrimination. Look at the relevant policies and procedures in your place of work. How do these reflect this legislation?

Choose one policy and discuss it with your manager – do you think you and your colleagues are working within the 'spirit' of the policy. What, if anything could you improve in your everyday practice?

2.1b A breach of rights

Research a 'human interest' story, either nationally or locally – for example abuse in a care setting or a person with a disability being denied access to a public building

What does the story tell you about the principles of equality and diversity – how was the individual/s discriminated against. What lessons can you and your organisation learn from this – and what do you do well already and why?

Codes of practice

Codes of Practice (or standards) set out safe and effective practice in the professions that are regulated by the different professional bodies. The codes draw from relevant legislation and aim to:

- Protect the public
- Ensure workers are accountable for their conduct
- Give guidance on behaviour related to care and interaction with individuals and the public.

Regulatory bodies include:

- Skills for Health and Care National Occupational Standards which also hosts current standards for health and care support workers (NOS) www.skillsforcare.org.uk
- Nursing and Midwifery Council (NMC), www.nmc-uk.org, whose professional standards (2015) include:
  - 'Avoid making assumptions and recognise diversity and individual choice'
  - 'Respect and uphold people's human rights'.
  - 'Act as an advocate for the vulnerable, challenging poor practice and discriminatory attitudes and behaviour relating to their care'. This expects staff to not only act in an anti-discriminatory way themselves but to challenge poor practice. This is partly a reflection of the issues unearthed at Winterbourne View and Mid Staffordshire hospital.

Health and Care Professions Council has its own set of 'Standards of Proficiency' which include:

- 'Be aware of the impact of culture, equality and diversity on practice' – treat every person as an individual, and do not make assumptions – the traveller may in fact be very content to stay on the ward, but may need support with communication.
- 'Be able to reflect on and take account of the impact of inequality, disadvantage and discrimination on those who use social work services and their communities'.
- 'Understand the need to adapt practice to respond appropriately to different groups and individuals' a 'problem' and approach them in a way that reassures the individual that you are considering and valuing their preferences.

In 2011 CQC produced guidance on the equality and human rights aspects of the essential standards of quality and safety. This was done jointly with the Human Rights Commission. The aim is to:

Know the steps to take if they are concerned that a provider may be in breach of equality or human rights laws.

The new standards for inspection of care providers ask – 'is the provider:'

- Safe? – would anyone from any cultural background, experiencing particular difficulties, feel safe with the staff and the environment they are being supported by?
- Effective? – does the organisation work effectively in delivering care in line with legislation and policies?
- Caring? – does the organisation deliver the right care at the right time, with empathy and a real understanding about the different needs of individuals?
- Responsive to people's needs? – does the organisation find out about the different cultures, preferences and needs of individuals and ensure all these factors are taken into account in the delivery of care?
- Well-led? – is the organisation led in a way that encourages excellent anti discriminatory and inclusive practice – is there a culture that welcomes diversity and challenges poor practice?

Source: Care Quality Commission, www.cqc.org.uk

AC 2.2 Show interaction with individuals that respects their beliefs, culture, values and preferences

In the previous sections you have looked at the effects of discrimination on the individual, and how within organisations and as practitioners we must work in an anti-discriminatory manner.

The nature of our work means that we support some of the most vulnerable and disadvantaged people in society. Inevitably this also means we are in a position of power. We are the ones who assess, make decisions and clinical judgements and deliver care in a way that we feel meets needs.

Beliefs

Beliefs values and attitudes are shaped throughout our lives from a very early age. Beliefs are the strong ideas and principles (or ideology) that help to guide us through life.

Family and community background can influence our belief in a particular religion or how we should treat more vulnerable members of society, for example.

Education can help to formalise that belief- give it structure and context, so that you can, for example understand where your religious beliefs sit with other faiths, or where the ideology of caring for vulnerable people came from.

The Human Rights Act protects our right to choose what we think and believe. As health and care workers it is your responsibility to support the individual who wishes to participate in their religious or other customs. An example of this might be inviting the **Imam** into the care home, or arranging for someone to attend a local Green Peace meeting. It is irrelevant whether you are a Muslim or support Green Peace.

Values

Values are principles, that an individual or group of people hold dear to them. Values guide the way we live. Values and beliefs are linked – if you have a belief in something then you will value certain principles. For example if you believe that it is immoral to expect people to live on the streets you will see great value in supporting homeless charities.

Values can influence many of the judgments we make as well as have an impact on the support we give individuals which is why we must respect their values rather than impose our own. The Human Rights Act 1998 protects our right to freedom of conscience; in other words, to decide for ourselves what to respect and value, and what is right, decent, fair and principled.

Culture

A **culture** is formed by people bonding due to their ethnic or racial backgrounds, or gender, or shared beliefs, values, and activities. Sociologists define society as a group of people who share these bonds. It is likely a particular culture will share a moral code and have a particular identity and heritage or history. You will come across people from a variety of cultures and one of their biggest problems will be access to information. Do you know, for example, how to access a translator, or the particular food preferences of a person from the Indian Sub-Continent? We still tend to wait until the situation arises and then unfortunately it can be seen as a 'problem' or 'barrier' rather than a celebration of difference and an opportunity to learn from others and enrich our own lives.

Preferences

Preferences are very personal, and may be shaped by culture, beliefs and values. We all make choices based on our preferences, and they affect all aspects of our lives from the food we eat, the clothes we wear to the job we prefer to do. To be able to choose according to our preferences adds to our mental wellbeing. Imagine how you would feel if your preferences were ignored and it was assumed you would comply with another's choice.

We should provide support to the individual based on their particular needs, not on the preference of the worker.

Legislation and policies

Recent legislation and policies give us clear guidance on how to fulfil these duties in a way that respects human rights, but as individuals we must adhere to these principles all the time and not let any personal beliefs or values cloud our judgement.

It is also important to consider the principle of 'whistle blowing'. As a health and social care worker you have a '**duty of care**' to highlight and bring to attention any poor practice and this includes practice that discriminates or ignores the individuals' values or beliefs.

Figure 3.9 Show warmth and respect for beliefs, culture, values and preferences

Key terms

An **Imam** is the worship leader of a mosque.

Duty of care is the requirement of a service provider to take reasonable care with respect to the interests of others, including protecting them from harm.

Time to think

2.2a Respecting values

As a care worker, you may be rushed for time and decide to persuade Emily, who has dementia, to wear a particular outfit because it is quicker to put on. Emily hates the outfit – whose needs are you meeting and perhaps it is worth asking, are you also taking advantage of her condition – what kind of practice is this? Is it respecting Emily's values?

2.2b Who are you?

Ask an individual you work with or a colleague if you can talk to them about the following:
- How has their childhood influenced them?
- How would they describe themselves now in terms of their values and preferences?
- How do they think they have changed in their attitudes and beliefs as they have grown older?

Case study

2.2 The Lunch Club

A local lunch and social club for people with learning disabilities is run by a committee. The cultural makeup of the club is mixed with people from Asian, West Indian and white British backgrounds attending. Most of the members of the committee are parents and support workers. There is one white male service user on the committee. At a recent meeting it was decided that 'grace' should be said before each meal and that 'food fads' could not be accommodated at meal times.

As an advocate for the service users, what do you think you would be saying to the committee about respecting beliefs values culture and preferences?

Evidence activity

2.2 Interaction and inclusive work practice

This activity gives you an opportunity to practice becoming competent at inclusive working.

Look at some care plans for individuals in your organisation. Do they reflect beliefs, values, preferences and cultural backgrounds? Talk to the individuals concerned- what do they think is missing from the care plan?

Put their suggestions into practice. If you have any difficulties, get help from a colleague or your supervisor Monitor improvements in your practice by checking with each individual that you are indeed showing respect for their beliefs, values, preferences and cultural background. In other words, that you are developing inclusive work practices.

LO3 Be able to promote support diversity, equality and inclusion

Know how to access information, advice and support about diversity, equality and inclusion

AC 3.1 Demonstrate actions that model inclusive practice

Modelling or demonstrating good practice is a useful method of training and supporting staff. For example, the worker can demonstrate respect for the privacy of an individual when carrying out personal care whilst recognising cultural preferences in their choice of clothing. Inclusivity is demonstrated by consulting with the individual and accepting their cultural norms.

The way in which the health and social care worker understands and carries out their role will impact on inclusive practice. By their actions they can either support or damage inclusivity.

It is accepted that when people feel included and valued they are more likely to function better. This is also the case when their cultural differences are acknowledged and taken into account.

The people you support may not have had many positive experiences of inclusion. In these circumstances it is important to practice in a way that confirms their inclusion. A feeling of acceptance and belonging is vital. For example, you may be working with a single parent who has been rejected by her family. She has found it difficult to find employment because of reduced opportunities and feels excluded from not only their family, but their previous circle of friends and the work environment. Your role is to support them in seeking other opportunities and to foster a feeling of inclusion, for example, in a mother and baby support group.

People can feel excluded simply by the use of language and stereotyping. The 'single mother' may have a degree, she may be an older parent – but as a society we tend to stereotype and assume she will be young, with an incomplete education and an over reliance on the benefits system.

As a health or social care worker you have a duty of care to support people regardless of their differences. Having an open respectful attitude can empower the individual, making them feel valued and able to be fully included in your interaction rather than alienated and alone. Understanding their life story and their previous experiences gives you a context in which to work – a better understanding of what makes the individual 'tick'.

You have already looked at the legislation, policies and professional standards (or **principles of**

care) that inform and guide health and social care workers in inclusive and anti-discriminatory practice. Having a good understanding of the concept of inclusive practice will help you to work in a way that demonstrates:

- Respect for the individual and the cultural group they belong to
- A willingness to learn from the individual
- Ensuring that thy are not excluded from their social group and are welcomed into any new social groups.

It is important to see this process as on-going learning and development. There are a wealth of books, academic articles and journals about anti discriminatory practice. Ensure that it is discussed openly with your colleagues and do not be afraid to challenge (in a professional manner) negative practice.

Reflective practice is also a helpful way of understanding your own practice. This means that you analyse the way in which you dealt with a particular situation and think about the ways you could you have improved your interaction, and how it demonstrated inclusive practice?

Key term

Principles of care – guidance on good attitudes and practice.

Time to think

3.1 Are we labelling people?

- Look at some examples in the media, particularly health or social care stories. What labels and stereotypes do they use?
- How do they affect the people they are describing?
- How does it affect the principle of inclusive practice?

Research and investigate

3.1 Who are we?

Talk to someone you know and who has a different cultural or social background from you. Discuss their beliefs, values, preferences, and way of life, expectations, customs and traditions. Compare what they have to say with your original perspective. Have you learnt anything? Why would you recommend your colleagues to research cultural differences?

AC 3.2 Demonstrate how to support others to promote equality and rights

Once you have an understanding of equality and inclusion, the extremely damaging effects of discriminatory practice and the laws and standards that support positive practice, you can begin to support others to promote equality and uphold the rights of vulnerable and disadvantaged people.

The concept of equality suggests that all individuals should have the same opportunities to achieve their goals. This is also termed 'equal opportunities' meaning that barriers are removed and the individual is actively helped to access support, services, education etc. It also means that we should not impose 'artificial' barriers, for example people who need a hip replacement should be offered one based on clinical need – 'you are too young to need a hip replacement!' is not the appropriate response.

Challenging behaviour and whistleblowing

Sometimes it can be difficult for others to accept that they have an approach that does not respect the rights of others or promotes equality. This might be a long standing belief and the individual may become angry or upset when challenged. This type of behaviour includes giving preferential treatment to one individual rather than another (perhaps this is justified by the worker saying that the individual they prefer to work with is more polite or cooperative). This is clear discrimination and does not uphold the values of inclusivity. Making fun of an individual also ignores their right to be treated with dignity and respect. Recently two nursery nurses were convicted because they had deliberately made fun of a child in their care. The court heard that the defendants denied bullying the girl

when they were interviewed by the police and described some of the incidents as 'fun' and 'a joke'. This is obviously totally unacceptable and contravenes codes of practice, as well as some legislation.

In some situations like the one above you may need to 'whistle blow 'and draw inappropriate practice to the attention of your manager. In these circumstances the confidentiality of the individual must still be respected. Always be clear about what you witnessed and report it objectively without giving your opinion.

It is likely that an investigation and an action plan would be put in place.

However, before getting to this extreme situation it is more productive and positive to lead by example. Supporting an individual is not enough. It is also about the way in which you support them.

Encouraging and supporting the promotion of equality and rights

There are a number of ways you can encourage and promote equality and rights and model this through your own behaviour:

- You can talk to the individual about their life-go at their pace and actively listen.
- Think about whether they feel included in their care. Are there issues in their past that you need to take into account – were they disadvantaged or marginalised in any way – does this impact on the way they view their current situation?
- Find out more about their culture, preferences etc.
- Read their care plan. Does it give you the correct information?

It is also important that as a group of staff you encourage discussion about equality and the rights of the individuals you support. Do you think you are offering support that respects their rights and promotes equality?

Do you think you have training needs in these areas? Look for relevant courses and guidance. Organisations like Social Care Institute for Excellence and the Joseph Rowntree Trust provide information and advice.

How aware are you of the policies of your organisation. Seek them out – are they still relevant, and accessible to all staff? Would it be helpful to discuss policies on equal opportunities etc. with your manager or as a staff group?

Do you discuss these issues regularly at staff meetings? Could it be a set item on the agenda?

Do you know what your whistle blowing policy? How supportive is your organisation with regard to whistle blowing?

How effective is your induction for new staff in emphasising your policy of tolerance, inclusion and equal opportunities? Do new staff 'shadow' experienced staff who demonstrate inclusive practice that upholds the rights of the individual.

Are there opportunities for you to discuss this in supervision with your supervisor or line manager? If this is not the case can you suggest this as part of your personal development?

Key term

Whistle blowing means alerting managers and others to the poor practice of another staff member or drawing attention to institutional abuse, etc.

Case study

3.2 Jorge

Jorge is a Polish man who has been admitted to hospital with pneumonia. He is currently homeless and arrives in a disheveled condition. He speaks very little English and appears to be uncooperative. The nurses are frustrated because they are struggling to look after him. One nurse has been overheard saying 'well, what do you expect, it shouldn't be allowed. I don't see why we have to put up with this'.

The rest of her colleagues are very upset by her attitude and decide to deal with it. What issues in her practice do you think they need to bring to her attention?

What can they do for Jorge to improve his situation?

Evidence activity

3.2 Personal and professional development

Start to build a resource of statutory and voluntary services that offer advocacy and organisations that have an expertise in championing and defending equality and human rights, to which you could refer the people you work with. Record your findings.

Does the philosophy of care or stated written objectives of your organisation include a commitment to upholding the rights and equality of service users? Does it need updating? Have service users been consulted about the philosophy? Do they consider it truly reflects how staff interact with them?

AC 3.3 Describe how to challenge discrimination in a way that promotes change

In order to challenge discrimination in a way that will be effective means that you need to understand how to challenge and how to sustain the change.

How to challenge

In order to challenge discrimination, it is also necessary to understand what discrimination is and how it manifests itself. As you read in AC 2.1 discriminating against someone implies putting them at a disadvantage or oppressing them. Feeling oppressed or disadvantaged affects the individual's sense of self, their dignity, their confidence and mental well-being.

Discrimination can also be demonstrated by one individual or it can be 'institutionalised', i.e. part of the culture of an organisation. For example the Metropolitan Police have, in the past been accused of institutional racism.

It is not enough to confront an individual and tell them that they are being discriminatory. Most of us do not respond well to this kind of behaviour and it will not immediately change your **mindset**. You have already learnt that discrimination can be direct or indirect, and it can also be intentional or unintentional. The effects can be the same, however and when challenging discriminatory practice it is important that you have some understanding of the person's mindset. Do they realise they are discriminating and if not, why not? It is helpful to understand whether they have experienced discrimination themselves, or were they brought up in a culture where discriminatory attitudes were acceptable as the norm? In these circumstances it is probably more beneficial to discuss the 'roots' of their attitude and why it now has no place in the work they do.

How to sustain the change

By challenging discrimination and making changes you enhance the experience of the individuals you support. This improves not only their well-being but their relationship with both you as the care worker but also the organisation. Positive feedback nurtured by inclusive and anti-discriminatory practices of staff encourages a sustained and continued improvement in working practices.

It is helpful to use checks and balances, not just through formal feedback in questionnaires and care reviews, but also on a day to day basis. Ask friends and family for their opinions, if an issue is raised, deal with it immediately before a situation escalates, and always make sure individuals and their carers and family have access to the complaints and comments procedure.

Key term

A **mindset** is a state of mind that affects an individual's attitude and behaviour and their ability to make decisions.

Time to think

3.3a Learning to change

Think about the training courses you have attended and the books and manuals you have read that were aimed at improving your work practice. Can you honestly say that your practice really changed as a result? If so, in what ways did it change? If not, why not? What would have been more effective in changing the way you work?

Consider the use of appraisals and personal development plans. How could these improve to your knowledge skills and understanding of anti-discriminatory practice?

3.3b Changing the mindset

We have all behaved in a discriminatory or unfair way at some time or another. It may not have been intentional, but reflecting on the reasons for our behaviour can help us to overcome these issues. We can all learn from our mistakes and by analysing them we can change our practice and move on. It is helpful to take advice and guidance from others – try to be open-minded and accept positive criticism and feedback in a professional manner. It is aimed at improving both your professional practice.

Evidence activity

3.3 Challenging discrimination in a way that promotes change

Describe how you can challenge discrimination in such a way that people begin to confront and change their behaviour. What barriers might you encounter and how could you try to deal with them in a way that promotes change and good practice?

Legislation

- The Equality Act 2010
- The Human Rights Act 1998
- The Care Act 2014

Useful resources

Websites

Joseph Rowntree Foundation
www.jrf.org.uk

Government Equalities Office
www.equalities.gov.uk

Equality and Human Rights Commission
www.equalityhumanrights.com

Department of Health
www.dh.gov.uk

Care Quality Commission
www.cqc.org.uk

The Nursing and Midwifery Council
www.nmc-uk.org

NHS Scotland
www.healthworkerstandards.scot.nhs.uk

Skills for Care
www.skillsforcare.org.uk/home/home.aspx

Social Care Institute for Excellence (SCIE)
www.scie.org.uk/

Unit SHC 34

Principles for implementing duty of care

This unit is worth 1 credit

What are you finding out?

Working in the health and social care sector involves acting in a person's best interests at all times. As a practitioner you have a duty of care to the people you support, your colleagues, your employer and yourself. Everyone has a duty of care; it is not something we have a choice about.

In this unit you will find out about ways to address the dilemmas, conflicts or complaints that you may encounter where there is a duty of care.

The unit also covers making sure that individuals feel safe, valued and respected, and that you offer as much choice and independence as possible, and have the opportunity to evaluate and reflect upon the key factors involved in service delivery. Information is also given on how complaints systems work and how you can help people access them. If conditions are not ideal, it is important for individuals to feel supported in telling someone. This is why it is important for organisations to have a complaints system which people can use.

By the end of this unit you will:

1 Understand how duty of care contributes to safe practice.
2 Know how to address conflicts or dilemmas that may arise between an individual's rights and the duty of care.
3 Know how to respond to complaints.

Links to Level 3 Certificate in Preparing to Work in Adult Social Care

Unit SHC 34 is one of the knowledge units included in the Level 3 Certificate in Preparing to Work in Adult Social Care. This units is the same across both qualifications.

LO1 Understand how duty of care contributes to safe practice

AC 1.1 Explain what it means to have a duty of care in own work role

All health and social care professionals and organisations must exercise a level of care towards individuals who use their services, put their interests first, and avoid injury to them or their property. This is what is meant by duty of care.

Duty of care in health and social care involves thinking about our actions at work and making sure we do everything we can to keep people safe. This starts at the very early planning stages and needs careful thought in relation to the safety or security of certain tasks. For example, if you are enabling a person to move from their bed to a chair, are there enough members of staff to support this? Are the moves the correct ones, and is the person's independence and dignity maintained?

Health and social care workers provide care and support for a range of vulnerable people with different needs, abilities and preferences. As a result, staff owe a duty of care to the people they support; they cannot always keep themselves safe from harm and need staff to work to a duty of care and to look after their best interests.

A breach of that duty?

In a health and social care setting, a duty of care usually exists where the health and social care worker has some professional or work responsibility for delivering a service to an individual. A breach would arise if an individual was harmed as a result of negligence, an oversight and failure to act, and if this could have been predicted and prevented.

What it means to have a 'duty of care'

As a care worker, you have a duty to:

- take reasonable care for your own health and safety, and for the health and safety of others, while at work
- follow reasonable directions given by, or on behalf of, the employer on issues related to health or safety
- use relevant safety equipment provided for your use
- report a workplace accident to the employer as soon as practicable after it occurs.

As a care worker you must not:

- intentionally or recklessly interfere with or misuse safety equipment provided by your employer
- intentionally create a risk to the health or safety of another at your workplace.

Figure 4.1 What does 'duty of care' mean to you?

In 1932 a court was asked to think about a case relating to snails that had found their way into a glass of ginger beer! The woman who drank the ginger beer suffered from nervous shock as a result of seeing the snails in the bottom of her glass and, in a landmark case, she brought an action against the publican who had served her the drink. She was able to establish that the publican owed her a duty of care and that he had breached that duty of care by unwittingly allowing the snails to get into her glass. In recent years the courts have been full of people claiming that a duty of care was owed to them by someone, that the person has been negligent in observing that duty of care and has, as a result, breached it.

Time to think

1.1 **Duty to individuals**

You are working in a health and social care setting. Time is limited and you are very busy on your shift. Care plans state that two people are required to work with certain individuals, but your colleague says this is not really necessary and you do not have time to do this.

● What do you think your duty to individuals is?
● Does it match up with the expected duty of care?

Research and investigate

1.1 **GSCC**

The General Social Care Council Codes of Practice for Social Care Workers, and Code of Conduct for Healthcare Support Workers and Adult Social Care Workers in England offer advice and guidance in relation to best practice and the support which should be offered to people.

Research section 3 of the Code of Practice. Find out how you can ensure the health and safety of service users, protect them from danger and harm,

but promote their independence at the same time. How can you apply this to your role?

Note that following the closure of the GSCC, Skills for Care houses the Code of Practice until the purpose of the new joint code of conduct and minimum training standards for healthcare support workers and adult social care workers in England has been clarified. However, it will still be useful for you to research the Code of Practice.

Evidence activity

1.1 Duty of care

Ask your manager or senior in charge what they understand by 'duty of care'. How do they ensure that they are meeting these requirements? Have they experienced any breaches of this duty?

Case study

1.1 Following duty of care

We know that as health and social care workers 'Duty of Care' is a legal obligation.

Caitlin works in a residential care home for older people. One of the residents, Molly, enjoys walking and although she was advised not to, she has been walking about in a new pair of shoes that have rubbed her feet. Molly has some cognitive impairment but it was 'felt' that she had the capacity to make that decision, and no intervention was discussed.

As a result of walking in the shoes, she has sustained two nasty blisters on her heels. The care home deputy manager decides to treat them herself, as she is a qualified nurse. She asks Caitlin to assist her by holding a bowl of hot water and some cotton wool.

Caitlin observes the manager 'treating' the blisters, but notes that the deputy manager does not:

1 Ask for Molly's consent
2 Explain the procedure to her
3 Use sterile equipment
4 Observe hygiene precautions.

As a result the blisters become infected and the GP is asked to visit.

Consider the issues highlighted, and decide in terms of Duty of Care:

1 Whether Caitlin or the Deputy Manager were acting in the best interest of Molly- and if not why not?
2 Are there any legal or registration implications – what are they?
3 Was Caitlin or the Deputy Manager acting within their competence, or taking on something that they could not do safely – what should they have done instead?
4 Did they fail to act in a way that resulted in harm – and if so what should Caitlin and the Deputy Manager do now?

AC 1.2 Explain how duty of care contributes to the safeguarding or protection of individuals

Health and social care professionals have a duty of care to ensure the safety and well-being of individuals. Most professions have set out good practice guidelines, and not following these guidelines may amount to abuse or neglect. All health and social care professions have identified certain principles and ways of working as 'good practice'. Being aware of what good practice means can help you to identify abuse or neglect.

Health authorities, including Clinical Commissioning Groups (CCGs) and local authority social services, are legally responsible for all the staff they employ. This responsibility includes making sure that appointed staff have the necessary qualifications and skills to carry out their roles, and that there is no reason to believe that staff could pose a risk to others. Initial recruitment checks involve following up references and checking with the Disclosure and Barring Service that prospective staff have no criminal convictions which may affect their work. Work settings should ensure that staff receive the ongoing supervision, training and support needed to carry out their work. Employers are liable if a member of their staff is found guilty of professional misconduct.

Health and social care services as a whole are regulated by a national regulatory agency, the Care Quality Commission (CQC). This agency inspects health and social care services to check that standards are being met.

Key terms

Safeguarding means to prevent harm and abuse, and involves all actions necessary to do so.

Protection means to keep a person safe.

Evidence activity

1.2 Duty of care

Make a list of responsibilities that you have under your duty of care.

Most health and social care professions are also regulated by independent agencies relevant to their profession, such as the General Medical Council for doctors, and the Nursing and Midwifery Council for nurses. The General Social Care Council's code of practice requires all social care workers to:

[bring] to the attention of your employer or the appropriate authority resource or operational difficulties that might get in the way of the delivery of safe care.

Following the closure of the General Social Care Council (GSCC) in 2012, Skills for Care houses the Code of Practice until a new joint code of conduct and minimum training standards for healthcare support workers and adult social care workers in England is agreed.

See www.skillsforcare.org.uk/developing_skills/ GSCCcodesofpractice/GSCC_codes_of_practice.aspx for more information.

Duty of care therefore forms part of the safeguarding and protection procedures. They work hand in hand and enable workers to carry out work safely for all concerned. Workers are guided by codes of conduct which further support a duty of care at all times. This is covered in more detail in HSC 024. Here you will also find information on supporting the rights and choices of individuals which is useful to the reading of this unit.

LO2 Know how to address conflicts or dilemmas that may arise between an individual's rights and the duty of care

AC 2.1 Describe potential conflicts or dilemmas that may arise between the duty of care and an individual's rights

Duty of care

In your role you have a duty of care to raise any concerns you have about any aspect of your work.

These can range from ineffective working conditions, poor equipment and bad practice by other staff to raising concerns about potential safeguarding cases and situations of harm or neglect.

Individuals' rights

It is the right of every individual accessing services to make choices and take risks and, as previously mentioned, it is your role to enable them to make those choices and to reduce any identified risks without compromising their rights. An individual may be restricted in the activities they take part in if their behaviour presents a serious risk of harm to themselves or to other people.

For example, if an individual is refusing to take their prescribed medication and their health and well-being depend on this medication, you cannot force them to take it. You should contact your supervisor or manager and seek advice. You should also make sure you record what has happened and any action taken in the person's care or support plan.

Capacity

The issue of capacity, or the ability to make decisions, is also involved here. The Mental Capacity Act 2005 initiated a framework to provide protection for people who cannot make decisions for themselves. The Act identifies times where a person may lack capacity and may not be able to make decisions; for example, a person with a head injury, with dementia or learning disabilities. The person will need to be assessed to determine whether they have capacity, and decisions will then be made for them or with them, depending on the outcome of the assessment.

The Mental Capacity Act 2005 is governed by five core principles.

1 **A presumption of capacity**: every adult has the right to make their own decisions if they have the capacity to do so. Carers and practitioners must assume that a person has the capacity to make decisions, unless they can establish that the person does not have capacity.

2 **Maximising decision-making capacity** means that people should receive appropriate support to help them make their own decisions. Before deciding that someone lacks capacity to make

a particular decision, it is important to take all possible steps to try to help them reach a decision themselves.

3 **Right to make unwise decisions**: people have the right to make decisions that others might think are not sensible. A person who makes a decision that others think is unwise should not automatically be labelled as lacking the capacity to make a decision.

4 **Best interests**: any act done for, or any decision made on behalf of, someone who lacks capacity must be in their best interests.

5 **Least restrictive option**: any act done for, or any decision made on behalf of, someone who lacks capacity should be the least restrictive option possible.

The key principle of the Mental Capacity Act 2005 is that any decision made or action taken on behalf of a person who lacks the capacity to make the decision or act for themselves must be made in their best interests.

The Mental Capacity Act 2005 Code of Practice is an official document that places certain legal duties on health and social care practitioners. The Code of Practice also offers more general guidance and information to anyone supporting or caring for someone who may lack capacity to make a decision.

In addition, the Mental Capacity Act 2005 created the criminal offences of ill-treatment or wilful neglect. The offences can be committed by anyone responsible for the person's care or support.

See the legislation section on page 78 for more laws and legislation relevant to this unit.

Consequences of breaching a duty of care

A duty of care is breached if a person acts unreasonably or fails to act to prevent harm from happening. Duty of care requires individuals to take reasonable care, but also to ensure that everything 'reasonably practicable' is done to protect the health and safety of themselves and others. The decision about how to respond or what action to take differs for every one and every activity. For example a person may be fully able to make their own decisions but you should make it known the level of risk involved.

There may be occasions when a worker is not able to fulfil a duty of care. A person may have been given all the information and facts in relation to a risk or hazard but chooses to ignore this. For example, they have been asked not to smoke as they have often left lit cigarettes in their room. The person chooses to continue smoking.

It is important that rights are supported by:

- making sure that all staff understand the organisation's policies and guidelines relating to the rights of individuals
- ensuring that individuals are made fully aware of the organisation's complaints procedures
- discussing choices and preferences with individuals
- ensuring that colleagues are made aware of an individual's choices and preferences
- supporting individuals to maintain their rights and independence
- refusing to participate in discriminatory or prejudicial behaviour.

The duty of care in childcare may involve conflicts in some situations. Issues related to the duty of confidentiality about children and their parents are an example. A dilemma may arise which would normally require complete confidentiality, but which if not disclosed to parents of other children may put those children at risk. This would then be a breach of the duty of care to the other children. A decision to observe one duty could result in a breach of the other, and it is not always the case that one duty automatically has priority over the other.

> ### Time to think
>
> **LO2 Do you know how to address conflicts or dilemmas?**
>
> Have any conflicts or dilemmas arisen in your work setting between the duty of care and an individual's rights?
>
> What were the issues for the individual? What were the issues for the health or social care professional?
>
> How were these conflicts or dilemmas managed in your work setting?

AC 2.2 Describe how to manage risks associated with conflicts or dilemmas between an individual's rights and the duty of care

Risk is part of everyday life and is present in everything we do. Often it is risk-taking that allows us to grow and learn, and this has been acknowledged in the development of guidance across the sectors. Each area of health and social care has different issues with regard to consent, capacity, service involvement and areas of risk.

In situations where there is a conflict or a dilemma between an individual's rights and your duty of care, best practice involves making sure that the individual is aware of the potential effects of their choice, and that they have the mental capacity to understand the risks involved in the choice they are wanting to make. It is their right to be able to make informed choices about their own lives even if you disagree with their choice.

People accessing services are often vulnerable, and the law requires that an assessment is carried out to look at any risks there might be to the individual or to others. The aim of this assessment is not to remove the individual's right to take risks, but to recognise and reduce them where possible to an acceptable and safe level. This may relate to the dilemma a person presents when they refuse to follow a specific diet to meet their needs; or they choose to smoke and know they should not. The decision reached must be in the best interests of the person and must safeguard the individual and keep them free from harm and high-level risk.

A worker can provide all the information for the person but the person may still choose to exercise their right to carry out that activity. The risk could be reduced by, for example, asking the person to smoke in one area where they can be monitored.

Key term

Risk is the possibility of suffering harm or loss; danger.

Evidence activity

2.1, 2.2 Risks

Look around your workplace. What can you see that you think could be a risk? Is it the behaviour of someone or how the service is delivered?

Make a note of the risks you identify and of how you think you could reduce them.

Are there any issues which are causes for concern and a conflict for you in relation to duty of care?

How can you manage risks associated with conflicts between an individual's rights and the duty of care?

AC 2.3 Explain where to get additional support and advice about conflicts and dilemmas

When accessing health and social care services, the individual usually has contact with a number of staff. This could include frontline staff, a manager, volunteers, the local authority complaints manager, and inspectors and regulators as well as contract monitors. This involves support from a number of people which can be confusing for the individual. It is important to try to reduce duplication, but it is also important that staff are not confined to roles that detract from a holistic approach to services. For example, in domiciliary services, even though the service might be monitored by both inspectors and a contract monitor, good practice might involve domiciliary staff being trained to spot potential safeguarding issues or changes in the well-being of an individual that might trigger the need for a care plan review. If domiciliary staff are not trained to do this, it increases risk to the individual and wastes a resource that might reduce that risk. The same argument could be seen to apply to contract monitoring staff.

Accessing advice and guidance in relation to conflicts and dilemmas is important. Your manager should be your first point of contact, but you could also contact the inspectorate, your union or the person responsible for health and safety in your setting, for example.

If a local authority becomes aware of risks to an individual they have a duty of care and obligations under the Human Rights Act 1998, and potentially under No Secrets guidance, to take action, whether or not a breach of contract is involved. Further advice and guidance is available from your manager, also from trade unions and organisations with a specific focus on such issues.

Ongoing discussions, self-evaluation and a **critique** of practices and professional development will help to ensure that policies and procedures are thorough, up to date, understood by all and most importantly that they translate into sound daily practice. In addition, establishing relationships with individuals, carers and relatives where there is open communication and where they are encouraged to ask questions and voice concerns will result in a shared care experience which is better for carers, parents and most importantly the individual concerned. This all helps worker address conflicts and dilemmas in a more confident manner.

Key term

A **critique** is a critical discussion of a specified topic.

Evidence activity

2.3 Hierarchy of roles

In your workplace, ask about the hierarchy of roles. Who is responsible for what? Do you think the individuals you provide care for know all of this?

Draw a diagram or map illustrating key roles and functions and how they link to managing conflicts and dilemmas.

Where would you get additional support and advice about managing conflicts and dilemmas?

LO3 Know how to respond to complaints

AC 3.1 Describe how to respond to complaints

What is a complaint?

An individual may make a complaint if they are dissatisfied or unhappy about employees' actions, lack of actions or the standard of service that is provided. A complaint could be one of the following:

- A person who is unhappy with the service provided.
- Action or lack of action by the organisation affecting an individual or group.
- An allegation that the organisation has failed to follow correct procedures.
- An allegation that there has been a delay in dealing with a matter or about how an individual has been treated by a member of staff.

Within the health and social care sector, a complaint is an expression of dissatisfaction that requires an investigation and a response. Serious complaints are dealt with under the NHS and Social Care Complaints Procedure. Where there is doubt as to whether a complaint is a 'formal' complaint or a concern, the 'complainant' (person making the complaint) should be asked whether they wish the matter to be dealt with through the complaints process, leading to a formal response from the chief executive.

The benefits of complaints

Prevention is most definitely better than cure in relation to complaints. A well-organised setting with sound and effective procedures in place covering a wide range of service delivery and safety expectations will receive fewer complaints. Good communication with individuals ensures that they have the information they need as they enter the setting and during their time with you. Policies regarding health and safety and patient care will all help the smooth running of your setting. They will also reduce the likelihood of misunderstandings or dissatisfaction leading to complaints.

The legal framework

The Health Service Ombudsman – 'Principles of Good Complaints Handling'

From 1 April 2009, the Health Service Ombudsman takes responsibility for investigating NHS complaints that cannot be resolved locally, and the new approach to complaints is based on the Health Service Ombudsman's Six Principles of Good Complaints Handling. In summary, good complaint handling means:

1 Getting it right.
2 Being customer-focused.
3 Being open and accountable.
4 Acting fairly and proportionately.
5 Putting things right.
6 Seeking continuous improvement.

It is important that workers have an understanding of their organisation's complaints procedure and their role in this. At times it might be appropriate for the worker to assist the person to initiate a complaint, particularly if the person has no knowledge of the complaints procedure or if they are disadvantaged by language or disability. In this situation the worker may be acting as an 'advocate'.

Research and investigate

3.1 Dealing with complaints

Have any complaints been dealt with at your work setting? What process was used?

Evidence activity

3.1 Complaints

Think about a complaint you have made. How was it dealt with and were you happy with the outcome? Describe how to respond to complaints in your setting?

Dealing with conflict and disputes

If you are asked to deal with a conflict or dispute as a worker you should:

- Remain calm and speak in a firm, quiet and controlled voice.
- Be quite clear that neither verbal nor physical abuse will be tolerated.
- Listen to both sides of the argument, without any interruption.
- Identify ways in which a compromise might be achieved without either party losing face.
- Be clear that compromise is often the only way of achieving a resolution.

AC 3.2 Explain the main points of agreed procedures for handling complaints

The complaints arrangements for health and social care have been reformed. Reports frequently identified that some complaints took too long to resolve and services did not systematically try to learn from the important feedback that complaints offer. In addition, there is strong evidence that some people do not complain either because they do not know how to, or because they believe that doing so will not result in any action.

Who is a complaint made to?

Complaints can be made to the organisation providing care, for example to a hospital or GP surgery, or direct to the commissioning body, usually the Clinical Commissioning Groups (CCGs) or social services. If a CCG or social services receive a complaint about a provider, and they consider that they can deal with the complaint, they must seek consent from the complainant so that they can send details of the complaint to the provider. On receiving consent, the details must be sent as soon as possible. If, however, the CCG or social services consider it more appropriate for the provider to answer the complaint, and the complainant consents, the complaint can be passed to the provider for a response.

Complainants must choose at the outset whether to make a complaint to a primary care provider or the CCG. A complainant who makes an initial complaint to a provider and who does not agree with the provider's response cannot then seek a review from the CCG. Complainants who are dissatisfied with the response they receive from a primary care provider can refer the complaint to the Ombudsman.

If a responsible body considers that it is not required to consider a complaint, it must inform the complainant in writing of the decision and the reasons for it.

The complainant

Complainants or the person making the complaint should normally be current or former users of services or nominated representatives, which can include a solicitor or a person's elected representative. The investigation of a complaint does not remove the need to respect a person's right to confidentiality. People over the age of 16 whose mental capacity is unimpaired and children under the age of 16 who are able to do so should make their own complaint.

If someone other than a user of services makes a complaint, you will need to make sure that they have authority to do so. If a person lacks capacity to make decisions for themselves, the representative must be able to demonstrate sufficient interest in their welfare and be an appropriate person to act on their behalf. This could include a partner or relative, or someone appointed under the Mental Capacity Act 2005 with lasting **power of attorney**.

Time limits

The regulations require a complaint to be made within 12 months from the date on which the matter occurred, or from when the matter came to the attention of the complainant. The regulations state that a responsible body should consider a complaint outside that time limit if the complainant has good reason for not making the complaint within that limit and, despite the delay, it is still possible to investigate the complaint fairly and effectively. While the regulations do not set timescales for the procedure to take place they do require a timely, appropriate response. If a response is not provided within six months from the date the complaint was made, or a later date if one was agreed with the complainant, the complaints manager has to write to the complainant and explain why it is delayed. The complaints manager must ensure that the complainant receives a response as soon as possible.

Evidence activity

3.1, 3.2 Dealing with complaints
Locate a flow chart of how complaints are dealt with. Make a copy of this for your own evidence.

Key term

Power of attorney is the authority to act for another person in specified or all legal or financial matters.

Legislation

- **The Local Authority Social Services and NHS Complaints (England) Regulations 2009** came into force on 1 April 2009 and introduced a revised procedure for the handling of complaints by local authorities, in relation to complaints about adult social care, and by NHS bodies, primary care providers and independent providers about the provision of NHS care. The regulations brought adult social care and health complaints processes into a single set of procedures.
- **Children Act 1989/2004** provides a statutory basis for social care complaints.
- **Data Protection Act 1998** governs the protection and use of person-identifiable information (personal data). The Act does not apply to personal information relating to the deceased.
- **The Human Rights Act 1998** – Article 8.1 provides that 'everyone has the right to respect for his private and family life, his home and his correspondence'. Article 8.2 provides that 'there shall be no interference by a public authority with the exercise of this right except as in accordance with the law and if necessary in a democratic society in the interest of national security, public safety or the economic well-being of the country for the prevention of crime and disorder, for the protection of health or morals, or for the protection of the rights and freedoms of others'.
- **The Freedom of Information Act 2000** – the Act creates rights of access to information (rights of access to personal information remain under the Data Protection Act 1998) and revises and strengthens the Public Records Act 1958 and 1967 by reinforcing records management standards of practice.
- **The Mental Capacity Act 2005** – see pages 70–71.

Useful resources

Websites

Skills for Health

www.skillsforhealth.org.uk

Skills for Care and Development

www.skillsforcareanddevelopment.org.uk

Care Quality Commission

www.cqc.org.uk

Nursing and Midwifery Council

www.nmc-uk.org

Publications

Barksby, J. and Harper, L. (2011) *Duty of care for learning disability workers (Supporting the Learning Disability Worker),* Learning Matters.

Principles of safeguarding and protection in health and social care

This unit is worth 3 credits

What are you finding out?

In this unit you will learn about the different types of abuse as well as why it may occur. Knowing how to recognise the signs and symptoms of abuse and the procedures to follow for reporting unsafe practices as well as suspicions and **allegations of abuse** will help you to understand your responsibilities in responding to abuse.

You will also learn more about the legislation and procedures in place, the roles of different safeguarding agencies and sources of information and advice that you can access and how you can reduce the likelihood of abuse from occurring.

By the end of this unit you will:

1 Know how to recognise signs of abuse.
2 Know how to respond to suspected or alleged abuse.
3 Understand the national and local context of safeguarding and protection from abuse.
4 Understand ways to reduce the likelihood of abuse.
5 Know how to recognise and report unsafe practices.

Links to Level 3 Certificate in Preparing to Work in Adult Social Care

Unit HSC024 is one of the knowledge units included in the Level 3 Certificate in Preparing to Work in Adult Social Care. This unit is the same across both qualifications.

LO1 Know how to recognise signs of abuse

AC 1.1 Define the different types of abuse

What is abuse?

Working in health and social care settings will involve you meeting and working with individuals with a wide range of needs and abilities. All individuals you provide care and support to are potentially at risk of danger, harm and abuse, with some being more vulnerable than others.

In 2000 the government's Department of Health issued guidance in England about protecting adults from abuse, entitled 'No Secrets'. It defined abuse as:

the violation of an individual's human and civil rights by any other person or persons.

Abuse can occur once or may be repeated over and over again. It can take place in any setting where care and support are being provided. This includes in an individual's home or in a service providing day care, nursing care, residential care or in hospital. It can take place by different people, i.e. another individual, a family member, a partner, a friend, a professional, a volunteer or even a stranger to the individual. Whether abuse takes place deliberately or unintentionally, it can lead to individuals being placed in significant danger and facing harm.

What are the different forms that abuse can take?

Abuse not only takes place in different settings and in different relationships but it can also appear in different forms as shown in Table 5.1.

It is important to remember that sometimes more than one type of abuse may occur at the same time, or at different times with one individual or a group of individuals.

AC 1.2 Identify the signs and/or symptoms associated with each type of abuse

Having considered the different forms that abuse can take, it is also important that you can recognise each of these types of abuse. Individuals may display outward signs to indicate that they are being abused, and/or experience emotional and physical changes in their behaviour. These may not be present in all individuals; as individuals are unique, the signs and symptoms they display will be different and may or may not be indicators of abuse.

To be able to recognise when there might be a problem and what the cause could be (which may or may not be abuse), you must get to know the individuals you work with, their personalities, their individual ways and how they personally express how they are feeling.

Table 5.2 shows some of the signs and symptoms of the main forms of abuse to look out for that may indicate that abuse is occurring or has occurred.

> ### Key terms
>
> **Abuse** means ignoring an individual's human and civil rights.
>
> **Allegations of abuse** are when it is reported that abuse has happened or is happening.
>
> **Signs of abuse** are visible indications of abuse such as bruises, cuts.
>
> **Symptoms of abuse** are what an individual experiences and feels as a result of the abuse, such as fear, sadness.

> ### Research and investigate
>
> **1.1, 1.2 Abuse**
>
> Find out more about how abuse is defined and the different types of abuse that exist.

Type of abuse	What is it?
Physical	Inflicting physical injuries on another individual. Examples can include: hitting, slapping, pushing, pulling, pinching, being thrown, kicking, being strangled, stabbed, burnt or scalded, inappropriate restraint, misuse of medication.
Sexual	Forcing or pressuring an individual to take part in a sexual activity, unwanted sexual behaviour or exposure to pornography; it may involve physical contact as well as non-contact. Examples of physical contact can include: rape, sexual assault, oral sex, kissing, unwanted touching. Examples of non-contact can include: being forced or pressured to be photographed, look at photographs or video recordings, or being sexually harassed.
Emotional or psychological	Treating an individual in a way that undermines their sense of worth and confidence. Examples can include: shouting, swearing, intimidation, humiliation, threats, harassment, being isolated from others, being controlled and pressured into saying and thinking what the abuser wants, deprivation of sleep, denial of rights.
Financial or material	The misuse of an individual's money or property. Examples can include: theft of money or property, fraud, misuse of financial information.
Institutional	Day-to-day activities and work practices that are designed for the benefits of staff or the organisation rather than for the needs and well-being of individuals. Examples can include: individuals rights not being respected, fixed routines with little individual choice being made available such as for when and where meals take place, as well as denial of access to the local community and arrangements to have visitors.
Self-neglect	Individuals' behaviour that causes danger, harm or injury to themselves. Examples can include: an individual not eating or drinking, not co-operating with others in relation to their well-being such as regarding their personal care or their safety at home.
Neglect by others	Failing to meet an individual's physical, emotional, social needs. Examples can include: not providing suitable or sufficient care or support to an individual, ignoring or denying an individual their human rights.

Table 5.1 Different types of abuse

Evidence activities

1.1, 1.2 Types of abuse, signs and symptoms

Think about the following types of abuse that exist: physical, sexual, emotional/psychological, financial, institutional, self-neglect and neglect by others.

Imagine you are inducting a new member of staff who has never worked in the health and social care sector before. In your own words, tell them what each of these types of abuse mean and include the signs and symptoms that you and/or others might notice.

AC 1.3 Describe factors that may contribute to an individual being more vulnerable to abuse

Abuse can happen in different ways and take place in a variety of settings by a variety of different people. Some individuals may be more vulnerable to abuse than others due to their individual needs, the setting they are in and the people involved in their lives. For example:

- if an **individual** has a memory or sensory impairment, they may need to depend on others for care or support which can be stressful

Types of abuse	Signs to recognise	Symptoms to recognise
Physical abuse	Unexplained injuries, injuries that are the shape of objects, injuries that have occurred at different times, finger marks, bruises, black eyes, fractures, scratches, bite or slap marks, burns.	Individual becoming anxious, in particular in the presence of the abuser, less confident, withdrawn, losing weight, deterioration in health, reluctance to undress in front of others.
Sexual abuse	Bruises, scratches, soreness, or bleeding around genital and rectal areas, incontinence, pregnancy, blood on clothing, unexplained stomach pains and cramps.	Individual becoming withdrawn, anxious, frustrated, aggressive, displaying uninhibited sexual behaviour, reluctance to undress.
Emotional/ psychological abuse	The individual avoiding making eye contact, being fearful and anxious, incontinence, the individual telling you that they are not worthy and not able.	Individual displaying changes in eating and sleeping, low self-esteem, becoming withdrawn, anxious, frustrated, aggressive.
Financial/ material abuse	Unexplained lack of money or wish to spend money, sudden debts and unpaid bills, possessions disappearing, sudden changing of the individual's will, enduring power of attorney obtained when individual is unable to consent.	Individual becoming anxious over money and increasingly talking about inability to make payments and buy items.
Institutional abuse	Poor working practices and low standards of care and support, inadequate staffing, withholding care and lack of access to care, support, activities and visitors, failure to uphold individual's rights to choice, privacy and dignity.	Individual becoming withdrawn, passive, frustrated, feeling isolated, losing interest in themselves and others.
Self-neglect	Unexplained injuries to arms, face and body including bruises, scratches and cuts.	Individual becoming passive, losing interest in themselves and their values in life.
Neglect by others	Poor standards of care that do not meet the individual's needs, i.e. poor personal hygiene, dirty surroundings, development of pressure sores, untreated medical conditions, repeated falls.	Individual becoming anxious, depressed, withdrawn, losing weight.

Table 5.2 Signs and symptoms of main forms of abuse

- if a **work setting** has poor standards of care and working practices this can lead to low expectations and a lack of awareness of what abuse is which can make it difficult to recognise and report abuse
- if the **people providing care** and support have personal problems such as misuse of drugs or alcohol or stress resulting from family pressures, this can lead to mistakes being made which can place individuals and others at risk.

It is important to remember that just because these factors are present it does not mean that an individual will be abused, but they may make the circumstances for abuse to happen more likely.

Time to think

1.3 Can you recognise the signs of abuse?
- Think about a time when you read about or heard about a vulnerable adult who was abused.
- What do you think made them vulnerable?
- What do you think were the short-term and long-term effects on their lives?

1.1, 1.3 May

May has returned home after spending four weeks in hospital due to an injury from a fall. The hospital has arranged for May to have some intermediate care to provide support with maintaining personal hygiene and preparing meals as May is finding it difficult to carry these out for herself. May is feeling anxious about having support at home as she has not required this until now, and her son is also uncomfortable about having people he does not know in the house when he is not there. May's daughter is also concerned.

1 Do you think May's daughter is right to be concerned?
2 Do you think May is at risk of any danger, harm or abuse?
3 What would you advise May and her son?

Evidence activity

1.3 Factors that contribute to abuse

Think about two individuals who may be vulnerable to abuse.

For each individual detail different factors that may make them more vulnerable to abuse.

Key terms

Actions to take constitute the learner's responsibilities in responding to allegations or suspicions of abuse.

Suspicions of abuse are when you witness either abuse or signs that make you suspect it is happening.

Disclosures of abuse are when an individual tells you that abuse has happened or is happening to them.

Case study

2.1 Jim

Mary is Jim's support worker and she has known Jim for twelve years; Jim has no family and Mary is his only regular visitor. Mary supports Jim with his shopping, housework and paying his bills. When Mary supports Jim with his food shopping, Jim always gives the 'buy 2 for 1' offer items he does not want to Mary. Jim also buys Mary a coffee and a cake on their way back from paying his bills.

1 Do you think abuse is happening?
2 Does action need to be taken? Why?
3 Should Mary accept gifts from Jim?

LO2 Know how to respond to suspected or alleged abuse

AC 2.1 Explain the actions to take if there are suspicions that an individual is being abused

Once you have understood what abuse is and how to recognise the signs and symptoms of abuse, the next step is to consider what to do when you suspect an individual is being abused or someone shares their suspicions with you. You may notice some signs and/or symptoms that may lead you to suspect that abuse is going on, but you may not be sure. Not acting on suspicions you or others may have is not an option; you have to be prepared to take action as not doing so may put individuals' safety and well-being in serious danger. It is your legal duty to take action and you must not delay in reporting your suspicions.

The flow chart in Figure 5.1 indicates the actions you should take if there are suspicions that an individual is being abused; your workplace procedures will include more information about the actions the organisation you work for will expect you to take.

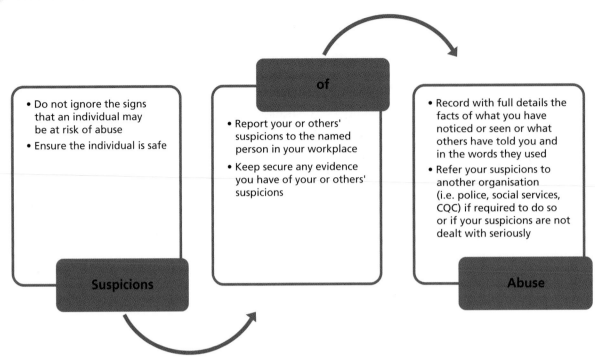

Figure 5.1 Actions to take when there are suspicions of abuse

AC 2.2 Explain the actions to take if an individual alleges that they are being abused

Your role as a health or social care worker will also mean that you will work closely with individuals, and over time they will begin to trust you and confide in you and could disclose to you that they have been abused.

The flow chart in Figure 5.2 on page 83 indicates the actions you should take if an individual discloses to you that abuse is happening to them; your workplace procedures will include more information about the actions the organisation you work for will expect you to take.

The key **principles** you must uphold when acting on both suspicions and allegations of abuse include:

- **protecting** the individual from any further risk of abuse
- **reporting** your concerns in line with your workplace procedure and while maintaining confidentiality
- **preserving** any evidence available

- **recording** the details of what you have noticed, others have witnessed or you have been told
- **referring** to an external agency when required to do so.

You may have concerns over whether an individual has the mental capacity to make an informed decision about their safety and well-being; if an individual does have capacity then you must record the details about the concerns as well as what has been said and done to support the individual to maintain their safety. On the other hand, if an individual does not have capacity then the actions taken on their behalf as well as the reasons for these must be explained to them and recorded in full. An individual may have concerns about what will happen to them or to their abuser. It is important that you provide the individual with reassurance, explain what is happening and what will happen next and talk to them about the support available. See Figure 5.3 on page 83.

Key term

Principles are the beliefs or theories on which working practices are based.

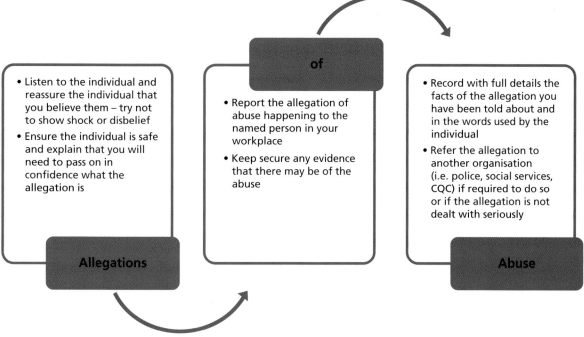

- Listen to the individual and reassure the individual that you believe them – try not to show shock or disbelief
- Ensure the individual is safe and explain that you will need to pass on in confidence what the allegation is

Allegations

of

- Report the allegation of abuse happening to the named person in your workplace
- Keep secure any evidence that there may be of the abuse

- Record with full details the facts of the allegation you have been told about and in the words used by the individual
- Refer the allegation to another organisation (i.e. police, social services, CQC) if required to do so or if the allegation is not dealt with seriously

Abuse

Figure 5.2 Actions to take when there are allegations of abuse

Figure 5.3 Responding to suspected or alleged abuse

Research and investigate

LO2 Actions to take

Find out how to respond to suspicions and allegations of abuse in your work setting.

Evidence activities

2.1, 2.2 Responding to suspicions and allegations of abuse

Read through your workplace procedure about how to respond to suspicions and allegations of abuse.

List the actions you must take when there are suspicions and allegations that an individual is being abused and then explain the reasons why you must take these actions, including the consequences of not doing so.

AC 2.3 Identify ways to ensure that evidence of abuse is preserved

As you read in the previous section, your role in safeguarding individuals from abuse is an important one. Being aware of how to ensure that any evidence of abuse is preserved is crucial.

Below is a list of some of the ways that you can do this:

- Keep the immediate area where the abuse is suspected or alleged to have happened secure by not letting anyone enter into it and by not touching anything within it.
- Do not clean, remove or destroy any items within the area where the abuse is suspected or alleged to have happened.
- Encourage the individual not to change their clothes, wash or destroy anything.
- Do not question the individual or the abuser.
- Keep accurate records of what you have seen, what others have witnessed and what has been told to you.

Evidence activity

2.3 Preserving evidence of abuse

Think about the different types of abuse you identified for AC 1.1.

Choose three types of abuse and then for each one list at least two ways to ensure that any evidence of abuse taking place is preserved.

Time to think

2.1, 2.2 Do you know how to respond to abuse?

- Have you ever had to report suspected or actual abuse?
- Reflect on the actions you took at the time and consider why and whether these were effective.
- What could you have done differently?

LO3 Understand the national and local context of safeguarding and protection from abuse

AC 3.1 Identify national policies and local systems that relate to safeguarding and protection from abuse

Once you have understood how to respond to suspicions and allegations of abuse, the next step is to learn more about the national and local policies and arrangements in place for protecting and safeguarding vulnerable adults. There are no laws that relate specifically to the protection of vulnerable adults from abuse, but legislation and guidance are in place to protect vulnerable individuals from abuse. An overview of key legislation and guidance and how these relate to safeguarding adults from abuse is provided in Tables 5.3 and 5.4.

Key terms

Local systems may include employer/organisational policies and procedures and multi-agency adult protection arrangements for a locality.

Safeguarding means ensuring that vulnerable adults are kept safe from danger, harm and abuse.

Safeguarding policies are the safeguarding principles and guidelines adopted by organisations that influence how they keep individuals safe from danger, harm and abuse.

Safeguarding systems are the detailed methods of keeping individuals safe from danger, harm and abuse.

Legislation

Name of Act	Purpose of Act
The Care Standards Act 2000	The Act aims to promote high-quality standards of care and protect individuals from abuse.
Safeguarding Vulnerable Groups Act 2006	The Act implemented the vetting and barring scheme to ensure that people considered unsuitable to work with vulnerable adults and children are not able to do so.
Mental Health Act 1983	The Act aims to protect vulnerable adults from abuse and maintain individuals' safety and well-being.
The Human Rights Act 1998	The Act aims to set out the rights and freedoms that all individuals have access to.
The Equality Act 2010	The Act aims to protect people from discrimination, harassment and victimisation.
The Public Interest Disclosure Act 1998	The Act protects workers who disclose information about malpractice including abuse at their current or former workplace and provides the legal framework for whistleblowing.
The Criminal Justice Act 2003	The Act allows the police to prosecute people who commit assaults on others including expanding the range of aggravating factors in hate crimes to include sexual orientation and disability.
Sexual Offences Act 2003	The Act allows the police to prosecute people who commit rape, indecent assault and other sexual offences.
Theft Act 1978	The Act allows the police to prosecute people who commit theft including in relation to obtaining services by deception such as through loans.
Fraud Act 2006	The Act allows the police to prosecute people who commit fraud; it makes it unlawful to make a dishonest gain from another person, make a false representation and abuse a position of trust.

Table 5.3 Legislation and its purpose

Guidance

Name of guidance	Purpose
'No Secrets' (England) and 'In Safe Hands' (Wales) 2000	These guidance documents set out how different agencies must work together to respond to, investigate and prevent abuse of vulnerable adults wherever possible.
'Safeguarding Adults' 2005	This guidance document provides a national framework of 11 sets of good practice standards to ensure the implementation of high-quality and consistent work in protecting vulnerable adults from abuse.

Table 5.4 Guidance and its purpose

As well as knowing about the different pieces of legislation and guidance documents available to you, your role involves being a guide to vulnerable adults in terms of raising their awareness about what constitutes abuse, how to report it and who and where to go to for support and advice.

AC 3.2 Explain the roles of different agencies in safeguarding and protecting individuals from abuse

As you will probably be aware, it is not just you who is responsible for safeguarding and protecting individuals from abuse: there are teams of different professionals who work in different agencies that also have a number of specific responsibilities. Look at Figure 5.4 which provides details about different agencies.

The work of these different agencies is founded on some shared safeguarding principles and values, based on national guidance for achieving positive outcomes for adults at risk of abuse. These principles recognise that adults should be in control of their lives, and that everyone has a role to play in preventing abuse from happening and responding to abuse when it occurs.

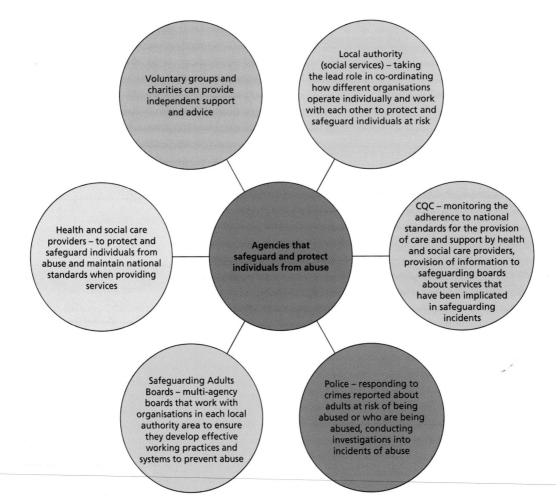

Figure 5.4 Agencies responsible for safeguarding and protecting individuals from abuse

AC 3.3 Identify reports into serious failures to protect individuals from abuse

When organisational policies and procedures in place for safeguarding and protecting individuals from abuse are not complied with or used effectively this can result in serious failures to protect individuals from abuse. Such failures are reported in the media and can make us aware all too often of the different types of abuse that individuals who are vulnerable may be subjected to. It is only after such serious failures have taken place that serious case review reports are published that look into the abuse that happened and how it could have taken place.

For example, the serious case review report published into the abuse of people with learning difficulties at Winterbourne View Hospital that occurred in 2011 found that the abuse that happened was in the main due to professionals and others not responding to incidents of abuse that took place, not challenging poor working practices as well as not understanding their own and each other's roles and responsibilities.

Responding to abuse is everyone's responsibility, and although we can all learn lessons from reports published into serious failures to protect individuals from abuse, the ultimate goal is for us all to be able to recognise and respond to individuals at risk from abuse before abuse has actually happened.

AC 3.4 Identify sources of information and advice about your role in safeguarding and protecting individuals from abuse

Responding to incidents, suspicions and allegations of abuse can be stressful and upsetting. If you are a survivor of abuse yourself then carrying out your role in safeguarding and protecting individuals from abuse may evoke other feelings and thoughts. It is important therefore that you know about all the different sources of information and advice that are available to you if you require additional support or guidance at any time.

Information and advice about your role in safeguarding and protecting individuals from abuse are available from both within the setting where you work and externally. Your workplace policies and procedures as well as your line manager can be useful sources of information and advice. Support centres, helplines and your GP can also provide additional advice when required.

Evidence activity

3.4 Sources of information and advice

Reflect on your role in safeguarding and protecting adults from abuse in the setting where you work.

Meet your manager and discuss the different people, documents, agencies and other outside sources of information and advice available to you in relation to your role in safeguarding and protecting adults from abuse.

LO4 Understand ways to reduce the likelihood of abuse

AC 4.1 Explain how the likelihood of abuse may be reduced by working with person-centred values, encouraging active participation, promoting choice and rights

Once you have understood the national and local procedures available, including the roles of different agencies and the sources of information and advice available to you,

Key terms

Active participation means supporting individuals to live their lives the way they want to.

Person-centred values are the important aspects of an individual's life such as being individual, independent, being able to make own choices and decisions. See HSC036 for information on person-centred approaches.

the next step is to understand more about different ways to reduce the likelihood of abuse happening.

Working with person-centred values

Underpinning all work in health and social care involves working with person-centred values because this is how practitioners can ensure that individuals remain in control of their lives (see Figure 5.5). The eight main values are:

1 Valuing individuality.
2 Supporting people to make their own choices.
3 Respecting privacy.
4 Treating people with dignity.
5 Ensuring that people feel respected.
6 Valuing people's rights and supporting them to access their rights.
7 Supporting people's independence.
8 Working in partnership.

Working with these person-centred values can reduce the likelihood of abuse happening. The following section explains why.

- the individual will feel empowered, be more aware of what high-quality care and support involve and what their rights are.

Encouraging active participation

Active participation in health and social care involves encouraging and supporting individuals to learn and develop skills for themselves. The

Figure 5.5 How do you encourage active participation in physical well-being?

likelihood of abuse happening can be reduced by encouraging active participation because:

- the individual will become more independent, thus reducing their dependency on others and the risk of being abused by others.

Promoting choice and rights

By working with person-centred values and encouraging active participation you will also be promoting individuals' choice and rights to live their lives as they want to. The likelihood of abuse happening can be reduced by promoting choice and rights because:

- the individual's needs, wishes and preferences will form the focus of their plan of care and support, thus avoiding care and support being planned around organisational and practitioners' preferences and reducing the risk of abuse happening.

Working in these ways will create a culture where abuse is less likely to happen and where it does happen, will be more likely to be reported and responded to.

AC 4.2 Explain the importance of an accessible complaints procedure for reducing the likelihood of abuse

Having a complaints procedure that is accessible can also reduce the likelihood of abuse occurring. All organisations that provide health and social care services are required by law to have a process in place to respond to complaints. Having an accessible complaints procedure means one that is:

- understood by those who will access it, i.e. uses clear and plain language
- presented in a range of formats to meet individuals' different needs, i.e. with pictures, signs, symbols, in writing, in audio, in different languages
- available at all times, i.e. in locations that are familiar and easy to reach
- reinforced on a regular basis, i.e. by raising people's awareness of its purpose and use,

how confidentiality will be maintained, the timeframes that can be expected for all responses to complaints

- reviewed on a regular basis for its effectiveness with participation from those who use it, i.e. by discussion at forums or through completion of questionnaires.

An accessible complaints procedure will not prevent abuse but it does empower individuals and others to play a significant role in reducing the likelihood and risks of individuals being subjected to abuse. It can raise people's confidence in the services being provided as well as their rights to a high standard of care and support.

Case study

4.1, 4.2 White Lodge

White Lodge nursing home offers high-quality 24-hour nursing care. Its principles include providing a homely and comfortable home for residents to live in and a pleasant and welcoming place for staff to work in. Family and friends are welcomed to visit their relatives/friends at any time and are encouraged to spend quality time together. Each resident is also provided each day with a choice of different and stimulating experiences to take part in; their wishes to participate or not are always respected.

1 Do you think White Lodge's philosophy and ways of working may reduce the likelihood of abuse occurring?
2 Why?

Time to think

4.1, 4.2 Do you understand the different ways of reducing the likelihood of abuse?

- Think about your work setting and how you and others work to reduce the likelihood of abuse.
- Are these ways and approaches effective? Why?
- What improvements if any do you think are needed?

LO5 Know how to recognise and report unsafe practices

AC 5.1 Describe unsafe practices that may affect the well-being of individuals

Once you have understood the different ways that working practices and an accessible complaints procedure can reduce the likelihood of abuse occurring, the next step is to understand more about how to recognise and report unsafe practices. You will consider how unsafe practices can include different types of abuse as well as the risk of the likelihood of individuals being subjected to danger, harm or abuse.

Unsafe practices

Not practising safely can manifest itself in a number of different ways and can be related to working practices, the environment and the health

or social care provider. Table 5.5 includes some examples of unsafe practices.

Unsafe practices	Examples
Working practices	Not respecting individuals' rights to privacy, dignity, choice, independence and individuality.
The environment	A poorly maintained environment with unsafe fittings and fixtures, dirty or poorly ventilated areas.
The health or social care provider	A lack of available information, support and guidance about your and others' roles and responsibilities.

Table 5.5 Examples of unsafe practices

It is very important that you are able to recognise unsafe practices so that when you witness them or when someone asks you to carry out an activity that you deem to be unsafe, you are able to stop, think and ensure that you and others work safely at all times. Not to do so can lead to individuals being abused and their physical, mental, emotional and social needs being unmet. An unsafe environment can lead to the likelihood of accidents occurring and hazards going undetected which puts individuals' safety and well-being at serious risk. An unsafe health or social care provider may find it difficult to retain, motivate and train staff; this in turn can lead to poor care and support and a lack of monitoring and supervision, which can put individuals' well-being at risk and make them more vulnerable to abuse.

AC 5.2 Explain the actions to take if unsafe practices have been identified

Recognising unsafe practices is important but it is also your responsibility to take action if you identify that unsafe practices are being used. Taking no action is not an option, neither is ignoring unsafe practices that you have witnessed or been asked to carry out as you will be placing yourself and others in danger.

Key terms

Negligence means failing to carry out your duty of care that results in placing individuals at risk of danger, harm or abuse.

Duty of care means your responsibility to safeguard individuals from danger, harm and abuse and uphold their rights.

Whistle-blowing is reporting concerns about unsafe practices or abuse to management and/or other authorities.

Case study

5.1, 5.2 Sandra

Sandra works as a night care assistant in a residential care home and is concerned that she does not have sufficient aprons and gloves made available to her at night. Sandra has also noticed that the ceiling hoists in two of the residents' rooms have still not been fixed. Sandra has reported these concerns to her manager, who has told her to be patient as the home is going through some financial difficulties at the moment.

1 What do you think Sandra should do next?
2 Why?

The five steps below include some of the key actions you must take:

1 **Read** and **follow** your workplace procedure for reporting unsafe practices.
2 **Challenge** in a constructive way any unsafe practices you witness or are asked to carry out – be prepared to explain why you believe these practices are unsafe.
3 **Do not continue** with an activity if you deem it to be unsafe.
4 **Talk your concerns through** with your manager or supervisor.
5 **Record** your concerns.

AC 5.3 Describe the action to take if suspected abuse or unsafe practices have been reported but nothing has been done in response

Ensuring that any concerns you report in relation to suspected abuse or unsafe practices are

Time to think

5.2, 5.3 Do you know how to recognise and report unsafe practices?

● Have you read your work setting's whistle-blowing procedure?
● Do you know when and how to use it?

Research and investigate

LO5 Unsafe practices
Find out more about your responsibility to recognise and report unsafe practices.

followed through and addressed is also important. You may find it uncomfortable to do so but to do nothing would be deemed as negligence and a failure of your duty of care.

The 'No Secrets' guidance states that

it is the responsibility of all staff to act on any suspicions or evidence of abuse or neglect and to pass on their concerns to a responsible person or agency.

Under the Public Interest Disclosure Act 1998 all health and social care providers are required to have a whistle-blowing procedure in place for staff to be able to use to report unsafe practices to management or another authority.

It is important therefore that you are aware of how to report to the next level of management if your manager does not address your concerns or is involved in the unsafe practices. If your concerns are not addressed within the setting you work in then you will need to report these to an outside authority such as the Safeguarding Team or CQC; you will need to know how to do this. Recording your concerns is also crucial.

Although we may not be able to prevent abuse, understanding more about what abuse is, how to recognise it and what to do when it occurs will make it more difficult for others to continue to exploit and harm vulnerable adults.

Evidence activity

5.1, 5.2, 5.3 **Unsafe practices and the actions to take**

Provide details about three unsafe practices that either you have witnessed or someone else has told you about that have taken place at work.

Think about your work setting and then detail with reasons why this practice is unsafe; the actions to take if you notice unsafe practices; and the action to take if you have reported suspected abuse or unsafe practices but nothing has been done in response.

Legislation

- The Care Standards Act 2000
- Safeguarding Vulnerable Groups Act 2006
- Mental Health Act 1983
- The Human Rights Act 1998
- The Equality Act 2010
- The Public Interest Disclosure Act 1998
- The Criminal Justice Act 2003
- Sexual Offences Act 2003
- Theft Act 1978
- Fraud Act 2006

Useful resources

Websites

Care Quality Commission

cqc.org.uk

Public Concern at Work

pcaw.co.uk

Action on Elder Abuse

elderabuse.org.uk

Abuse Survivors

abuse-survivors.org.uk

Mind

mind.org.uk

Publications

Heller, T., Reynolds, J., Gomm, R., Muston, R. and Pattison, S. (1996) *Mental Health Matters*, Macmillan Press Ltd.

Read, J. and Reynolds, J. (1996) *Speaking Our Minds: An Anthology*, Macmillan Press Ltd.

Unit HSC 025

The role of the health and social care worker

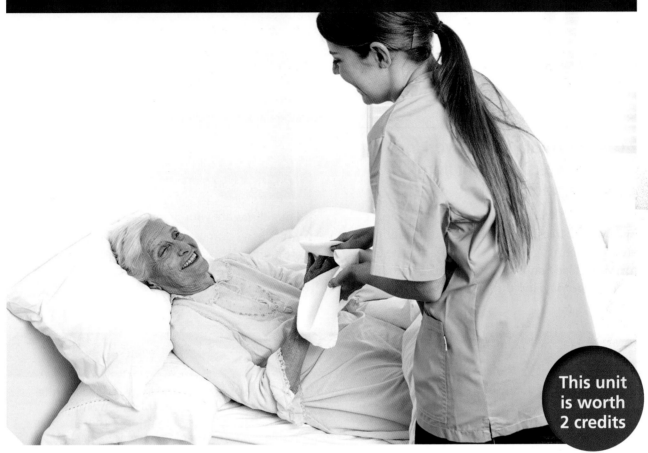

This unit is worth 2 credits

What are you finding out?

In this unit you will learn about the key features of working relationships in health and social care settings which will help you to understand your role and responsibilities as a health and social care worker.

You will also learn more about how to carry out your duties and responsibilities in line with your job description and the expectations of your employer. Being able to work in partnership with others who are involved in individuals' lives is central to carrying out your role effectively and

providing quality care and support; this unit will also help you look at how you can improve working in partnership with others, as well as the skills and approaches needed for resolving conflicts that may arise.

By the end of this unit you will:

1 Understand working relationships in health and social care.
2 Be able to work in ways that are agreed with the employer.
3 Be able to work in partnership with others.

Links to Level 3 Certificate in Preparing to Work in Adult Social Care

SHC32 Assessment criteria	Unit PWCS32
AC 1.1, 1.2	ACs 1.1, 1.2
AC 2.1	AC 2.1
AC 3.1, 3.2, 3.3, 3.4	ACs 3.1, 3.2, 3.3, 3.4

LO1 Understand working relationships in health and social care

AC 1.1 Explain how a working relationship is different from a personal relationship

Personal and working relationships form part of all of our lives and involve communicating and interacting, getting to know each other and forming close bonds. Relationships continually change and develop throughout our lives.

Personal relationships

Personal relationships can be formed with family, friends and partners. Table 6.1 details some of the main features of each of these personal relationships.

Key terms

Boundaries are your limits (see page 95).

Agreed ways of working means complying with workplace procedures (see page 95).

Type of personal relationship	Examples of who are involved	Key features
Family	Parents, brothers, sisters, aunties, uncles, grand-parents, cousins	The meaning of family varies from one individual to another depending on their main influences in childhood and adulthood. The term 'family' is used to refer to those people we feel comfortable with, trust and feel we are a part of; these people may or may not be related by birth, marriage or adoption. The roles of family can vary over time and between different cultures and families.
Friends	Friends you see regularly, friends you see from time to time, best friends	The term 'friends' is used to refer to those people we have a close bond with. Friendships develop out of shared experiences and mutual interests. Friendships can vary over time and throughout our lives both as children and adults.
Partnerships	Long-term partners, short-term partners, sexual partners, married partners, unmarried partners	The term 'partners' is used to refer to those people who know us intimately, and perhaps in a loving and/or sexual way. Partnerships develop out of affection and physical closeness which makes them different to family relationships and friendships. The length and types of partnerships we have will vary depending on our values, beliefs, culture and expectations.

Table 6.1 Types of relationships

Working relationships

It is essential for health and social care workers to be able to develop and maintain effective working relationships in health and social care settings (see Figure 6.1). There are many benefits of having good working relationships with the different people you work with, including providing job satisfaction, making your work setting an enjoyable place to be as well as encouraging mutual trust and respect among the team and positive outcomes for individuals.

Although working and personal relationships are built on some of the same values such as trust, respect and open communications, there are also some significant differences that you need to be aware of as a health and social care worker. Table 6.2 details some of the main differences.

Figure 6.1 Working relationships can be constructive and supportive

AC 1.2 Describe different working relationships in health and social care settings

Having considered the differences that exist between working and personal relationships, it is also important that you are aware of the many different working relationships that exist in health and social care settings, including their purpose so that you can understand their importance for carrying out your job role effectively.

Key features of working relationships	How these differ from personal relationships
Working relationships **develop in a planned and structured way**, i.e. as a result of applying for a job or furthering your career	Family relationships happen naturally and we choose who we want to be friends with; we do not choose the people we work with.
Working relationships have **clear boundaries** in place, i.e. what is acceptable as part of your job role, and what is acceptable behaviour in the setting where you work	Relationships with family, friends and partners involve socialising at birthdays, weddings and parties and sharing personal moments and information together. In working relationships it is not acceptable to socialise with individuals outside of your working hours or to give and accept gifts or to share personal information about your relationships and family, as this blurs professional boundaries.
Working relationships are bound by **agreed ways of working**	Relationships with family, friends and partners do not include prescribed ways of behaving. In working relationships there are professional and working codes of conduct and guidelines that set out ways to behave and expectations of what you can do in your job role.
Working relationships include **unequal balances of information and time**	Relationships with family, friends and partners involve the giving and receiving of information between you and them. The nature of working relationships means that you and other colleagues know more about the individuals you work with than they know about you. How long you spend with family, friends and partners is variable depending on your commitments and theirs; how long you spend with an individual is agreed beforehand and time bound.

Table 6.2 Differences between relationships

Figure 6.2 provides details about the purpose, of some of the different working relationships in health and social care settings.

Effective working relationships involve complying with ways of working agreed by the professional and employer, and are also based on a core set of values: valuing and respecting each team member, being honest and openly communicating when positive outcomes for individuals are achieved, as well as when changes and improvements need to be made. Working well and consistently with others is an important skill to have as a health and social care worker, as this can lead to innovative and person-centred approaches.

Effective teamworking can ensure that tasks are completed quickly and efficiently and that any difficulties or challenges are shared and acted on by the whole team. In turn this enables team members to begin to trust and support one another by offering suggestions and practical solutions.

Research and investigate

LO1 Values

Values Research values that are important when building and developing working relationships in health and social care settings.

Case study

1.1, 1.2 Tony

Tony attends a day service twice a week; his sister takes him there in her car and then picks him up after collecting the children from school. The day service is supported by a manager, two full-time day care assistants and three volunteers.

1 What are the different relationships that Tony has?
2 How will these relationships be different?
3 Why?

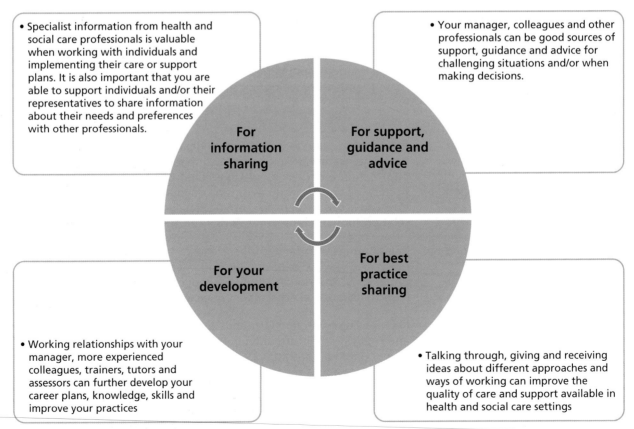

- Specialist information from health and social care professionals is valuable when working with individuals and implementing their care or support plans. It is also important that you are able to support individuals and/or their representatives to share information about their needs and preferences with other professionals.

- Your manager, colleagues and other professionals can be good sources of support, guidance and advice for challenging situations and/or when making decisions.

For information sharing

For support, guidance and advice

For your development

For best practice sharing

- Working relationships with your manager, more experienced colleagues, trainers, tutors and assessors can further develop your career plans, knowledge, skills and improve your practices

- Talking through, giving and receiving ideas about different approaches and ways of working can improve the quality of care and support available in health and social care settings

Figure 6.2 The purpose of working relationships

LO2 Be able to work in ways that are agreed with the employer

Once you have understood more about the different working relationships in health and social care settings, you need to learn more about how to work in ways that are agreed with your employer.

AC 2.1 Describe why it is important to adhere to the agreed scope of the job role

Most health and social care employers develop **job descriptions** and **person specifications** to

formalise the requirements of the job and their expectations of employees carrying out different work roles. These can include:

- specific information about the aims of the work setting
- where your work will take place
- the level of knowledge, experience and skills required
- the qualities that are essential such as patience, understanding and a commitment to supporting individuals to be in control of their lives
- the responsibilities of the role
- who you will report to
- any staff you are responsible for
- who will supervise you
- details about your pay
- your hours of work
- any other benefits you are entitled to.

Read through Figure 6.3, which gives an example of a job description for a Senior Care Assistant; how does this compare to your job description?

Working within the agreed duties and responsibilities of your job role as a health or social care worker is also therefore part of your duty of care; not doing so can have consequences for the individuals you provide care and support to, for the rest of your team and for you. Not fulfilling your job role and responsibilities may put your colleagues and other professionals you work with at unnecessary risk, i.e. not completing a risk assessment may mean that unsafe working practices will result in injuries and fatalities. Not complying with your job role will mean that you are putting yourself in danger and risking

HIGHTREE CARE HOME

JOB DESCRIPTION

SENIOR CARE ASSISTANT

JOB TITLE: Senior Care Assistant

REPORTING TO: Registered Manager

CONTRACTED HOURS: Full time

JOB PURPOSE:

To work alongside the Home Manager.

To act as a role model to other care assistants and provide them with support and regular supervision.

JOB DESCRIPTION:

- Lead shifts and develop the rotas for all care assistants.
- Assist in the formal supervision of other care assistants.
- Respect the rights, dignity and choices of individuals.
- Respect the cultures, values and diversity of individuals.
- Ensure the health and safety of everyone at all times.
- Report any health and safety issues or concerns to the Manager.
- Communicate effectively with colleagues, managers and visitors.
- Carry out manual handling in accordance with training and the Home's policy.
- Assist in the administration of medicines.
- Provide individual and holistic care to individuals in line with their daily living needs and preferences.
- Assist individuals in retaining independent living skills.

Note: The post holder may from time to time be asked to undertake other reasonable duties to reflect the service's changing needs. Any changes will be made in discussion with the post holder.

Figure 6.3 An example of a job description

allegations being made about you and your working practices; this may result in you losing your job and ultimately not being able to work in the health and social care sector again.

How well you carry out your job role and further training and support available to you will form part of your discussions during supervision with your manager and your appraisal at the end of the year. Carrying out your job role to a high standard will ensure you fulfil your employer's requirements and expectations of you.

AC 2.2 Access full and up-to-date details of agreed ways of working

Knowing when and how to access complete and up-to-date details of ways of working that your employer expects from you is essential to ensure that you carry out your job role to the best of your knowledge and ability. Employers in the health and social care sector will have in place **policies** (how the employer and the work setting are complying with legislation), **procedures** (how your employer expects day-to-day work activities to be carried out) and **guidelines** (how to work in specific situations with different individuals).

Some smaller employers may have less formally documented policies and procedures.

Policies belong to the service or organisation and reflect the aims to be achieved, while procedures belong to the employees and reflect how the service or organisation expect its employees to meet their aims. For example, a complaints policy would set out an organisation's commitment to take all complaints seriously and deal with them fairly, and also its aim to ensure that everyone is aware of how to complain; the complaints procedure would then detail the steps to go through to make a complaint including who to report to, how and the timescales for each stage of the process.

Policies, procedures and guidelines have to be accessed by health and social care workers so that they can carry out their job roles and responsibilities accurately and fully. How effective these are depends on whether they are understood by those who read them and whether they are reviewed regularly to ensure they are up to date and relevant. Each employer in the health and social care sector may also provide access to these through the induction process, through regular updates and discussions with staff.

AC 2.3 Implement agreed ways of working

As we read in the previous section, having access to policies, procedures and guidelines in your work setting is essential to carrying out your job role well. Below is a list of five practical steps that can help you put these into practice effectively:

● **Step 1** – Read the policies, procedures and guidelines in place; ensure that colleagues are aware of these too and where to find them.

● **Step 2** – If you are unsure or do not understand any policy, procedure or guideline, let your manager know; ensure that colleagues do so too.

● **Step 3** – Attend all training and updates provided to you by your employer; be honest with your manager if there are any skills or areas of knowledge that you do not feel competent or knowledgeable about.

● **Step 4** – Take an active part in discussions around policies, procedures and guidelines.

● **Step 5** – Be a good role model to others and follow agreed ways of working at all times; always challenge constructively and report any working practices that do not follow agreed ways of working.

Case study

2.1, 2.2, 2.3 Simeon

Simeon leads a team of carers who support individuals to develop and maintain independent living skills at home. As part of his job role Simeon undertakes risk assessments, reviews the support in place regularly with each individual and provides support and guidance to the team of carers. Next month Simeon is planning on inducting a new senior carer to work with him.

1 What sources and types of information will Simeon need to have access to, to complete the new senior carer's induction? Why?

2 How can Simeon monitor whether the new senior carer is working in agreed ways?

3 Why is it important that the new senior carer understands his job role and responsibilities and is able to work within these?

Research and investigate

LO2 Agreed ways of working

Compare the agreed ways of working in your work setting with those from one other work setting with which you are familiar.

Evidence activities

2.2, 2.3 Accessing and implementing agreed ways of working

Reflect on the policies, procedures and guidance available to you in your work setting and then consider how you ensure that you work within these.

You will also need to be observed by your assessor accessing full and up-to-date details of agreed ways of working and putting the knowledge you have gained about these into practice.

Time to think

2.1, 2.2, 2.3 Do you always work in ways agreed with your employer?

● Have you or someone else you know not worked within the boundaries of the job role?

● What could you have done differently and why?

LO3 Be able to work in partnership with others

Once you have understood how to work in agreed ways with your employer, the next step is to learn more about how to work well in partnership with others. Working with different people and agencies may mean that you come across different ways of thinking and practising that may be in conflict; it is important therefore that you are also aware of the skills and approaches that are required for resolving any conflicts that arise.

AC 3.1 Explain why it is important to work in partnership with others

As a health or social care worker, your role will involve working alongside a range of people who have different roles, responsibilities, values, beliefs and needs; this may include the individuals you provide care or support to, their families, friends, advocates or representatives, your colleagues, your manager as well as professionals from other agencies.

As we read in AC 1.2, effective partnership working with others involves being committed to sharing a common set of values. It is also important to note that there are often specific reasons for different agencies and professionals to work together towards shared goals over both short and long periods of time.

Working well and in partnership with others is important for:

- **You** – to improve your understanding of others' roles, practices and approaches, and in turn improve your knowledge and skills and deliver a good-quality service.
- **Your work setting** – to create a more skilled workforce.
- **The individuals** you provide care and support to – to ensure that the care or support provided is consistent, co-ordinated and holistic.
- **Other people** you work in partnership with – for team building and to share skills, knowledge and expertise.
- **Other agencies** you work in partnership with – to pool resources and help everyone to work together effectively.

AC 3.2 Demonstrate ways of working that can help improve partnership working

There are many benefits to effective partnership working with others, and it is important that you are able to recognise and use different approaches and methods that can help improve partnership working. (see Figure 6.4).

In order for partnerships to work well it is important that the role of each partner and

Figure 6.4 Partnership working

the aims of the partnership are made clear to everyone involved to improve trust and knowledge of each other's contributions. It is also essential for all the partners involved to be able to communicate openly, be clear about decisions reached as well as listening to and addressing ideas and conflicts. Improving partners' skills and knowledge, sharing good practice with others and learning together from mistakes can lead to the development of more flexible and holistic ways of working and the development of mutual trust and respect.

AC 3.3 Identify skills and approaches needed for resolving conflicts

Working with different people and agencies can at times be challenging because although everyone is working towards a shared goal, disagreements may result over the best way forward. If these are not managed effectively then this can be very damaging to how the team works together. For this reason it is important that you are aware of the main skills and approaches needed for resolving conflicts that may arise.

Table 6.3 includes details about key skills and approaches required for resolving conflict.

Skills required for resolving conflict

- **Empathy** – to gain a better understanding of another person's view
- Assertiveness – to clearly state your point of view
- Honesty – to express how you feel
- Creativity – to see how a conflict could become an opportunity
- Willingness to work with others – to share ideas for improvements
- **Negotiation** and **mediation** – to enable others to move towards making improvements and agreeing on ways forward

Approaches required for resolving conflicts

- Being constructive – to treat others respectfully
- Focusing on the conflict – to avoid blaming an individual
- **Active listening** – to understand others' perspectives

Table 6.3 Skills and approaches for resolving conflict

Being aware of and using these skills and approaches can help you to work positively and constructively with others to agree on how best to resolve any conflicts that arise.

Key terms

Empathy means the ability to understand how someone else may be feeling.

Negotiation is reaching an agreement.

Mediation is intervention to resolve a conflict.

Active listening requires the listener to feedback and acknowledge that they have understood what is being said. See SHC31 for more information an active listening.

AC 3.4 Demonstrate how and when to access support and advice about partnership working and resolving conflicts

Depending on your experience, you will have developed over time a range of skills and approaches that have proved useful when working in partnership with others and resolving conflicts. There may be times, however, that you need to seek support and advice from someone else; for example, in relation to partnership working you may be finding it difficult to communicate with a particular person or agency, or you may have witnessed or been told about unsafe working practices. In relation to resolving conflicts you may be uncomfortable about the decision that has been reached, or not feel that the decision reached is in the best interests of the individual concerned or for the team in your work setting.

Being able to recognise when you must ask for support and advice is just as important as knowing how to do so. Sources of support and advice available within your work setting can include your manager or a more experienced or senior colleague. If you are unable to access any support or you are dissatisfied with the advice you have been provided with, you may need to inform the next level of management within your work setting. If you are still dissatisfied you may need to access support and advice from independent external sources available to you; depending on what the issues are, these may include a confidential helpline or a service such as the Advisory, Conciliation and Arbitration Service (ACAS).

Time to think

3.1, 3.2, 3.3, 3.4 Do you have the skills to work in partnership with others?

- Read through the skills for resolving conflicts identified in Table 6.3; on a scale of one to five, with five being the most competent, how do you rate the skills you have for resolving conflicts? Why?
- How effective are you in working in partnership with others? Ask three or four people you work with to provide you with feedback on how effectively you work with them. How does this compare to your original thoughts? What improvements do you need to make?

Case study

3.1, 3.2, 3.3, 3.4 Grace

Grace moved into Park Residential Home three weeks ago but is finding it difficult to settle in. She is not used to being surrounded by so many different people, having lived on her own for many years, and finds the noise in the home particularly at meal times very stressful. Lewis, Grace's friend who visits her every week, knows that Grace is not happy and has made the staff and Grace's social worker aware of what she thinks and how she would like to live with him. Grace also has a daughter who lives in Norfolk who thinks that Grace should live with her.

1 Do you think effective partnership working is taking place? Why is this important? (AC 3.1)
2 How can partnership working be improved? (AC 3.2)
3 How can the conflict about where Grace should live be resolved? (AC 3.3)
4 What skills and approaches do you think may be needed to resolve the conflict that has arisen? (AC 3.3)
5 What sources of support and advice could be accessed in relation to improving partnership working and resolving the conflict that has arisen? (AC 3.4)

Evidence activities

3.1, 3.2, 3.4 Working in partnership

Make a list of all the people you work in partnership with in your work setting; choose three of these and then detail why it is important to work in partnership with each person, include the consequences of not doing so and the different methods that can be used to improve the way you work together.

You will also need to be observed by your assessor demonstrating ways of working that can help improve partnership working, and how and when to access support and advice about resolving conflicts. If a natural opportunity for you to access support and advice about resolving conflicts does not arise, you need to ask your manager or supervisor for an expert witness testimony that provides evidence of an occasion when a conflict was resolved, and how.

3.3, 3.4 Resolving conflicts

Reflect on a conflict that arose in your work setting and that was resolved.

Make a list of the skills and approaches that were used to resolve this conflict.

Research and investigate

LO3 Across support

Find out from professionals who work in other agencies the best practice models they use for working in partnership and resolving conflicts.

Legislation

- The Equality Act 2010
- The Health and Social Care Act 2012
- The Human Rights Act 1998

Useful resources

Websites

Advisory, Conciliation and Arbitration Service

acas.org.uk

Care Quality Commission

cqc.org.uk

Skills for Care

skillsforcare.org.uk

Skills for Health

skillsforhealth.org.uk

Publications

Davies, C., Finlay, C., Bullman, A. (2000) *Changing Practice in Health and Social Care*, Sage Publications.

Hawkins, R., Ashurst, A. (2006) *How to be a Great Care Assistant*, Hawker Publications.

Knapman, J., Morrison, T. (1998) *Making the Most of Supervision in Health and Social Care*, Pavilion Publishers.

Promote person-centred approaches in health and social care

This unit is worth 6 credits

What are you finding out?

The essence of a person-centred approach is that it is individual to, and owned by, the person being supported. But how can we ensure that this happens, and how can we support others to work in a person-centred way?

The reading and activities in this chapter will help you to understand what person-centred approaches are, understand how to work in a person-centred way and understand the role risk assessment plays in enabling a person-centred approach.

By the end of this unit you will:

1. Understand the application of person-centred approaches in health and social care.
2. Be able to work in a person-centred way.
3. Be able to establish consent when providing care or support.
4. Be able to implement and promote active participation.
5. Be able to support the individual's right to make choices.
6. Be able to promote individuals' well-being.
7. Understand the role of risk assessment in enabling a person-centred approach.

Links to Level 3 Certificate in Preparing to Work in Adult Social Care

HSC 036 Assessment criteria	Unit PWCS36
AC 1.1	ACs 1.2 and 1.3
AC 1.2	AC 2.3
AC 3.1	AC 3.3
AC 5.4	AC 5.2
AC 6.1	AC 6.1
AC 7.1	AC 7.1
AC 7.2	ACs 7.2 and 7.3
AC 7.3	AC 7.4

LO1 Understand the application of person-centred approaches in health and social care

AC 1.1 Explain how and why person-centred values must influence all aspects of health and social care work

Person-centred care is a way of providing care that is centred around the person themselves, and not merely focused on their health or care needs. To explain this in simple terms, we are all unique – no two people are the same –so it is not appropriate to say, for example, that two people will have the same care and support needs just because they both have dementia. Person-centred values are outlined in Figure 7.1 on page 105.

Person-centred values ensure a comprehensive understanding of individual needs and the development of appropriate individual care plans for all. An individual's plan of care is the document where day-to-day requirements and preferences for care and support are detailed. It may be known by other names, e.g. support plan, individual plan or care delivery plan.

- **Practical or physical support**: this must be discussed and agreed with the person involved to ensure their needs and preferences are met at all times. What is agreed must be included in their care plan so that all staff can follow correct procedures. This could include, for example, bathing or hygiene routines.
- **Emotional support**: observation of how a person is feeling is vital to make sure workers communicate effectively at all times. A person may feel frustrated at change or anxious about how their needs are going to be met so clear communication and guidance are vital at all times.

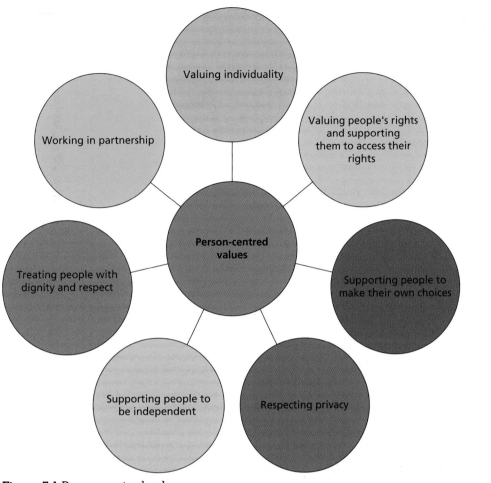

Figure 7.1 Person-centred values

- **Intellectual or cognitive support**: we all have different levels of intellectual ability and identifying this for everyone is important, as it develops our interests and knowledge and involves us in valuable learning activities. You could support individuals with this through courses, discussion and other activities such as reading.
- **Social support**: exclusion from activities and social groups and meetings can leave a person feeling unwanted and ignored. Making sure a person can voice their views and opinion about the activities they would like to participate in helps them to feel valued and included.

The White Paper 'Our health, our care, our say' confirms a vision of high-quality support meeting people's hopes for independence and greater control over their lives, making services flexible and responsive to individual needs.

Time to think

1.1 What do you like doing?
What things do you like to do in your spare time? Compare this with the things your best friend or partner likes to do. Do you notice how we vary in the things we like.

Research and investigate

1.1 Person-centred values
Person-centred planning is central to the White Paper 'Valuing People' (Department of Health, 2001). Research a key White Paper or Act and list its features.

The Mental Capacity Act 2005

It may be that an individual cannot always make decisions for themselves; the Mental Capacity Act (MCA) 2005 is intended to support such individuals. The Act came into effect on 1 April 2007 and covers England and Wales. It promotes fair treatment for people who may be affected, and protects the rights of some of the most vulnerable people in society.

The Mental Capacity Act 2005 helps people to make their own decisions. It also protects people who cannot make their own decisions about some things. This is known as 'lacking capacity'.

The Act provides a statutory framework for the more than 2 million people in England and Wales who lack the capacity to make decisions by or for themselves. The Act tells people:

- what to do to help someone make their own decisions
- how to work out whether someone can make their own decisions
- what to do if someone cannot sometimes make decisions about some things.

A lack of mental capacity could be due to:

- a stroke or brain injury
- a mental health problem
- dementia
- a learning disability
- confusion, drowsiness or unconsciousness that results from an illness or a treatment for an illness
- substance misuse.

The types of decisions that are covered by the MCA range from day-to-day decisions such as what to wear or eat, through to more serious decisions about where to live, whether to have an operation, or what to do with a person's finances and property. Some types of decisions (such as marriage or civil partnership, divorce, sexual relationships, adoption and voting) can never be made by another person on behalf of someone who lacks capacity. This is either because these decisions or actions are so personal to the individual concerned, or because they are governed by other laws. The MCA applies to situations where a person may be unable to make a particular decision at a particular time because

their mind or brain is affected. See AC 3.1 for information on consent and providing support to individuals to make decisions.

Evidence activity

1.1 The impact of The Mental Capacity Act 2005

What impact would the Mental Capacity Act 2005 have on individuals in your care?

Who could you ask for help and guidance?

How do you think person-centred values must influence health and social care work?

AC 1.2 Evaluate the use of care plans in applying person-centred values

A **care plan** sets out in some detail the daily care and support that it has been agreed should be provided to an individual. If you are employed as a carer, the care plan acts as a guide in terms of what sorts of activities are expected of you. There will be regular reviews, and the individual and you should be involved in discussions about how it is working and whether parts of it need to be changed. On-going review of a care plan is vital to ensure the person's changing needs are met and that workers are fully aware of what is required. A person's abilities and what they want to achieve going forward also change so they need to be assessed and reviewed with them.

Person-centred planning

Person-centred planning is a process of continually listening and learning, focusing on what is important to the person now and in the future, and acting upon this in alliance with their family and friends. It is vital that we think about how the person can be central throughout the process, from gathering information about their life, preparing for meetings, monitoring actions and on-going

Key term

A **care plan** is the document where day-to-day requirements and preferences for care and support are detailed. It may be known by other names, e.g. support plan, or an individual plan.

learning, to reflection and further action. There is a danger that efforts to develop person-centred planning focus simply on having better meetings. If you do not put into practice the things that you have planned and discussed people may feel frustrated and cynical, however, which is often worse than not planning at all.

Very often you will be caring for and supporting people only when they are in a vulnerable position. The quality of care that you provide will be improved by having knowledge of the whole person, not just the current circumstances: for example, knowledge of an individual can help you to understand better why they behave in the way they do. A care plan, based on a person-centred approach, will help in understanding some of this, but what else might help? In thinking about this, you will see that person-centred planning demands that you see the person as the central concern. You need to find ways to make the care and support individual to the person, not 'one size fits all'. The relationship should move from being one of carer and cared for, towards one based on a partnership – you become a resource to the person who needs support.

LO2 Be able to work in a person-centred way

Person-centred planning is a way of helping people to think about what they want now and

in the future. It is about supporting people to plan their lives, work towards their goals and get the right support. It is a collection of tools and approaches based on a set of shared values that can be used to plan *with* a person, not *for* them. Planning should build the person's circle of support and involve all the people who are important in that person's life.

Person-centred planning is built on inclusion, and looks at what support a person needs in order to be included and involved in their community. Person-centred approaches offer an alternative to traditional types of planning, which are based on the **medical model** of disability and are set up to assess need, allocate services and make decisions for people.

Person-centred working

Person-centred working involves a number of approaches that carers can use to help them work in a more person-centred way, such as:

- How to sort what is important *to* an individual from what is important *for* them.
- How to address issues of health, safety and risk while supporting choice.
- How to identify the core responsibilities for those who provide paid support.
- How to consider what makes sense and what does not make sense about a person's life.
- How to ensure effective support by matching characteristics of support staff to the person's needs.

Person-centred teams

Person-centred approaches are beneficial not only for the people who use services, they can also be very useful tools for enabling teams to work effectively together. Person-centred team plans help teams to be clear about their purpose, and to understand what is important to each team member and what support they need to do a good job.

Evidence activity

LO2 Teamworking

Draw a spider diagram to show the people you think would be part of a care team. What are their roles?

Research and investigate

2.1 New ways of working

Carry out some research into new ways of working and how these can improve individuals' lives.

AC 2.1 Work with an individual and others to find out the individual's history, preferences, wishes and needs

Person-centred planning can work for anyone. It is especially useful for people who may need help planning their future, or who find that services often do the planning for them. Lots of people feel like this, so person-centred planning suits a lot of different people.

There are key features of person-centred planning that will help anyone reviewing plans to ensure the person is at the centre and has their say.

- The new Care Act 2014 stresses the importance of beginning the process of **person-centred care** by assuming that the individual is best-placed to judge their own **well-being** and the care and support they need to maintain or enhance their well-being.
- The concept of person centred care can only work in practice if care and support begins with the individual.
- If the person is at the centre, they are in a position to exercise real **choice** about the care and support they require and the way in which it is delivered.

Person centred care should ensure:

- **Consent** – the person should consent to an assessment and the care and support agreed. If they lack capacity to consent to this, the Mental Capacity Act should be used and action taken 'in the best interests of the person.'
- **Positive risk taking** – there should be an acknowledgement that as long as the person has insight they have the right like anyone else to take positive risks if they feel they add to their quality of their life. This also ensures greater **self-esteem** and adds to a sense of **personal**

identity because the person is **empowered** to take decisions.

- By working **in partnership** with the person, their family/carers can ensure their active participation in the care and support process.

There is no single approach that can be applied to working with someone in a person-centred way, and no approach that exclusively covers all of the processes that may be needed in developing a person-centred plan.

It is important for you to find out a person's history, preferences, wishes and needs. These things shape who the person is, they affect the way the person should be supported and they may explain reactions to certain types of situations or support. You can ask the person, speak with carers, refer to their records, put together a story board, with their input.

Other team members, colleagues and other individuals may have noticed skills or abilities a person may have, or identified needs that are not always obvious to others. This valuable information can identify a person's on-going needs and wishes. Families, friends, carers and advocates can also offer valuable insight which helps with meeting a person's preferences and needs.

AC 2.2 Demonstrate ways to put person-centred values into practice in a complex or sensitive situation

Person-centred planning is a process of life planning with individuals, using the principles of inclusion and using a social model rather than a medical model. In a medical model, a person is seen as the passive receiver of services and their impairment is seen as a problem; this often leads to being separated or segregated and to them living and working away from the community. A social model sees a person as being disabled by society. In this model, a person is proactive or planning for positive action in the fight for equality and inclusion.

The concept of person-centred planning is not new. One of the first people to develop the model was John O'Brien. His 'five accomplishments' (respect, choice, participation, relationships and ordinary places) were the foundation for person-centred planning in the USA.

Person-centred planning has five key features:

- The person is at the centre of the planning process.
- Their family and friends are partners in planning.
- The plan shows what is important to a person now and for the future, and what support they need.
- The plan helps the person to be part of a community of their choosing and helps the community to welcome them.
- The plan puts into action what a person wants for their life and it does not remain static – the plan remains 'live'.

If a worker is faced with a complex or more sensitive situation then person-centred values can be even more crucial and effective. The plan can be referred to but also used to carry out a review of a person's needs and preferences, with them.

Person-centered values in practice

With person centred ways of working it is important you make sure you provide the time the individual wants and needs to take in any sensitive or complex information, and answer any questions they may have. You also need to make sure that the information is provided in the form that the individual wants, for example verbally, or written. You also need to ask who they want the information given to. For example they may not want information to be shared and they may be the ones to inform others, so you should ensure that they are at the centre and feel involved.

AC 2.3 Adapt actions and approaches in response to an individual's changing needs or preferences

An important first step in person-centred approaches is to understand each person's unique way of getting their message across. This can vary from person to person, and can depend on the person's level of spoken language, their eye contact and their body language. It is important, when starting your person-centred planning, that each individual is recognised as having their own particular way of communicating. Without an understanding of this we will struggle to achieve a person-centred approach, to hear about people's hopes and needs, or to achieve a better life for each person.

Communication

Effective communication depends on how well we use language. Language is not just about speaking – there will be some people you will work with who are unable to communicate using speech or they may have hearing problems. To communicate with each individual, it is important to understand their unique communication needs, and the adaptations you may have to make.

- Hearing loss can affect communication because the individual may misinterpret what is said, or is reluctant to participate in groups because they cannot hear the conversation.
- Poor vision can also affect confidence. It can feel uncomfortable when you cannot 'read' body language.
- Effective communication can depend on your attention span, and your ability to follow a conversation or a set of instructions.

Case study

2.3 Communication

You have been asked to produce an information poster for the people who use your service. The majority have poor literacy skills and do not like to be 'bombarded' with information.

What basic principles do you need to consider in the design and layout of the poster?

How would you engage with the service users?

How would you ensure that equality and diversity was being recognised, bearing in mind that for some of the service users, English is not their first language?

- Communication is a two way process – the individual may not only struggle to understand what is being communicated to them, but is also unable to express themselves. This includes 'word finding' difficulties, or an inability to start a conversation.

Bearing all this in mind it is important that you:

- Take practical measures. Are spectacles and hearing aids in good, clean working order? Are they are comfortable to wear and regularly checked?
- Check the individual's care plan. Do they use particular nonverbal methods of communication such as body language, signing, Makaton or pictures and symbols?
- Ensure the individual can see you- gently attract their attention, try to ensure you are in a good light and that you are at their eye level, particularly if they need to lip read
- Use body language appropriately to reinforce what you are trying to say. Be observant- the individual might use body language to indicate a need, and actively listen. What is the individual really communicating to you?
- Are aware of the environment. Is there too much noise or too many distractions?

Adapting actions and approaches to meet needs makes the intervention more effective and individuals changing needs or preferences can determine the communication method used. Being aware of the need to change is important, for example you may need to slow your speech down, or to use sign language.

Evidence activity

2.1, 2.2, 2.3 Responsibility for care plans

How can you work with individuals and others to find out about the individual's history, preferences, wishes and needs?

How can you put person-centred values into practice in a complex or sensitive situation?

Who is responsible for reviewing care plans and service delivery in your setting? How can you adapt actions and approaches in response to an individual's changing needs or preferences?

LO3 Be able to establish consent when providing care or support

AC 3.1 Analyse factors that influence the capacity of an individual to express consent

Consent means making an informed agreement to an action or decision (see Figure 7.2). The process of establishing consent will vary according to an individual's assessed capacity to consent, but every adult must be presumed to have the mental capacity to consent or refuse treatment, unless they are:

- unable to take in or retain information provided about their treatment or care
- unable to understand the information provided
- unable to weigh up the information as part of the decision-making process.

Valid consent must be given by a competent person (who may be a person lawfully appointed on behalf of the person) and must be given voluntarily. Another person cannot give consent for an adult who has the capacity to consent, however. It may be that a person needs support to enable them to understand what they are consenting to. For example, it might be a surgical procedure that they do not understand the need for. Workers should be able to explain the importance of the procedure and ensure the person fully understands what is involved. See unit HSC 036 for more information on consent.

In exceptional cases, for example where consent was obtained by deception or where not enough information was given for consent to be informed, this could result in an allegation of battery (or civil assault in Scotland). Only in the most extreme cases is criminal law likely to be involved, however.

Usually the individual performing a procedure should be the person to obtain consent. In certain circumstances, you may seek consent on behalf of colleagues if you have been specially trained for that specific area of practice.

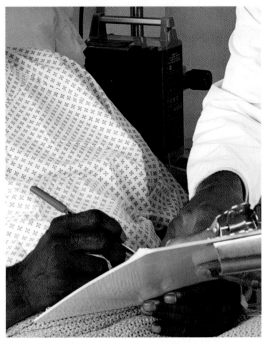

Figure 7.2 The consent process

Forms of consent

A person may demonstrate their consent in a number of ways. This can be informed consent, implied consent, written or verbal. Informed consent is when a person understands what they are consenting or agreeing to. They may agree to treatment and care verbally, in writing or by implying (i.e. by co-operating) that they agree. Equally, they may withdraw or refuse consent in the same ways. Verbal consent, or consent by implication, not necessarily verbally but perhaps through body language or even not saying anything, will be enough evidence in most cases. Written consent should be obtained if the treatment or care is risky, lengthy or complex. This written consent stands as a record both that discussions have taken place and of the person's choice. If a person refuses treatment, making a written record of this is just as important. A record of the discussions and decisions should always be made.

When consent is refused

Legally, a competent adult can either give or refuse consent to treatment, even if that refusal may result in harm or death to him or her. Nurses and midwives must respect an individual's refusal just as much as they would their consent. It is important that the person is fully informed and that, when necessary, other members of the healthcare team are involved. A record of refusal to consent must be made, as for consent itself.

Evidence activity

3.1 Refusing consent

Why do you think someone might refuse to give consent? What action should you take if this happens? Analyse three factors which might mean an individual refuses to give consent.

Consent of people under 16

If the person is under the age of 16 (i.e. a minor), carers must be aware of local protocols and legislation that affect their care or treatment. Consent of people under 16 is very complex, so local, legal or membership organisation advice may need to be sought. Children under the age of 16 are generally considered to lack the capacity to consent to or refuse treatment. The right to consent to or refuse treatment lies with the parents, or those with parental responsibility, unless the child is considered to have significant understanding and intelligence to make up his or her own mind.

Children of 16 or 17 years are presumed to be able to consent for themselves, although it is considered good practice to involve the parents. Parents, or those with parental responsibility, may override the refusal of a child up to the age of 18 years. In exceptional circumstances, it may be necessary to seek an order from the court. Child minders, teachers and other adults caring for the child cannot normally give consent.

Consent of people who are mentally incapacitated

It is important that the principles governing consent are applied just as rigorously to people who are mentally incapacitated. A person may be described as mentally incapacitated for a number of reasons. These may be temporary reasons, such as sedatory medicines, or longer-term reasons, such as mental illness, coma or unconsciousness.

AC 3.2 Establish consent for an activity or action

If your work involves treating or caring for people (including anything from helping people with dressing to carrying out major surgery), you need to make sure you have the person's consent for what you propose to do, if they are able to give it. This respect for a person's right to determine what happens to their own body is a fundamental part of good practice. For consent to be valid, the person must be:

- capable of taking that particular decision
- acting voluntarily (i.e. not under pressure or duress from anyone)
- provided with enough information to enable them to make the decision.

Seeking consent

Seeking consent is part of a respectful relationship and should usually be seen as a process, not a one-off event. When you are seeking a person's consent to treatment or care, you should make sure that they have the time and support they need to make their decision. People who have given consent for a particular intervention are entitled to change their minds and withdraw their consent at any point if they have the capacity (are 'competent') to do so. Similarly, if they have refused an intervention, they can later on change their mind and consent. It is important to let the person know this, so that they feel able to tell you if they change their mind.

Adults with the capacity to take a particular decision are entitled to refuse the treatment or care being offered, even if this will be clearly detrimental to their health. Mental health legislation does provide the possibility of treatment for a person's mental disorder without their consent (in which case more specialist guidance should be consulted). Detention under mental health legislation does not, however, give a power to treat unrelated physical disorders without consent.

The consent process

Consent is a process. Legally, it makes no difference if people give their consent verbally, non-verbally (for example, by holding out an arm for their blood pressure to be taken) or by signing a consent form. A consent form is only a record, not proof that genuine consent has been given. It is good practice to seek written consent if treatment or care is complex, or if it involves significant risks or side effects. If the person has the capacity to consent

Evidence activity

3.2 Seeking consent

You are seeking consent from an individual. What information do they need? How can you help them get this?

to a treatment or care for which written consent is usual but is unable to write or is physically unable to sign a form, a record that the person has given verbal or non-verbal consent should be made in their notes or on the consent form. See AC 3.1 for more information on the types of consent.

Some people may have capacity to consent to some treatment or care provisions but not others. For example, people suffering from the early stages of dementia would probably still have the capacity to make many straightforward decisions about their treatment or care but may lack the capacity to make very complex decisions. You should never assume that people cannot make decisions for themselves, just because they have been unable to make a particular decision in the past. A person's capacity may fluctuate: they may, for example, be able to make a particular decision one day, even if they had not been able to make it the day before. Where a person's capacity is fluctuating you should, if possible, delay treatment or care decisions until a point when the individual has the capacity to make their own decision. People close to the individual may sometimes be able to assist you in choosing an appropriate time to discuss their health or social care wishes and options.

AC 3.3 Explain what steps to take if consent cannot readily be established

When adults lack capacity

Even where information is presented as simply and clearly as possible, some people will not be capable of making some decisions. You must not proceed with any care or clinical activity without consent. Make sure you report any refusal, and it will be important to repeat any information to ensure that you are understood. This will apply when a person is in a coma, for example. It may also apply to people with severe dementia, although you should

Evidence activity

3.3 When consent cannot be given

What steps should you take if consent cannot be given? For example, if a person is not conscious or has communication difficulties.

never automatically assume that a person lacks capacity simply because they have dementia. If a person is not capable of giving or refusing consent, it is still possible for you lawfully to provide treatment and care, unless such care has validly been refused in advance. But all treatment or care must be in the person's 'best interests'.

No one (not even a spouse or others close to the person) can give consent on behalf of adults who are capable of giving consent for themselves. Those close to the incapacitated person, however, should always be involved in decision making, unless the person has earlier made it clear that they don't want such involvement. Although legally the health and social care professionals responsible for the person's care are responsible for deciding whether or not particular treatment or care is in that person's best interests, ideally decisions will reflect an agreement between professional carers and those close to the person.

LO4 Be able to implement and promote active participation

AC 4.1 Describe different ways of applying active participation to meet individual needs

A crucial aspect of relationship building in your job role is to make sure that people are able to make choices and take control of as much of their lives as possible. This is known as **'empowerment'**, and simply means doing everything you can to enable people to make their own decisions. Many people who receive care services are often unable to make choices about what happens in their lives. This might be due to many factors, for example their physical ability, where they live, who provides their care and the way services are provided.

Key terms

Active participation is a way of working that recognises an individual's right to participate in the activities and relationships of everyday life to the best of their ability and as independently as possible. The individual is regarded as an active partner in their own care or support, rather than a passive recipient.

Empowerment is supporting a person to make choices for themselves.

Self-esteem is a person's view of their self-worth or how the value themselves.

Self-image is how people see themselves.

Active participation involves finding ways of supporting individuals to do as much as they can for themselves so they remain independent and able to take control of their lives. Achievements, however large or small, give a person a sense of value and purpose and you should consider the importance of encouraging this when working with individuals.

Self-esteem

Individuals who are unable to make choices or exercise control may suffer from low self-esteem and lose confidence in their own abilities as a result. There are other factors that may impact on self-esteem, including the degree of encouragement and praise a person is given from important people in their lives, the amount of satisfaction someone gets from their job, and whether a person has positive and happy relationships with their friends and family.

Self-esteem has a major effect on people's health and well-being. Individuals who have a more positive and confident outlook are far more likely to be interested and active in the world around them than those who lack confidence or belief in their own abilities. It is therefore easy to see how this can affect an individual's quality of life and their overall health and well-being.

If self-esteem is about how we *value* ourselves, then self-image is how we *see* ourselves – both are equally important. As part of empowering individuals, you need to consider how you can

Evidence activity

4.1 **Active participation**

Describe different ways of applying active participation to meet individual needs.

Explain how you would support someone who has recently started accessing services and has learning disabilities. How would you support them through active participation?

Evidence activity

4.2 **Working with others**

Lisa is new to your service but requires a lot of support. How can you find out Lisa's needs and identify how these can be met through a person-centred approach? How can you agree, with Lisa, the support she needs? How can you support active participation?

promote their sense of their own identity. This involves making sure you recognise the values, beliefs, likes and preferences people have, and not ignoring or discounting them if they do not fit in with the care system. See AC 6.1 for more information on self-esteem, identity and self-image.

Thought and consideration

A little thought and consideration can ensure that people feel they are valued and respected as individuals. For example, finding out how an individual likes to be addressed is important. Some older people, for example, like to be addressed as Mr or Mrs X, rather than by their first name, as this indicates respect.

You will also need to make sure that people have been asked about their religious or cultural beliefs, particularly in relation to food, acceptable forms of dress and the provision of personal care.

AC 4.2 Work with an individual and others to agree how active participation will be implemented

Individuals should be enabled to have control over their lives. How can you support them with this? Person-centred approaches are about the service user being at the centre of any care plan. Person-centred approaches quite simply give people a life and not just a service. What is important to each person? What support do they need? What are their dreams and ideas for their future? In order to fully implement active participation it is important to communicate well with colleagues and other professionals. This ensures that everyone is working to the same principles and procedures.

AC 4.3 Demonstrate how active participation can address the holistic needs of an individual

AC 4.4 Demonstrate ways to promote understanding and use of active participation

The holistic needs of an individual include their intellectual, emotional and social requirements. Assessment involves looking at the person as a whole and not in a piece by piece way.

Active participation enables individuals to feel involved, to make choices and to feel empowered. This also supports the holistic needs of an individual, for example with their intellectual, emotional and social preferences and requirements.

The range of services and facilities that individuals may want to use is large and varied. First you must be sure that you give information on services and facilities in a way that can be understood by the individuals concerned. You must ensure that any specific communication needs are met. For example, people may require information in Braille, or to be communicated with using signing. You will need to find out how to change the format of information, or how to access it in a suitable format. Promoting choice and empowerment is about identifying the practical steps you can take in daily working activities to give individuals more choices and more opportunities to make decisions about their own lives and the activities in which they wish to become involved (see Figure 7.3).

4.3 Providing information

You need to provide some information to an individual for whom you provide care. How can you make sure they can understand this information?

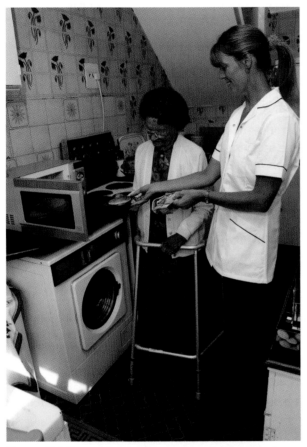

Figure 7.3 Promoting active participation in the home

When individuals want to make choices about their lives, you must ensure that you are doing your best to help them identify any barriers they may meet and to overcome them. When working with individuals in their own homes, it is generally easier for them to make day-to-day choices for themselves.

Once people have the information on the available services and facilities, the next stage is to support them to make use of it. This may involve completing application forms or other paperwork, and you may need to support individuals to fill in any forms that are required to access their selected networks or services.

Overcoming barriers

There are many barriers that can restrict access or prevent people from using support networks, or participating in or developing relationships. Information is one of the keys to overcoming these barriers. An individual with plenty of accurate and current information is far more likely to be able to challenge or overcome difficulties than someone who feels anxious or uncertain because of lack of information and support. Barriers to access tend to fall into three key categories: environmental, communication and psychological.

Environmental barriers include:

- lack of disabled facilities
- narrow doorways
- no ramps
- no lifts
- no interpretation of signage for those with a sensory impairment
- lack of transport
- lack of ease of access.

Communication barriers include:

- lack of loop systems
- poor communication skills
- lack of translators or interpreters
- lack of information about the network or facility
- lack of information in an appropriate format.

Psychological barriers include:

- unfamiliarity
- lack of confidence
- fear or anxiety
- unwillingness to accept help in accessing resources or networks.

It is always important to explain to a person what active participation is and how it can support them in their decision making and lifestyle choices. For example, you might need to adapt your communication approach to make sure they can state their wishes and preferences. It is also important that colleagues, carers and others are aware of the important role active participation plays. This can be reinforced through explaining methods of including people in all decision-making processes and demonstrating how decisions should be clearly recorded.

LO5 Be able to support the individual's right to make choices

AC 5.1 Support an individual to make informed choices

Informed choice involves a person knowing what they are saying yes or no to. They have made a choice based on the options and information given to them.

People need information about the options available to them if they are to be able to make choices about their lives. There are many ways of making information accessible to people. These include the different ways of communicating mentioned above, and presenting information in ways that enable people to become more engaged in the planning process. See unit SHC 31 for more information on barriers to communication.

As individuals, we can only make 'informed' choices if we have the right amount of information, in the right format and at the right time, and this is the same for the people who use our services.

How to prepare for a planning meeting
You need to consider:

- The preferred methods of communication used by the individual. Do you need adjustments like a hearing loop or an interpreter?
- Whether the appropriate consent has been gained to share information at the meeting. Is the individual aware of how information will be shared?

- Whether the appropriate people/organisations are attending the meeting, for example does the individual require an advocate?
- Do you have the required skills and knowledge to contribute to the meeting?
- The necessary information and documentation is ready and people have had sight of it in the right format, if appropriate.
- The environment. Try to avoid 'clinical' or more formal rooms. Is the environment comfortable, and are you able to maintain confidentiality by ensuring the door is closed and the meeting is not interrupted?
- You are working in partnership, so avoid an 'interview' type format. Try to make the seating arrangement as informal as possible, to make the individual feel at ease. It is important that they feel confident enough to express their opinions, and if they feel comfortable, they will be more empowered to do so.
- Treat the individual with respect. Make sure they are aware that you take their views and preferences seriously and that they will contribute to the care planning process.

See unit SHC 31 for more information on barriers to communication. Advocates may be used if a person has communication difficulties or generally does not find it easy to make decisions.

You may also want to refer to AC 3.3 for information on capacity to consent in relation to this.

AC 5.2 Use own role and authority to support the individual's right to make choices

Making choices is part of everyday life for most of us. It is an essential part of being recognised and respected as an individual and contributes to us having control over our lives. Individuals we support also have the right to participate in decisions that affect their lives.

Our practice should recognise the right of individuals to make their own choices. Alongside this, services also need to provide capacity to give their users options. Choosing whether to 'take it or leave it' is not a real choice. Choice for individuals is now rightly promoted as a quality standard when care organisations advertise their services, and it forms part of how organisations are judged. The vast majority of decisions – and virtually all choices – can ultimately be tackled by most adults if the right information and options are made accessible to them in a form they can understand. This can involve advocates and other measures to safeguard the choice or decision making; this may, for some parties, require considerable time and expertise in communication. Choice is one of the core elements of person-centred approaches.

The importance of choice

A person's rights can range from everyday human rights to civil and legal rights. Legal and civil rights help to eradicate discrimination in our society. There are also other rights that we might consider to be important, for example the right to be treated with dignity and respect, the right to complain. We could refer to these as moral rights. Generally these rights do not have the same legal force behind them as civil and legal rights; they depend more on the goodwill of people to recognise and support them.

Exercising choice is, for most people, part of everyday life. Whether these choices are minor or major they all contribute to having control over our lives. Minor choices are typically taken for granted. Major choices or decisions include where to live and work, whether to have a particular type of medical treatment or even with whom to be intimate. These are the decisions that can have a big impact and long-term effect on people's lives.

Consideration should be given to the difference between making a 'choice' and a 'decision'. Generally speaking, 'choice' is used when the options are not too important. A 'decision' is seen to relate to a more fundamental choice that can have a greater impact on an individual's life.

In order to make a major decision a person should have:

- access to appropriate and sufficient information
- the capacity to understand the information, the options and the consequences of the various outcomes
- the opportunity to make their decision freely and without any duress or biased encouragement.

Sometimes, presenting the same information in different ways, or presenting small pieces of information and continually checking understanding, can help with progression to an overall understanding and therefore to a decision. It may become apparent that the person cannot make a decision on their own. In this case, every effort should be made to ensure that they participate in the decision-making process to the fullest degree. Depending on the situation, it may be important to involve a person who knows the individual well. Those close to an individual can teach us a lot about their communication. On other occasions, it may be appropriate to use a person who is completely independent to work with a client, especially if there are concerns that there may be external pressures from another person, for example a relative or another carer.

Evidence activity

5.1, 5.2 Inability to make decisions

How can you support an individual to make informed choices?

Imagine that you are not able to make decisions and that they are all made for you instead. How would this make you feel?

AC 5.3 Manage risk in a way that maintains the individual's right to make choices

Risk is usually seen as the possibility that an event will occur, with harmful outcomes for an individual or for others. Such an event may be more likely because of risks associated with:

- disability or impairment
- health conditions or mental health problems
- activities while out in the community, or in a social care setting
- everyday activities, the risks of which may be increased by a disability
- delivery of care and support
- use of medication
- misuse of drugs or alcohol
- behaviours resulting in injury, neglect, abuse or exploitation by self or others
- self-harm, neglect or thoughts of suicide
- aggression or violence towards self or others.

A pure health and safety approach to risk identifies five key steps:

- Identify the hazard.
- Identify the risk (who may be harmed and how).
- Evaluate the risks and decide on precautions.
- Record findings and implement them.
- Review the risk assessment and update if necessary.

Choice

Exploring choice can also expose people to potential risk. Professionals and staff can feel a clear tension between choice and empowerment, and risk for the individual. While being aware of their duty of care and wishing to empower individuals to take reasonable risks on the one hand, on the other they are aware of being accountable for their actions and can fear a blame culture. They will need to balance the two, and this is where appropriate risk policies have a role to play, and organisations should develop a clear definition of risk that looks at probability and consequences.

In certain circumstances it may not be possible to comply with the choices of the person, for example where there are child protection risks or safeguarding risks. Taking risks can help people to learn and gain experience and confidence in leading their own lives. Not taking risks can mean that people are not able to develop and grow, and may be prevented from doing things that make them happy. Therefore people should be supported to make real choices, even when these choices may sometimes be unwise or could lead to harm – provided that the assessment and support planning has been undertaken in partnership with the person, that the planning has taken all the relevant factors into account and enabled the person to weigh up the advantages and disadvantages of a proposed course of action, and that they are able to make an informed choice. It is important when doing this to find out why the person wishes to make a particular choice, what this will bring to their life, and how their life may be adversely affected if they are prevented from making this choice.

Evidence activity

5.3 Risk versus choice

What do you think would cause tension between risk and choice in the setting where you work? How could a safe compromise be reached?

AC 5.4 Describe how to support an individual to question or challenge decisions concerning them that are made by others

Risk assessments

In social care, the relationship between the individual and the people involved in assessing their needs or helping them to arrange their support is one that gives rise to a duty of care. It is essential, therefore, that risk assessments are carried out in a transparent way, in partnership with people and their carers, and that agreement is reached about the risks, how they will be managed, and who will be responsible for them.

When carrying out risk assessments and risk management, the following factors should be considered:

- The identification, assessment and management of risk should promote independence and social inclusion.
- Risks may be minimised, but not eliminated.
- It may not be possible to manage all risks.
- Identification of risk carries a duty to do something about it, i.e. to manage the risk.
- Risks may change as circumstances change, and should then be reviewed – an assessment is a snapshot, whereas risk assessment is an ongoing process.

Advocacy

Advocacy is the process of speaking up about an issue that is important to the individual. This can either be self-advocacy, where the individual speaks on their own behalf, or citizen advocacy, where a volunteer from a local advocacy group speaks on the individual's behalf. From time to time, an issues advocate may be required to address a specific issue. The process of advocating is to address a specific problem, and once this is resolved it will come to an end. Because of the level of complexity or expertise required, the advocate could be a paid official or professional, e.g. a solicitor or welfare rights consultant. This form of advocacy does not replace the likes of citizen advocacy or self-advocacy, but works alongside it.

Evidence activity

5.4 Advocates

Find out when an advocate would be used and what they can do to help someone. Make notes on your findings. How can you support an individual to question or challenge a decision made by others?

Professionals, organisations and even family carers need to recognise the role and work of advocates in independently supporting people. An individual may be living in a care or supported setting, or with their family, and can still avail themselves of an advocate. In all cases the relationship is confidential to the person and their advocate. Such partnerships can grow into long-term friendships, which provide much support and safeguarding to people and their interests, particularly if they live in a long-term care setting.

There may be times when a person does not agree with a decision made by another person. This may, for example, relate to changes to their diet. This has been a necessary change but the person is not keen at all. There may be a compromise but how can this be reached? A first step would be to discuss these changes with the person, then with the practitioner involved in the decision-making process. If an agreement cannot be reached the person may wish to use the complaints process. They may not feel able to go through this process on their own so may need support. Complaints can be made by anyone and, once made, must follow the organisation's complaints procedure.

LO6 Be able to promote individuals' well-being

AC 6.1 Explain the links between identity, self-image and self-esteem

Personal identity and self-image

Our personal identity is the way we see ourselves and is closely related to our self-image. It is very important to us because it affects the way we feel about ourselves and how we behave in challenging situations. Our personal identity includes:

- who we are
- what makes us unique
- what our values are
- our physical identity (what we think we look like to others); this is also known as body image
- our internal identity (who we think we are in terms of our personality, character, values, etc.)
- how we see ourselves in relation to others
- how we identify ourselves in terms of our job
- our personal goals.

The most important thing to realise about our personal identity is that it can be close to how other people see us, in which case we will be at harmony with the world and others around us, or it can be very different from how others see us, meaning we may feel we are misunderstood and that life is a battle to make others appreciate who we really are.

One of the biggest problems people have with their personal identity is that they may not accept or may be blind to who they are and what they believe. Most of us today suffer from this to a certain extent because society seems to want us to behave and live in ways that may not be exactly what we want.

Self-esteem

The first step towards higher self-esteem is to be clear about who you are and what you believe. This is the goal of self-awareness. Before you can improve your self-esteem, or indeed make any positive changes to your life, you need to devote time to this form of self-improvement. Understanding your personal identity is, therefore, a necessary first step and only after this step can you think about how to change your life positively.

How can our personal identity help improve our self-esteem?

- Who are you? What makes you tick? Knowing this can lead you closer towards decisions that help you live as you want to, not as others want or how you feel you should.
- What makes you unique? Nobody else among the billions of people living on this planet now or the billions of people who lived before is or was ever exactly like you.
- What are your values? If you want to feel good about yourself then you need to understand what your values are and to start living them. Many people compromise their values and believe they must live a certain way, but this is the road to unhappiness and low self-esteem.
- What is your internal identity? Your personality and character make you unique and you should value them. Focus on the positives you have in these two areas.
- How do you see yourself in relation to others? This is related to your status as you see it. If you believe you have very low status you will suffer low self-esteem, but if you feel you have a high status this will help you have higher self-esteem.
- Do you identify yourself in terms of your job? Don't make the mistake of thinking that a job defines who you are – it is only what you do and nothing more.
- What are your personal goals? These say a lot about who you are and the values you hold, but if you want to improve your self-esteem you should have goals that move you closer to being who you really are.

Evidence activity

6.1 Identity

Ask an older friend or relative how they think their needs and abilities have changed over the years. Do they need any more or less support or help now? Write a short explanation defining how identity, self-image and self-esteem are interlinked.

AC 6.2 Analyse factors that contribute to the well-being of individuals

Well-being may include aspects that are spiritual, emotional, cultural, religious, social or political. Many factors combine to affect the health and well-being of individuals and communities. A person's well-being may be affected by aspects that are spiritual, emotional, cultural, religious, social or political. Whether people are healthy or not is determined by their circumstances and environment. To a large extent, factors such as where we live, the state of our environment, genetics, income and education level, and our relationships with friends and family all have considerable impacts on health and well-being. Conversely, the more commonly considered factors, such as access and use of healthcare services, often have less of an impact. The context of people's lives determines their health, so blaming individuals for having poor health or crediting them for having good health is inappropriate. Individuals are unlikely to be able to control directly many of the things that determine health.

Evidence activity

6.2 Well-being

What do you understand by well-being? What can affect our well-being?

AC 6.3 Support an individual in a way that promotes their sense of identity, self-image and self-esteem

Figure 7.4 Involve individuals and families in monitoring and reviewing care plans

Promoting a person's sense of identity, self-image and self-esteem

Individuals and/or their relatives and friends should have a full part to play in the care planning process. This could mean becoming involved with the meeting – either at the meeting itself or in the preparations for it. Involvement ensures they have a say in all aspects of their life and this promotes their sense of identity, self-image and self-esteem as they are treated as individuals and valued for their differences (See Figure 7.4).

Part of your role is to encourage individuals and those close to them to play an active part. A first step may be to give them basic information about things such as:

- why your organisation is having the meeting
- where and when the meeting will take place
- whether transport will be needed for the individual to get to the meeting
- who will attend the meeting
- why the different people are there
- how the individual should present their views
- what will happen when the individual and/or relative/friend arrives
- what they will be asked to say or do
- what happens if they decide to say nothing.

The aim of a person-centred approach is to ensure that the individual is an equal partner with health and social care professionals in assessing, identifying options for and delivering the most appropriate package of care for that individual across organisational boundaries. The approach involves the provision of full information on all aspects of the individual's needs and available services, and requires the individual to be treated with respect, courtesy and dignity at all times.

To begin with the person must be the centre of the plan, i.e. they must be consulted and their views must always come first. The plan should include all aspects of care – social services, health services, family and the voluntary sector.

A person-centred setting

A proactive care setting will follow the principles of person-centred care. Person-centred care aims to see the person as an individual, rather than focusing on their illness or disability or abilities they may have lost. Instead of treating the person as a collection of symptoms and behaviours to be controlled, person-centred care takes into account each individual's unique qualities, abilities, interests, preferences and needs.

Dignity and respect

Personal dignity and privacy should be respected at all times. Individual cultural or religious beliefs should also be taken into account. For example, staff should address the person in whichever way the person prefers, whether by their first name or more formally. Individuals, for example those with dementia, have the right to expect those caring for them to try to understand how they feel and to make time to offer support rather than ignoring or humouring them. Staff should talk to residents while they are helping them with physical tasks such as washing and dressing. One member of staff should have particular responsibility for the care of each person. This staff member should have a clear idea of that person's life history, habits and interests.

AC 6.4 Demonstrate ways to contribute to an environment that promotes well-being

The environment we live and work in can have a huge impact on well-being. A dark, dull room can make us feel less motivated and less positive. The physical environment can help promote a sense of well-being. Windows with a view to a garden or outside space, good lighting, different, bright colours for cupboards and clear signage are just some of the ways in which the environment can be used positively. Often changes can be identified with the help of staff, individuals and relatives, and made with little expense.

Supporting care plan activities

When a care plan is in place, as well as carrying out your own duties under the plan you will need to support and supervise colleagues as they carry out their specified activities.

Monitoring is essential to ensure that any plan of care is continuing to meet the needs it was designed to meet. A care plan will have originally been assessed, planned and put in place to meet a particular set of circumstances. The original plan should include provision for monitoring and review, because plans put in place with even the most thorough assessment and careful planning will not necessarily be appropriate in six months' or a year's time, and may not continue to provide services of the quality or at the level originally expected.

Monitoring may seem a complex process but its principles are very simple. Monitoring of care services needs to pick up and address changes in the circumstances of those receiving the services, their carers and service providers. For example, someone recently discharged from hospital following treatment for mental health problems may receive quite extensive support under the care programme approach. Feedback on their progress, however, may show that their mental health has improved to the point that day care is no longer needed on the previous level and that as such a lower level of care input can be planned.

Checking resources

Checking on resources can also be important if changes in the availability of those resources mean that a care package will have to be altered in some way. A reduction in the availability or an increase in demand for a particular service may mean that adjustments in the level of service provision have to be made. Regular monitoring makes it easier to be aware of where resources are being used and where changes can be made.

Ways of monitoring

Whatever approach is taken to monitoring, how a particular plan of care will be monitored and the methods used will be agreed with the individual and their carers at the outset. Your feedback will be an essential part of the process. The monitoring process may involve the following key people:

- the individual concerned
- their carers and/or family
- other healthcare professionals
- the service provider.

The most important person in the monitoring process is the individual receiving the service, so they must be clear about how to feed back information on the way the care package is working. This can be achieved by completing a checklist on a regular basis, maintaining regular contact with the care manager or co-ordinator, or recording and reporting any changes in the needs or in the care provision.

LO7 Understand the role of risk assessment in enabling a person-centred approach

AC 7.1 Compare different uses of risk assessment in health and social care

The emphasis in thinking about providing support and care has moved over the past decade or so towards promoting independence. An important part of this must be the recognition that the people who we support have the same rights as any other citizens. This includes the right to take risks.

The assessment of risk is something that can leave us feeling very anxious. Questions, such as 'What if I get it wrong?', are normal. It makes sense, therefore, to talk about worries with your manager or mentor, because talking things through helps us to get a

better perspective on things. As a result we learn to feel more confident in our judgements. Policies and procedures can also help, and this requires you to look at the risk assessment policy in your setting. You also need to know what to do with the policy.

Most services are provided on the basis that the service user wishes to follow a plan of treatment/support and that carers are involved wherever possible. Other services also depend on good quality assessments of need and risk. Local authorities have rules about how much money and resources should be allocated to people with additional needs. Such rules are called 'eligibility criteria', and the entitlement to resources that an individual has increases according to the level of need they have. Taking risks is part of living a full life. This means that for service users to have choice and to live as full as life as possible they must also be supported to take risks.

The general public take risks every day of their lives. These may be day-to-day risks, such as playing sport, driving a car or drinking, or occasional risks, like going on an aeroplane. Some of us take great pleasure in pushing the boundaries of risk to the limit in 'extreme sports'. Of all the activities that we do, the only ones that require us to be risk assessed or to be tested are those through which others may get hurt, for example driving a car. Service users must also be allowed to make bad and good choices, and be supported in the risk and consequences that these bring. For people to learn things about their environment and themselves they must be supported while they make mistakes.

The Health and Safety at Work etc. Act 1974

Employers have responsibilities for the health and safety of their employees. They are also responsible for any visitors to their premises, such as relatives, suppliers and the general public.

The Health and Safety at Work etc. Act 1974 is the primary piece of legislation covering work-related health and safety in the United Kingdom. It sets out a lot of your employer's responsibilities for your health and safety at work. The Health and Safety Executive is responsible for enforcing health and safety at work.

Risk assessments

Your employer has a 'duty of care' to look after, as far as possible, your health, safety and welfare while you are at work. They should start with a risk assessment to spot possible health and safety hazards.

They have to appoint a 'competent person' to take on health and safety responsibilities. This is usually one of the owners in smaller firms, or a member of staff trained in health and safety in larger businesses.

You also have responsibilities for your own health and safety at work (see Figure 7.6). You have the right to refuse to do something that isn't safe without being threatened with disciplinary action. If you think your employer isn't meeting their responsibilities, talk to them. Your safety representative or a trade union official may be able to help you with this. As a last resort, you may need to report your employer to the Health and Safety Executive or to the environmental health department of your local authority. If you are dismissed for refusing to undertake an unsafe working practice, you may have a right to claim unfair dismissal at an employment tribunal.

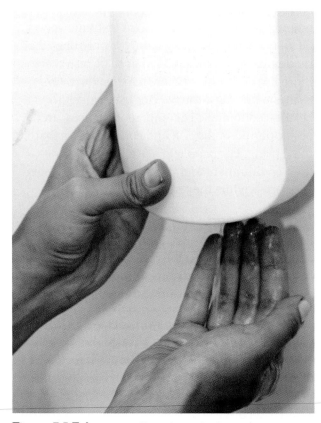

Figure 7.5 Take precautions to protect your health and safety and that of others

AC 7.2 Explain how risk-taking and risk assessment relate to rights and responsibilities

Addressing the issue of positive risk-taking is key to the implementation of person-centred planning and approaches, which are aimed at increasing inclusion and promoting people's participation in their communities as valued and contributing citizens. Responsible and responsive organisations (and services) strive to find ways to balance their responsibilities as employers with supporting people to live lives that work for them.

Our starting point is the principle that 'everyone in society has a positive contribution to make to that society and should have a right to control their own lives' ('Independence, well-being and choice', Social Care Green Paper, March 2005). Positive risk-taking is about people taking control of their own lives by weighing up the potential benefits and harms of exercising one choice of action over another. Positive risk-taking is not negligent ignorance of the potential risks. Risk is a part of everyone's everyday life. Everyone, including people with learning disabilities, has the right to take risks.

Practice outcomes

Given the support they need, people can take the risks they want and make informed choices. Taking part in new experiences and having greater community involvement potentially involves people in taking risks that offer opportunities for development of independence, confidence and autonomy.

Organisations must be able to demonstrate that a risk-assessing process (i.e. a process of thinking things through properly, involving the focus person and others who know them) has taken place. This may or may not result in a formal written risk assessment. This process is intended to complement the organisation's health and safety policy.

Everyone is assumed to have capacity unless proven otherwise (Mental Capacity Act 2005). Everyone is able to be involved in decision making, whether they are deemed to have capacity or not.

7.2 **Taking risks**

How can risk-taking be a positive thing? Think of some examples to illustrate this.

7.3 **Carrying out a risk assessment**

What are the steps involved in carrying out a risk assessment? Carry out a short risk assessment of a hazard you identify in your workplace or out in the community. Record your findings.

7.3 Explain why risk assessments need to be regularly revised

The following list gives an overview of the types of occasions when a risk assessment needs to be completed:

- when planning activities
- when planning and purchasing new facilities
- when new work practices are introduced
- when an individual develops a special need or there is a significant change to their existing needs.

In addition, there should be a system in place for regularly reviewing the risk assessments. No risk assessment should be written without a review date – this can be monthly, quarterly, six monthly or annually, depending on the need.

The risk assessment form allows risks to be recorded and the actions required to manage the risk easily communicated. This should be cross-referenced to other plans for the individual, especially the care plans. All plans need to be reviewed regularly. An additional review needs to take place, however, whenever a significant risk occurs. Forms must be dated and numbered.

Legislation

- **The Mental Capacity Act 2005**
- **The Care Act 2014**
- **The Health and Safety at Work etc. Act 1974**

Useful resources

Websites

Care Quality Commission
www.cqc.org.uk

Department for Education
www.gov.uk

Department of Health
www.gov.uk

Families Leading Planning UK
www.familiesleadingplanning.co.uk

In Control
www.in-control.org.uk

Support planning
www.supportplanning.org

Unit HSC 037

Promote and implement health and safety in health and social care

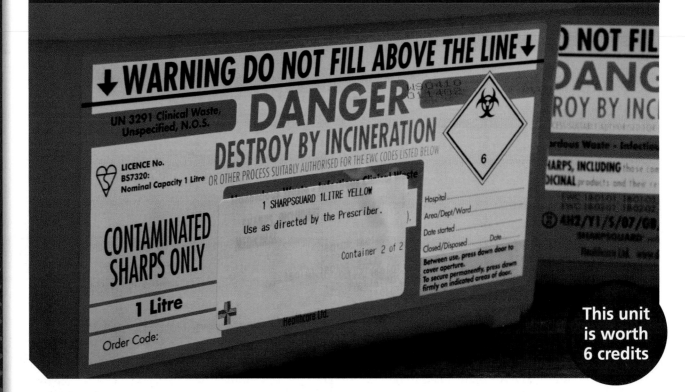

↓ WARNING DO NOT FILL ABOVE THE LINE ↓

DANGER

DESTROY BY INCINERATION
OR OTHER PROCESS SUITABLY AUTHORISED FOR THE EWC CODES LISTED BELOW

UN 3291 Clinical Waste,
Unspecified, N.O.S.

LICENCE No.
BS7320:
Nominal Capacity 1 Litre

CONTAMINATED
SHARPS ONLY

1 Litre

Order Code:

1 SHARPSGUARD 1LITRE YELLOW

Use as directed by the Prescriber.

Container 2 of 2

Hospital
Area/Dept/Ward
Date started
Closed/Disposed   Date
Between use, press down door to cover aperture.
To secure permanently, press down firmly on indicated areas of door.

Healthcare Ltd.

This unit is worth 6 credits

What are you finding out?

In this unit you will learn about the different ways to promote and implement health and safety in your work setting, including your responsibilities and those of others to ensure that it is a safe place for those who live and work there and where a sense of well-being is encouraged among everyone.

You will also learn more about how to respond effectively to health emergencies and environmental emergencies that may arise in your work setting, including preventative measures that can be taken. Being able to reduce the spread of infection, safely handle hazardous substances and materials, and move and handle equipment and other objects safely is also important in terms of being able to promote a safe and healthy environment for everyone. This unit will also help you learn more about how to recognise and manage stress, as being able to do so will impact positively on your own well-being and that of others.

By the end of this unit you will:

1 Understand your responsibilities, and the responsibilities of others, relating to health and safety.
2 Be able to carry out your responsibilities in relation to health and safety.
3 Understand procedures for responding to accidents and sudden illnesses.
4 Be able to reduce the spread of infection.
5 Be able to move and handle equipment and other objects safely.
6 Be able to handle hazardous substances and materials.
7 Be able to promote fire safety in the work setting.
8 Be able to implement security measures in the work setting.
9 Know how to manage stress.

Links to Level 3 Certificate in Preparing to Work in Adult Social Care

HSC 037 Assessment Criteria	PWCS 37
AC 1.1	AC 1.1
AC 1.3	AC 1.3
AC 2.4	AC 2.3
AC 3.1	AC 3.1
AC 3.2	AC 3.2
AC 4.1	AC 4.4
AC 5.1	AC 5.1
AC 6.1	AC 7.1
AC 7.3	AC 8.2 (fire)
AC 9.1	AC 9.1
AC 9.3	AC 9.3

LO1 Understand own responsibilities, and the responsibilities of others, relating to health and safety

AC 1.1 Identify legislation relating to health and safety in a health or social care work setting

Health and safety at work is very important as it involves the protection of everyone from accidents, injuries and illnesses. In health and social care settings accidents, injuries and illnesses can happen for a number of reasons, i.e. the frailty of individuals, including difficulties they may have with their mobility or vision or thinking and functioning, as in the case of those who have Alzheimer's, can mean that they are more susceptible to falls. Individuals and those they work with can also be susceptible to acquiring infections as tasks involve working closely with individuals who may have weakened immune systems.

Legislation is in place to ensure that everyone's health and safety is safeguarded. This includes all those who live, work and visit health or social care settings. Health and social care work settings are environments where accidents can happen for a number of reasons. For example, the age and frailty of individuals can mean accidents are more likely. Health and safety is therefore of the utmost importance in work settings, which may include one specific location or a range of locations, depending on the context of a particular work role.

Health and Safety at Work etc. Act 1974

The main piece of legislation that is relevant is the Health and Safety at Work etc. Act 1974 (HASAWA). This Act saw the establishment of the Health and Safety Commission (HSC) that merged with the **Health and Safety Executive** (HSE) in April 2008. It is responsible for **regulating** the health, safety and welfare for people in work settings in Great Britain.

The Act also formed the basis for other health and safety regulations and guidelines that are to be developed; Figure 8.1 provides details of some of the key ones.

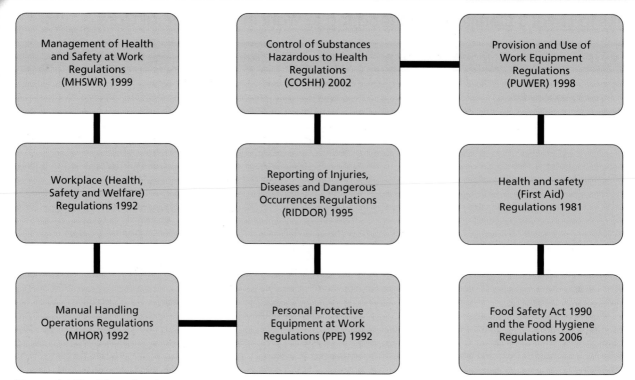

Figure 8.1 Health and safety legislation

Key terms

Legislation is a process that involves making laws.

Health and safety legislation covers laws relevant to health and safety.

The Health and Safety Executive (HSE) is the regulator or official supervisory body for the health, safety and welfare of people in work settings in the UK.

Regulators are organisations responsible for monitoring health and social care professionals.

Immune system is the process our body uses to protect us from infections.

Policies belong to the service or organisation and reflect the aims to be achieved.

Procedures belong to the employees and reflect how the service or organisation expects its employees to meet their aims.

Research and investigate

1.1 Your Health & Safety Policies and Procedures

Research the key points included in health and safety policies and procedures agreed with the employer. How well are you and others complying with these?

Visit **www.hse.gov.uk** and research the aims of the Health and Safety Executive. How are these aims relevant to your work setting and job role?

AC 1.2 Explain the main points of health and safety policies and procedures agreed with the employer

The health and safety legislation that exists requires employers to protect the health, safety and welfare of all their employees, as well as all those who may live in and/or visit their premises. Employers are therefore required to have in place policies and procedures that set out how people's health, safety and welfare will be safeguarded; these may include agreed ways of working as well as formal policies and procedures, and may relate to, for example:

- carrying out risk assessments
- the wearing of personal protective clothing when carrying out high-risk work activities
- the actions that must be taken in the event of an emergency
- how to carry out manual handling activities safely.

Health and SAFETY policies and procedures agreed with the employer include information on:

- **S**afe working practices
- **A**voiding the risk of injuries and diseases
- **F**ollowing safety signs and information
- **E**xposure to risks in the work setting and how to minimise them
- **T**raining available on health and safety
- **Y**our duties and responsibilities and those of others in the work setting.

A workplace that has five or more employees must have a written health and safety policy that includes a statement indicating the employer's aim to provide a safe workplace and who is responsible for the policy, as well as the arrangements in place to achieve the policy. **Health and safety policies and procedures** are important, therefore, for raising everyone's awareness of safe working practices, including how to reduce the risk of dangers, accidents and illnesses from occurring and those responsible for preventing specific and general health and safety hazards as well as the procedures for recording incidents at work and carrying out evacuations.

> ### Key term
>
> Health and safety policies and procedures are an employer's agreed ways of working relevant to health and safety.

AC 1.3 Analyse the main health and safety responsibilities of yourself, the employer or manager and others in the work setting

The main health and safety responsibilities for employees and employers

As we read in the sections above, the Health and Safety at Work etc. Act 1974 (HASAWA) set out legal duties and responsibilities for both employers and employees. Table 8.1 provides details about these.

As well as responsibilities, employees have rights in relation to their health and safety. These include the right to make your employer aware if you feel your health or safety is being put at risk, and to have those concerns fully addressed by your employer or another authority, such as the HSE, if your employer does not address these. You also have rights in relation to being provided with protective and safety equipment free of charge to carry out your work activities and to have time to rest during your time at work and time off from your work duties.

The main health and safety responsibilities of others

Although as we read employers and employees are jointly responsible for ensuring the health, safety and welfare of others who may live in and/or visit the work setting (see Table 8.1), others such as team members, other colleagues, individuals who use or commission their own health or social care services, their families, friends and advocates are also responsible for:

> ### Case study
>
> #### 1.1, 1.2 Fareed
>
> Fareed is a senior support worker providing support to individuals who live in their own homes. Fareed will soon be attending a health and safety training update and has been asked by his manager to share his learning from this with the rest of the team.
>
> 1. What are the key pieces of health and safety legislation that will be relevant to Fareed and the team?
> 2. What key details of his employer's health and safety policies and procedures will Fareed need to explain to the team?

Employers' health and safety responsibilities	Employees' health and safety responsibilities
1 Provide a workplace that is safe for everyone. E.g. properly maintained fittings and fixtures.	Take reasonable care of your own health and safety and that of others. E.g. follow safe working practices at all times when you work on your own and with others
2 Make the workplace free from risks to health. E.g. ensuring temperature, ventilation and lighting meet health and safety welfare requirements.	Take reasonable care to not put yourself or others at risk. E.g. report any health and safety concerns you have to your employer
3 Provide information, training and supervision around health and safety. E.g. how to use hazardous materials, carry out risk assessments, operate moving and handling equipment.	Co-operate with your employer on all health and safety information, training and procedures to follow. E.g attend health and safety training updates
4 Provide safety signs. E.g. on fire safety, security.	Understand the meaning of safety signs and follow these. E.g. understand the precaution s to take when using and storing different types of hazardous substances
5 Provide adequate first aid facilities. E.g. maintain fully stocked first aid kits.	Do not misuse first aid facilities or access these without authorisation. E.g. follow your work setting's procedures for how to access first aid facilities
6 Provide adequate welfare facilities. E.g. provision of toilet and washing facilities.	Use welfare facilities provided. E.g. take regular breaks in designated rest areas
7 Provide protective clothing free of charge. E.g. provision of disposable aprons and gloves.	Wear and understand how to dispose safely of protective clothing. E.g. remove aprons and gloves carefully and in designated area, wash hands before and after wearing and disposing of protective clothing
8 Provide equipment free of charge. E.g. provision and maintenance of hoists, maintain lifts in safe working order.	Use equipment provided and in accordance with instructions and training provided. E.g. read manufacturer's instructions before operating a hoist, avoid wearing loose clothing when operating a hoist, report any faults with moving and positioning equipment immediately
9 Assess risks and take precautions against risks of injury. E.g. carry out and update risk assessments.	Take reasonable care that you follow safe working practices at all times and comply with all risk assessments in place. Read individuals' risk assessments before moving and positioning them, ask if you are unsure or do not understand any aspects of individuals' risk assessments
10 Report accidents, injuries, diseases and dangerous occurrences to the appropriate authority. E.g. ensure accidents, injuries, diseases and dangerous occurrences are documented and reported in required timescales.	Report all accidents, injuries and diseases to your employer. E.g. report if you are pregnant to your employer or report if you have eczema to your employer

Table 8.1 Legal duties and responsibilities for both employers and employees

- maintaining a safe, healthy and secure environment, e.g. when entering and leaving the premises
- following all health and safety instructions and guidance provided, e.g. when assisting with a move, observing safety signs
- being aware of and complying with emergency procedures, e.g. in the event of a fire.

AC 1.4 Identify specific tasks in the work setting that should not be carried out without special training

In section AC 1.2, you read about two important responsibilities in relation to health and safety – taking reasonable care to not put yourself and others at risk, and co-operating with your employer on all training provided. It is important therefore that you undertake only those work activities that you have been trained to do and that you feel competent to undertake. There are some specific tasks in health and social care settings that require high levels of expertise and in-depth knowledge, which must only be undertaken if you have been trained; Figure 8.2 identifies what some of these are.

Figure 8.2 Tasks that require special training

Special training

Food preparation and handling will include knowing about safe techniques for preparing, cooking, storing food as well as precautions to take to avoid food poisoning.

Using equipment to assist and move individuals will include knowing about the different types of equipment available, safe techniques to use when moving individuals including the factors to take into account.

First aid will include knowing about your role as a first aider, how to manage accidents such as minor and severe bleeding or burns and scalds or head injuries and health emergencies such as seizures, a stroke, chest pains as well as techniques like resuscitation and knowledge of relevant legislation such as the Health and Safety (First Aid) regulations.

Administering medication will include safe administering of different medications i.e. inhalers, topical, tablets, use of PRN medication, risk assessments for self-medication and managing the risks associated with non-prescribed medicines.

Undertaking tasks that you are not competent to do or that you do not fully understand how to carry out can mean that you put yourself and others at risk of injuries and/or illness. For example, assisting an individual using a hoist that you do not know how to use could result in you and/or the individual being injured. Another example may be administering medication when you have not been trained to do so. This is a serious breach of your contract and can prove fatal for the individual concerned.

It is your employer's responsibility to provide you with regular training so that you can maintain your knowledge and keep your working practices up to date to comply with both legislation and your organisation's policies and procedures. For example, your employer may require you to attend a manual handling training update on the use of equipment such as a hoist or a first aid course or a course about the safe handling of medication. Complying with your employer's requirements for training is very important so that you can ensure that you are practising safely and within the remit of your job role and responsibilities.

Evidence activity

1.1, 1.2 Health and safety legislation, policies and procedures

List the health and safety legislation that is relevant to your work setting (AC 1.1).

Reference your work setting's health and safety policies and procedures or agreed ways of working. Explain the key points contained within these (AC 1.2).

1.3, 1.4 Health and safety responsibilities

- Identify the main health and safety responsibilities for you, your employer or manager, and others in the work setting.
- Analyse what each of these responsibilities is and how they differ for you, your employer or manager, and others in your work setting.
- Provide a list of the specific tasks in your work setting that should not be carried out without special training.

LO2 Be able to carry out own responsibilities for health and safety

Once you understand more about the different legal and organisational responsibilities you and others have in relation to health and safety (see AC 1.3), the next step is to learn more about how to carry out your day-to-day responsibilities for health and safety effectively.

AC 2.1 Use policies and procedures or other agreed ways of working that relate to health and safety

All aspects of health and safety covered in your workplace's policies and procedures are important and, as we read in AC 1.1, it is a legal requirement for you to comply with your employer's health and safety procedures. Using policies and procedures or other agreed ways of working is also important for a number of other reasons, including:

- to keep you and others safe
- to reduce dangers and risks of dangers that may arise in the work setting
- to keep you and others informed about safe working practices

- to keep you and others up to date with agreed ways of working
- to create a healthy environment
- to create good working and living conditions.

Every work setting will have in place its own set of health and safety policies, procedures and agreed ways of working; it is important that you read these and check your understanding of what you have read so that you can ensure you are carrying out your health and safety responsibilities effectively.

AC 2.2 Support others to understand and follow safe practices

As we read in LO1, health and safety is everyone's responsibility in the work setting. You can support others to understand and follow safe practices by:

- Following safe health and safety working practices yourself. This is a good way of role modelling to your colleagues, individuals and others who may visit the work setting how to safeguard their own and others' health, safety and welfare.
- Taking the time to explain and discuss with others why you practise the way you do so that they can understand the importance of following safe practices as well as the consequences of not doing so.
- Providing others with information and guidance around health and safety through the provision of leaflets, documents (available on the HSE's website) and handouts from training sessions you've attended, and through the sharing of articles and/or case studies you've read or heard about in the media.

Supporting others to understand and follow safe practices also involves recognising and being prepared to take action on and constructively challenge any unsafe practices you notice; it is only by discussing these with others that you can make them aware of the dangers and risks in which they are placing themselves and others, and support them to learn from their mistakes. When challenging unsafe practices you must also always report these to your manager and record your concerns including what policies and procedures have not been followed and all those that have been put at risk.

AC 2.3 Monitor and report potential health and safety risks

As we read in the previous section, it is important that any unsafe practices that arise are identified and challenged. Monitoring and reporting potential health and safety risks involves being aware of how hazards and risks can occur and develop in work settings. **Hazards** have the potential to cause harm, e.g. they can be objects or situations that may cause deaths, injuries, ill health or damage. **Risk** is the likelihood of harm occurring as a result of a hazard; the risks may be high, medium or low in terms of their likelihood and extent.

The potential health and safety risks you may encounter in your day-to-day working activities will depend on what your role and responsibilities involve and the setting in which you work. The following are examples of hazards that may be found and that you or others may have come across before:

- **Environmental hazards**, for example:
  - rooms with poor lighting, rooms that are too hot or too cold, noisy areas
  - poorly maintained floor coverings, e.g. frayed carpets in hallways, loose rugs in rooms, worn vinyl flooring in kitchens and bathrooms
  - obstructions, e.g. boxes in hallways, too much furniture in one room.
- **Equipment and aids**, e.g. faulty hoists, worn or inappropriate mobility equipment such as wheelchairs and walking frames.
- **Materials**, e.g. flammable liquids, incorrectly stored cleaning materials.
- **People**, e.g. people who behave in a challenging way, visitors who do not follow security procedures or handling procedures.

Reporting hazards and risks

It is your responsibility to ensure that you report any hazards or risks that you identify or that others have told you about; taking no action is not an option. You will need to follow your work setting's procedure for reporting risks and hazards.

Your employer also has a responsibility under the Reporting of Injuries, Diseases and Dangerous Occurrences Regulations (RIDDOR) (1995) to report:

- fatalities and major injuries
- reportable diseases
- any injury that leads to more than three days' absence from work
- dangerous occurrences.

AC 2.4 Use risk assessment in relation to health and safety

Monitoring and reporting potential health and safety risks is part of the **risk assessment** process. This considers the hazards that exist, their likelihood of causing death, injury, ill health or damage, and the precautions that are required in order to reduce the risks that these hazards present. Risk assessments may be completed in relation to hazards that are present in certain areas or rooms of the work setting, e.g. in the kitchen, bathrooms or hallways, or in relation to a person's work activities, e.g. a person's health, their use of equipment or their compliance with the fire safety procedure.

Reporting and recording

Reporting of Injuries, Diseases and Dangerous Occurrences Regulations 2013 (RIDDOR) is the law that requires employers to report and keep records for three years of work-related accidents that cause death and serious injuries (referred to as reportable injuries), diseases and dangerous occurrences (i.e. incidents with the potential to cause harm). These records are important for managing health and safety risks.

Records must include:

- the date, time and place of the event
- the date and method of reporting
- the personal details of all those involved
- details of the injury, disease or dangerous occurrence
- a description of the event.

Employers are required to report all deaths that have been caused by an accident if it is connected to the work setting.

The following specified injuries must also be reported if they are connected to the work setting and have resulted in the person being unable to carry out their duties for more than three days:

fractures, other than to fingers, thumbs and toes	any injury to the head or torso causing damage to the brain or internal organs
amputations	serious burns
injuries that are likely to lead to permanent loss of or reduction in sight	scalping requiring hospital treatment
any other injury arising from working in an enclosed space that leads to hypothermia or heat-induced illness or requires resuscitation or hospital admittance for more than 24 hours.	any loss of consciousness caused by a head injury or asphyxia

(Source: HSE)

Procedures for recording and reporting accidents in your work setting must be followed and an accident book or an accident report must be used to do so.

The risk assessment process has **five key stages**, as shown in the Figure 8.3.

After carrying out a risk assessment, risk control measures to reduce these risks must also be put in place. These include providing staff with additional training or further guidance on how to manage these risks effectively. As stated above, in the last stage of the risk assessment process, risk assessments must be updated as and when required to ensure that they are still valid in terms of safeguarding the health, safety and welfare of yourself and others. For example, an individual's mobility may have decreased due to a recent fall

Key term

Risk assessment is the framework for identifying, avoiding, minimising and controlling risks so that day-to-day duties can be carried out safely.

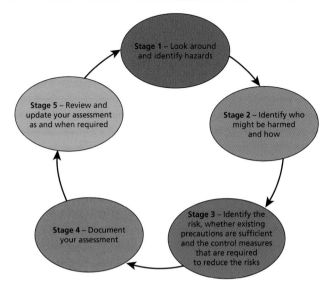

Figure 8.3 The risk assessment process

and the individual may no longer be able safely to use the stairs in their home on their own. A risk assessment would explore with the individual, as well as with the important people in their life, how best to manage this new risk. It may be that the individual would prefer to have a stair lift installed or would prefer to live downstairs; the individual may also benefit from some physiotherapy. However the risk is managed, what is important is the way forward that is agreed – one that does not prevent the individual from being independent but rather encourages them to retain their independent living skills while maintaining, as far as possible, their safety and that of others.

AC 2.5 Demonstrate ways to minimise potential risks and hazards

Using and revising risk assessments is one way to minimise potential risks and hazards that may occur in the work setting (see Table 8.2). Other ways may include:

Hazards	Risks	Actions to minimise these
A wet floor	Slips, fracturing of limbs	● Put up a safety sign to alert others that the floor is wet
A faulty hoist	An individual falling, a carer hurting their back	● Place a warning sign on the hoist indicating that it is faulty ● Remove the hoist from use ● Maintain regular checks to ensure the hoist is safe to use
An unauthorised visitor	May cause harm to others in the work setting or damage to the building or theft of property	● Ensure all visitors are clearly identified ● Be vigilant ● Challenge anyone you do not recognise ● Report any concerns you have immediately

Table 8.2 Actions to minimise potential hazards and risks

- Being vigilant at all times of health and safety risks and hazards that may arise.
- Providing regular and consistent feedback to others if you witness them engaging in unsafe practices.
- Making others aware of how to identify and report potential risks and hazards.
- Monitoring others to ensure they are complying with the work setting's procedures for minimising and reporting potential risks and hazards.
- Taking preventative measures and encouraging others to do the same before hazards develop, e.g. using safety signs to alert others that a floor is wet, checking equipment and aids are safe to use prior to using them, and not obstructing hallways, entrances and exits.

Evidence activity

2.3, 2.4, 2.5 Using risk assessment and minimising potential risks and hazards

- Reflect on different occasions when you monitored and reported potential health and safety risks and hazards in your work setting, and how you used risk assessment to minimise and control these.
- You will also need to be observed by your assessor monitoring and reporting potential health and safety risks, using risk assessment and demonstrating different ways to minimise potential risks and hazards.
  If a natural opportunity for you to monitor and report potential health and safety risks arises, use risk assessment and demonstrate different ways to minimise potential risks and hazards. If a natural opportunity to do this does not arise then you will need to ask your manager or supervisor for an expert witness testimony that provides evidence of an occasion or occasions when you did so.

Research and investigate

2.5 Potential risks and hazards

Find out about your work setting's policies and procedures for minimising potential risks and hazards.

AC 2.6 Access additional support or information relating to health and safety

As you read in LO1 and LO2, there are numerous pieces of legislation and policies and procedures available in your work setting. These are a good starting point for information and guidance relating to the health and safety responsibilities for you, your employer and others who work and live in the work setting. Other sources of additional **support or information** can include:

- the health and safety officer in your work setting
- the HSE
- training
- articles
- journals
- books
- courses.

These additional sources of support and information will not only help you develop a greater awareness of your role and your health and safety responsibilities, but can also be useful sources of information and support for others to access.

Key term

Support or information is people and resources that can provide guidance and information in relation to health and safety.

Evidence activity

2.6 Additional support or information

- Reflect on an occasion when you accessed additional support or information relating to health and safety in your work setting.
- You will also need to be observed by your assessor accessing additional support or information relating to health and safety. If a natural opportunity for you to access additional support or information does not arise then you will need to ask your manager or supervisor for an expert witness testimony that provides evidence of an occasion when you did so.

LO3 Understand procedures for responding to accidents and sudden illness

Once you understand how to carry out your health and safety responsibilities, the next step is to develop your understanding of the procedures to follow when responding to **accidents** and **sudden illnesses** that may arise in your work setting.

AC 3.1 Describe different types of accidents and sudden illness that may occur in own work setting

Accidents and sudden illness may occur in work settings if hazards and risks have not been identified or reduced. Accidents could result, for example, if a safety sign has not been used to indicate that a floor is wet, or from using an unsafe bathing aid, or from supporting an individual who displays aggression.

Examples of accidents that can occur include:

● fractures
● cuts
● bleeding
● burns and scalds
● poisoning
● electrical injuries.

Sudden illnesses are medical conditions that begin unexpectedly. These can occur in health and social care settings as a result of an accident, an injury sustained or from an unexpected deterioration in an individual's health.

Examples of sudden illnesses that can occur include:

● cardiac arrest
● stroke
● epileptic seizure
● choking and difficulty with breathing
● shock
● loss of consciousness.

AC 3.2 Explain procedures to be followed if an accident or sudden illness should occur

The procedures to follow if an accident or sudden illness occurs will depend on your role and responsibilities, as well as on the setting where you work, i.e. residential or based in a hospital or community. It is important that you only work within the remit of your job role and knowledge and that you only administer first aid if you have been trained to do so.

You may have heard of the DR'S ABC acronym. This is a good way of helping you to remember what to do when you come across an accident or sudden illness:

D **Danger checks** – look around you and check for any risks or signs of danger.

R **Response assessment** – assess all casualties. Check whether or not they are conscious.

S **Shout for help** – call an ambulance or get someone else to do this for you, and ask them to come back and tell you when this is done.

A **Airway checks** – check that the casualty's airway is open and not blocked. Check that help is on its way.

B **Breathing checks** – check whether the casualty is breathing normally. If they are, place them in the recovery position. If the casualty is not breathing, start CPR only if you have been trained to do so. Check that help is on its way.

C **Circulation checks** – continue to monitor the casualty. Check that help is on its way.

Tables 8.3 and 8.4 provide details about the signs and symptoms you may notice, as well as some guidelines around the key actions to take for the examples of accidents and sudden illnesses identified in AC 3.1. Note that these are not comprehensive lists of actions or guidelines to follow and you should consult your work setting's emergency procedures.

Recording and reporting

It is a requirement that records are kept of all accidents and incidents, including when an individual has refused treatment. The following information must also be recorded:

- the name of the person injured or taken ill
- the date, time and place of the accident/incident
- the details of the injury/illness
- the treatment given, including what happened to the injured/ill person afterwards.

You must also sign the record.

When responding to accidents or sudden illnesses there are a number of other procedures that must also be followed so as to avoid causing further harm or injury to the casualty.

Training

You must ensure that you attend training and can demonstrate your competence on how to respond to different accidents and sudden illnesses, including the Do's and Don't's as well as specific actions to take such as CPR.

- Making the area safe

When an accident or sudden illness occurs you must make the immediate area as safe as possible by for example removing any broken items that could potentially cause harm.

- Helping, and getting help

Getting help as soon as possible and checking that it is on its way is essential, as is providing assistance to others who may require this – if for example the casualty is distressed or requires a blanket to keep warm.

Ensuring your own well-being and that of the casualty is of upmost importance and involves maintaining the casualty's privacy and dignity, i.e. by covering them over with a blanket or asking others to leave the area, maintaining the confidentiality of the situation and providing reassurance to the casualty and any others who have witnessed what has occurred.

Case study

3.1, 3.2 Liam

Liam is a senior residential worker in a residential care home and is inducting a new member of staff. As part of his induction Liam has agreed to discuss the procedures in place for responding to accidents and sudden illnesses.

1 Detail the different types of accidents that may occur in a residential care home.
2 Detail the different types of sudden illness that may occur in a residential care home.
3 What actions must be taken if an accident should occur? Why?
4 What actions must be taken if a sudden illness should occur? Why?

Evidence activity

3.1, 3.2 Accidents and sudden illness

- Make a list of the different types of accident and sudden illness that have occurred or that can occur in your work setting. For each one provide details about what was involved and how they occurred.
- Read through your work setting's procedure for how to respond to an accident or sudden illness. Explain in your own words the key actions to take, and how and why these are to be followed.

Type of accident	Signs and symptoms	Key actions to take
Fracture	• Swelling • Oddly positioned limbs • Pain around the fractured area	• Do not move the injured person. • Support the injured limb. • Reassure the injured person. • Call and ensure that the fracture is diagnosed correctly at a hospital – you should not try to bandage this yourself. • Do not give the injured person anything to eat or drink.
Cut	• Large or small amounts of blood	• Apply pressure to a cut that is bleeding. • Use a dressing if one is available. • Call for help.
Bleeding	• Large or small amounts of blood	• Apply pressure to a bleeding wound. • If there is an object in the wound, do not remove the object, but do apply pressure either side of the wound. • Protect yourself from coming into contact with blood that may get into your eyes, your month, nose or through any broken skin i.e. cuts. • Raise the injured body part if possible and ensure the casualty is comfortable. • Call for help.
Burn/scalds caused by heat/flames/ hot liquids/ chemicals/ electrical currents	• Swollen or blistered skin • The person may be in severe pain or shock	• Call for medical help immediately. • Cool the burn with cold water (keep it underwater for 10 minutes for burns, 20 minutes for chemical burns). Ensure that you safely dispose of water used to cool chemical burns. • Remove if possible any clothing or jewellery that is not stuck to the skin.
Poisoning caused by chemicals, plants or substances like drugs and alcohol	• The person may be unconscious • The person may be in severe pain • Swollen or blistered skin around the mouth and lips	• If the person is unconscious, place them in the recovery position and call for medical help. • Try to find out either from the person or from objects left in the area what the poison may have been and how much has been taken.
Electrical injuries caused by high voltages (e.g. railway lines) or low voltages (e.g. electrical appliances such as a kettle or heater)	• The person may have burns • The person may have had a cardiac arrest	• Do not touch the person until the electricity supply has been cut off. • For low-voltage currents switch off the electric at the mains if you can; if you can't then try to move the casualty using something dry and not made of metal, e.g. a wooden broom. • Call for medical help immediately. • When safe to do so, treat the injured person, i.e. for burns, and if the person is unconscious place them in the recovery position.

Table 8.3 Types of accidents (Note: The information offered in this table is advice only and you should consult your manager/supervisor for further guidance).

Type of sudden illness	Signs and symptoms	Key actions to take
Cardiac arrest is caused by a heart attack, shock or electric shock	• The person has no pulse • The person is not breathing	• Reassure the person. • Call for help. • Carry out cardio-pulmonary resuscitation (CPR) only if you have been fully trained to do so.
Stroke is caused by blood clots that block the flow of blood to the brain	• The person may have an uneven face • The person may not be able to raise and hold both arms • The person's speech may be confused	• Call for help. • Reassure the person.
Epileptic seizure is caused by changes in the brain's activity	• Involuntary contraction of muscles	• Make the immediate area safe. • Do not attempt to move or restrict the person; make sure the person's clothes are loose. • Once the seizure has ended place the person in the recovery position. • Reassure the person, ensure they are comfortable, and be particularly careful to prevent any head injury. • Call for help.
Choking and difficulty with breathing can be caused by food becoming stuck in the throat	• Coughing • Difficulty breathing (gasping) • Difficulty speaking	• Encourage the person to cough and remove their dentures if possible from their mouth. • If this fails, use the heel of the hand to give five blows between the shoulder blades while the person is bent forwards. • If this fails use abdominal thrusts (the Heimlich manoeuvre), but only if you have been trained to do so. • Call for help.
Shock is caused when blood is not flowing round the body effectively	• Cold, clammy and/or pale skin • Fast pulse • Fast breathing • May feel sick	• Call for help. • Lay the person on the floor and raise their feet off the ground if possible. • Monitor and reassure the person, ensure they are warm, that their clothing is not too tight, and regularly check on their breathing and pulse. • Do not give the casualty anything to eat or drink and do not leave them alone.
Loss of consciousness is caused by a faint or a serious illness	• Not being responsive, either partial or total unresponsiveness	• Check if the person is breathing and has a clear airway. • Reassure the person. • Look for reasons why they may be unconscious. • Place the casualty in the recovery position to maintain their safety but only if they do not have any injuries to their back or neck or any fractured limbs, in which case the casualty should not be moved. • Call for help.

Table 8.4 Types of sudden illness (Note: The information offered in this table is advice only and you should consult your manager/supervisor for further guidance).

LO4 Be able to reduce the spread of infection

Once you understand how to respond to accidents and sudden illnesses that may arise in the work setting, the next step is to learn more about how to reduce the spread of infection. You can find more information on this in Unit IC 01.

Infections can make people feel unwell and some are so serious that they can cause people to die.

Infections can spread between different places and people through for example water, air, dust, droplets, food, contaminated items, animals, insects as well as person to person. The spread of infection from person to person can occur indirectly, i.e. through contaminated items, food, animals or insects, or directly when there is physical contact with another person who has an infection.

Pathogens such as bacteria and viruses can also find their way into our bodies through natural openings, i.e. eyes, nose, mouth, and unnatural openings, i.e. cuts or wounds, and can also be ingested and inhaled. Infections spread through six key stages; these are often referred to as the chain of infection:

1 Pathogen – this is the first stage of an infection when a pathogen causing infection is present.
2 Environment – the necessary conditions for the pathogen to survive and multiply must then be present.
3 Transport – the different methods for the pathogens to move from place to place must then be available.
4 Route into the body – a point of entry for the pathogen to enter the body must be available.

5 Route out of the body – a point of exit for the pathogen to leave the body must be available.
6 Next person – another point for the pathogen to enter the body must be available. The next person to have an infection becomes the sixth link in this chain of infection; some people may be more vulnerable than others to infections if they have low **immunity**.

If an individual is unwell or older then their immune system will work less effectively and therefore protect them less against infections.

AC 4.1 Explain own role in supporting others to follow practices that reduce the spread of infection

Reducing the spread of infection is important for maintaining your own health and welfare and that of others. Not doing so can lead to ill health and in some cases even fatalities. Supporting others to follow practices that reduce the spread of infection can be done in a variety of ways; some of the key methods for doing this are included in Figure 8.4.

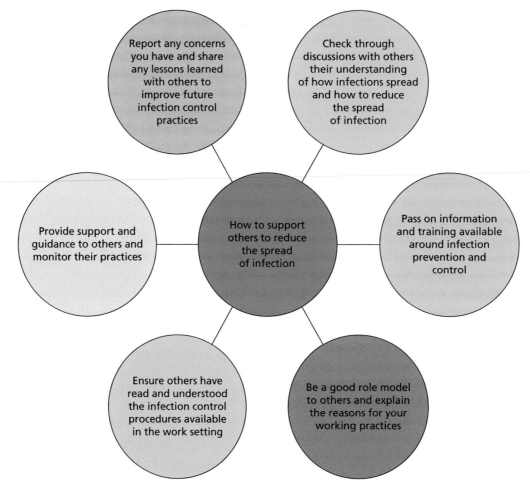

Figure 8.4 Supporting others to reduce the spread of infection

AC 4.2 Demonstrate the recommended method for hand washing

Infections can spread from person to person in health and social care settings by their hands; it is for this reason that it is essential that we wash our hands thoroughly (see Figure 8.4). Many work settings have a procedure for hand washing that details when hands must be washed, how to wash hands effectively and the training and information available.

It is important that you wash your hands before and after:

- all your work activities
- contact with an individual to whom you are providing care or support
- contact with bodily fluids (both your own and others')
- handling used laundry or waste products
- preparing and handling food

- eating
- wearing disposable gloves.

Washing and drying your hands effectively involves following good practice points (see Figure 8.5)

- **Duration** – minimum of 10 to 15 seconds.
- **Use of water** – use warm water to wash and rinse your hands; if the water is too hot or too cold this is likely to deter you from washing and rinsing your hands thoroughly.
- **Use of soap** – ensure you create a lather with the soap over all areas of your hands.
- **Washing technique** – rub your palms together, interlace the fingers, rub backs of hands, then round your fingers and thumbs.
- **Drying technique** – dry your hands thoroughly using a clean towel, disposable paper towel or air drier.
- **Use of hand-washing products** – alcohol-based hand rubs are not a substitute for hand washing

1 Wet hands with water

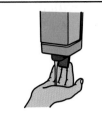
2 Apply enough soap to cover all hand surfaces

3 Rub hands palm to palm

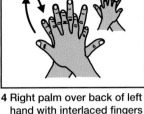
4 Right palm over back of left hand with interlaced fingers and vice versa

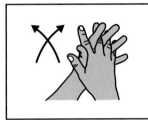
5 Palm to palm with fingers interlaced

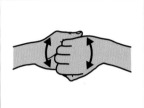
6 Backs of fingers to opposing palms with fingers interlocked

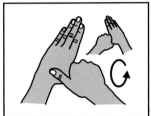
7 Rotational rubbing of left thumb clasped in right palm and vice versa

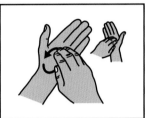
8 Rotational rubbing, backwards and forwards with clasped fingers of right hand in left palm and vice versa

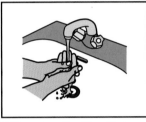
9 Rinse hands with water

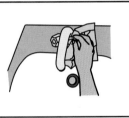
10 Dry hands thoroughly with a single-use towel

11 Use towel to turn off tap

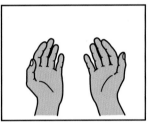
12 Your hands are now safe

Figure 8.5 Hand-washing technique

and should not be used when hands are visibly dirty; they can, however, be used alongside hand washing for additional protection. Disinfectant hand rubs can be placed in entry and exit points in rooms and can be used for disinfecting your hands.

AC 4.3 Demonstrate ways to ensure that own health and hygiene do not pose a risk to an individual or to others at work

As well as washing your hands effectively it is important that you look after your health and hygiene so you do not spread infections to individuals or others at work. Following your work setting's procedures for all high-risk activities you carry out – such as supporting an individual with an infection, handling soiled linen or cleaning equipment – is the first step to reducing the spread of infection to others.

Health, well-being and hygiene

In terms of your health it is important that you eat healthily, have sufficient sleep and relaxation, exercise regularly, take your breaks at work and have time off from work. Doing so will make you feel physically and emotionally well, and will make you a good role model for others. You will be less likely to have absences from work due to illness and more likely to be able to manage difficult and challenging situations and dilemmas you may come across in your day-to-day working activities. It is also important if you are unwell that you do not come into work as you will risk the spreading of infection to others.

In terms of your hygiene it is important that you maintain a good overall level of personal hygiene, and if you are required to wear a uniform that you do so and that you ensure it is clean and comfortable and fits properly. Shoes should also be comfortable and provide good support to your feet to enable you to carry out your activities safely. Not having your hair tied back can result in injury if it becomes tangled in equipment, or spread infection to others you come into close contact with such as individuals you are supporting. Jewellery and other accessories can be routes for infection and must be avoided; some items can also cause tears in aprons and gloves, and may prevent you from washing your hands effectively.

Other precautions in relation to maintaining good health and hygiene include ensuring you have all necessary vaccinations and boosters, following medical advice and taking necessary precautions for any temporary or long-term skin conditions, and always covering any breaks in the skin that occur with a dressing. Good food and kitchen hygiene such as cleaning utensils, washing your hands, wiping down surfaces and emptying rubbish is also essential to prevent the contamination of food that can result in food poisoning.

Protective clothing, cleaning equipment and dealing with waste

Gloves can be worn for different hazardous activities such as when handling laundry, carrying out personal care tasks and preparing and handling food. It is important to wash your hands before wearing gloves as well as after you dispose of them so as to minimise the spread of infection. You should also dispose of gloves carefully to avoid any micro-organisms being transferred onto other surfaces or areas.

Personal protective clothing (PPE) can also be worn for different hazardous activities such as when handling laundry, carrying out personal care tasks and preparing and handling food. It is important to put on your apron correctly so that it gives you the maximum protection from the spread of infection. Again, as with gloves, you should dispose of aprons carefully to avoid any micro-organisms being transferred onto other surfaces or areas, a process known as cross infection.

Clean equipment such as bed pans and wheelchairs before and after use as this will minimise the spread of micro-organisms that can be transferred to others. Cleaning linen at high temperatures will also reduce the spread of infections.

Dealing with different types of waste correctly can reduce the spread of infection. For example, clinical waste that may be contaminated by body fluids such as incontinence pads and wound dressings must be disposed of in yellow bags. Sharps waste such as needles and syringes must be disposed of in a sharps box that is then collected or taken to a disposal point.

Case study

4.3 Natsuko

Natsuko is an experienced senior carer and always ensures that she supports her colleagues, the individuals with whom she works, their families, friends and advocates to follow good working practices that reduce the spread of infections.

1 How can Natsuko support all these people to follow practices that reduce the spread of infection?

Evidence activity

4.1, 4.2, 4.3 Reducing the spread of infection

- Make a short presentation to your team about your role in supporting others to follow practices that reduce the spread of infection.
- Include in your presentation a demonstration of the recommended method for hand washing and the different ways to ensure that your health and hygiene do not pose a risk to others with whom you work.
- You will also need to be observed by your assessor demonstrating the recommended method for hand washing and ways of ensuring that your health and hygiene do not pose a risk to others with whom you work.

LO5 Be able to move and handle equipment and other objects safely

Promoting and implementing health and safety in the work setting also involves safe practices for **moving and handling** equipment and other objects.

Key term

Moving and handling refers to moving and handling individuals and objects from one position or place to another.

AC 5.1 Explain the main points of legislation that relates to moving and handling

The moving and handling of equipment and other objects in health and social care settings is governed by different pieces of health and safety legislation, as shown in Table 8.5. One piece of legislation, the Manual Handling Regulations (MHOR) 1992 (as amended 2002), defines moving and handling as:

Any transporting or supporting of a load (including the lifting, pulling down, pushing, pulling, carrying or moving thereof) by hand or bodily force.

(Source: Manual Handling Regulations 1992, as amended 2002)

Table 8.5 outlines information about the legislation that relates to moving and handling in health and social care.

Legislation	Relates to moving and handling equipment and other objects safely by stating that:
Health & Safety at Work etc. Act (HASAWA) 1974	• Risks must be identified, controlled and reduced. • Training must be provided and complied with. • Equipment must be provided and maintained.
Management of Health & Safety at Work Regulations (MHSWR) 1999	• Risk assessments must be undertaken. • Potential hazards and risks must be identified. • Risks must be evaluated.
Workplace (Health, Safety and Welfare) Regulations 1992	• Employers must ensure the health, safety and welfare of employees. • Employers must provide a safe environment. • Equipment must be maintained.
Manual Handling Operations Regulations (MHOR) 1992 (as amended 2002)	• Risks must be assessed. • The risks of injury must be reduced.
Provision and Use of Work Equipment Regulations (PUWER) 1998	• Equipment used must be suitable, safe and maintained. • Information, instruction and training must be provided to staff. • Health and safety stop devices and controls, warning devices and visible markings must be in place.
Lifting Operations and Lifting Equipment Regulations (LOLER) 1998	• Equipment used must be fit for purpose and maintained. • Problems with equipment must be reported and recorded.
Personal Protective Equipment at Work Regulations (PPE) 1992	• PPE must be provided free of charge. • Instructions, procedures, training and supervision must be provided to staff. • PPE must be maintained and appropriately stored.
Reporting of Injuries, Diseases and Dangerous Occurrences Regulations (RIDDOR) 1995	• Accidents, diseases and dangerous occurrences must be reported.

Table 8.5 Moving and handling legislation

AC 5.2 Explain principles for safe moving and handling

Moving and handling equipment and other objects safely is an integral part of some work settings. There is a wide range of moving and handling equipment available to meet different individuals' needs. These may include different types of equipment to:

- **lift individuals**, such as bath lifts, ceiling and mobile hoists
- **move individuals from one position to another without lifting**, such as slide sheets, transfer boards and turntables
- **assist individuals with their mobility**, such as wheelchairs, hand rails and walking frames.

Moving objects may also form part of an individual's duties, and may include lifting a box of items that has been delivered to your work setting or carrying a mobility appliance upstairs.

As well as legislation, general principles for safe moving and handling exist and provide clear guidance on practices to follow:

Always:

- check whether it is possible to avoid moving and handling
- follow your work setting's policies and procedures, and the individual's care plan and risk assessment for moving and handling
- follow your work setting's infection control policy when moving and handling
- check that equipment is safe to use before you use it
- check the safe weight limit of the load before you move it
- check that there is sufficient space to carry out the move safely before you do so
- use equipment in line with the manufacturer's instructions and check that it is stored appropriately

- respect an individual's privacy and dignity during moving and handling
- explain what you are going to do and gain the individual's consent to do so before you begin
- encourage the individual to assist in the move, and provide reassurance
- dress in a way that enables you to move around freely, and wear flat, enclosed shoes
- keep your spine in line during manual handling, create a good stable base and keep your knees slightly bent
- keep the load as close to you as possible
- use the large leg and buttock muscles to provide the power during manual handling.

Time to think

5.2 Are you moving and handling safely?
- How do you move and handle equipment and other objects?
- Do your working practices comply with the principles for safe moving and handling?
- If not, how will you improve these?

Case study

5.2 Gemma
Gemma works as a senior personal assistant and is also an accredited moving and handling trainer. As part of both her roles Gemma promotes and follows safe moving and handling working practices.

1 To what principles for safe moving and handling do you think Gemma adheres?
2 Why?

AC 5.3 Move and handle equipment and other objects safely

Implementing the principles for safe moving and handling discussed in AC 5.2 is essential if you are safely to move and handle equipment and other objects.

Before moving and handling equipment and other objects you must:

- Read and understand your work setting's policies and procedures, as well as the individual's care plan and risk assessment.
- Assess whether it is necessary that you move and handle equipment and other objects.
- Check that you have been trained to carry out the move, that you have the aids and equipment you need, that you feel competent and confident in using the equipment and carrying out the move, and that you are wearing suitable clothing and footwear.
- Assess whether you are able to move the load safely using a safe technique, whether there is sufficient space to carry out the move, and whether the equipment available is suitable for the move, clean, in good working order and safe to use.
- Discuss the best way to carry out the move with the person being moved when and wherever possible, encouraging them to do as much as they can but ensuring they are moved and handled safely at all times.

During moving and handling equipment and other objects you must:

- Plan the move by thinking about the equipment to use, what the move will involve, whether you will need any assistance from your colleagues.
- Keep the load close to your body and adopt a stable position to maintain your balance.
- Keep your back, hips and knees slightly bent and your head up.
- Seek advice from a senior colleague if you are unsure about the move, have concerns or need further clarification about how to carry it out safely.

Evidence activity

5.1, 5.2, 5.3 Safe moving and handling

- Read through the moving and handling legislation table on page 145, which identifies relevant moving and handling legislation. Then explain in your own words the key points of each piece of legislation and how they relate to moving and handling equipment and other objects.
- Discuss with a colleague the principles for safe moving and handling, what these include and why, as well as how you must move and handle equipment and other objects safely in your work setting.
- You will also need to be observed by your assessor moving and handling equipment and other objects safely.

Research and investigate

5.3 Using moving and handling equipment

Research the key practices to follow for using different types of moving and handling equipment.

LO6 Be able to handle hazardous substances and materials

In the previous section you learned about safe practices to follow for moving and handling equipment and other objects; in this section you will learn more about the different substances that may be found in work settings that can be **hazardous**, as well as the safe practices to follow when storing, using and disposing of these.

Key term

Hazardous substances are substances that have the potential to cause harm and illness.

AC 6.1 Describe types of hazardous substances that may be found in the work setting

Knowing what a hazardous substance is and the different types that can be found in your work setting is important in terms of promoting your own and others' health and safety.

Hazardous substances have the potential to cause harm and illness to others when stored, used or disposed of incorrectly. The Control of Substances Hazardous to Health Regulations (COSHH) 2002 classifies hazardous substances as toxic, very toxic, corrosive, harmful or an irritant. Hazardous substances can cause short- or long-term health problems, depending on the substance as well as on how long you or others are exposed to it. In your work setting examples of hazardous substances might be cleaning materials, adhesives and gas.

Research and investigate

6.1 Hazardous substances and COSHH
Research the different types of hazardous substances that may be found in different health and social care settings and how to dispose of these safely.

AC 6.2 Demonstrate safe practices for storing hazardous substances, using hazardous substances and disposing of hazardous substances and materials

Being aware of your work setting's policies and procedures for how to store, use and dispose of hazardous substances and materials is an integral part of keeping yourself and others safe.

When **storing** hazardous substances check the following:

- where they are being stored – the temperature and ventilation of the area
- how they are being stored – whether in line with the manufacturer's instructions
- the precautions to take – how to avoid any outbreaks of fire or illness.

When **using** hazardous substances check the following:

- how to use them – the PPE that is required
- the techniques to use – how to clean up spillages safely
- the precautions to take – use warning signs to alert others of the dangers (see Figure 8.6).

When **disposing of** hazardous substances and materials check the following:

- where to dispose of them – the location will vary for different substances
- the techniques to use – how to dispose of them safely
- the precautions to take – the PPE that is required.

Personal protective equipment (PPE)

Gloves, aprons, goggles and face masks are all examples of different types of protective equipment used in health and social care settings. Gloves and aprons are used to protect carers from micro-organisms that may transfer onto their hands or clothes and that may be transferred from their hands and clothes to individuals and other surfaces from hazardous activities such as handling waste or coming into contact with body fluids. Goggles and face masks are used to prevent micro-organisms present in for example body fluids entering the body through for example the eyes or mouth.

Figure 8.6 Hazard symbols

LO7 Be able to promote fire safety in the work setting

AC 7.1 Describe practices that prevent fires from starting and spreading

Fire safety in the work setting includes knowing how to prevent fires from starting, and the actions to take to prevent fires from spreading. Care workers are also responsible for supporting individuals to understand how to prevent fires from starting and spreading (see Figure 8.7).

For a fire to start it needs **all three** of these components:

1 **Oxygen** – oxygen is present in the air.
2 **Fuel** – items that can burn, can be a solid, liquid or gas.
3 **Heat** – items that can cause sparks or ignite, such as a heater or a cigarette.

If you take one of these components away, such as fuel or heat, then a fire cannot start. Practices that prevent fires from starting include ensuring that you keep items that can burn away from heat sources. For example, care workers can support an individual who lives in his own home not to dry his clothes (an item that can burn) over the door of his gas oven (a source of heat), or can support an individual to understand the reasons why electrical sockets must not be overloaded.

Figure 8.7 Combustion

There are also a number of preventative measures that can be taken to prevent fires when they first start from spreading, by ensuring that:

- fitted smoke detectors, fire alarms, sprinklers and fire extinguishers are maintained and are in good working order (to ensure they work effectively when a fire starts)
- smoke detectors and sprinklers are not obstructed by items piled up underneath them (to ensure they work effectively when a fire starts)
- windows and doors are kept closed (to keep the fire contained)
- you are trained in the actions to take when a fire starts (to keep the fire contained).

Research and investigate

7.1 Fire safety

Find out about the 'fire triangle' and why it is relevant to fire safety.

Research the different fire extinguishers, and for what each one should be used.

AC 7.2 Demonstrate measures that prevent fires from starting

Your work setting's fire safety policy and procedures will also include a number of important MEASURES to prevent fires from starting:

M   **M**aintenance schedules for all electrical items and fire safety equipment.

E   **E**veryday cleaning of all areas to avoid the accumulation of rubbish and dust.

A   **A**rrangements for where to smoke cigarettes.

S   **S**ystems to ensure that flammable items are kept away from heat sources.

U   **U**p-to-date fire risk assessments and records.

R   **R**isk assessment to identify sources of ignition and substances that burn to avoid, reduce and control fire risks and hazards.

E   **E**veryday monitoring of fire safety working practices.

S   **S**ystems for ensuring that all care workers are trained in and know about **measures** that prevent fires from starting and spreading.

Key term

Measures are a work setting's systems and equipment.

Evidence activity

7.1, 7.2 Preventing fires from starting and spreading

- Make a short presentation to your team about working practices that can prevent fires from starting and spreading quickly. Include details about the systems and equipment that are in place in your work setting to prevent fires from starting.
- You will also need to be observed by your assessor demonstrating how to use measures that prevent fires from starting.

AC 7.3 Explain emergency procedures to be followed in the event of a fire in the work setting

Your work setting's fire safety policy and procedures will also include details of the actions you must take in the event of a fire. It is important that you read through and understand what these actions are so that you do not place yourself or anyone else in danger. Below are some of the key actions to take, in the acronym ACT FAST:

A   **A**ct fast, do not panic, sound the fire alarm.

C   **C**ontrol and contain the fire only if you have been trained to do so and it is safe.

Case study

7.3 Juana

Juana is a senior night support worker in a mental health unit. One night Juana smells smoke coming from one of the individuals' rooms.

1 What actions must Juana take?
2 Why?

Time to think

7.3 Do you know how to respond to a fire in your work setting?

- Have you or someone you know ever had to deal with a fire at work?
- What happened?
- What actions were taken?
- Why?

T **T**elephone the fire brigade and provide them with details about you, your location and the fire.

F **F**ollow your **emergency** procedure to ensure the safety of everyone.

A **A**ssist in ensuring everyone is in a place of safety, either inside or outside the building.

S **S**upport others to ensure that no one stops or returns for personal belongings.

T **T**ry to remain calm and wait until the fire brigade informs you that it is safe to re-enter the building.

AC 7.4 Ensure that clear evacuation routes are maintained at all times

To be able to follow your work setting's emergency procedures in the event of a fire it is crucial that the setting's evacuation routes are kept clear at all times. You may work in a variety of different work settings, including individuals'

homes, and so it is very important that you are aware of the escape routes for each setting and that you ensure these are kept clear at all times so they can be used in the event of a fire. This will involve working with individuals to ensure that there are no items such as boxes or mobility appliances obstructing the escape routes, that floor coverings are not worn or damaged, and that the escape routes are well lit and signposted where possible.

Evidence activity

7.3, 7.4 Responding to a fire at work

- Discuss with your manager the emergency procedures to be followed in the event of a fire occurring in your work setting, and the consequences of failing to do so. Include details of the importance of maintaining clear fire escape routes at all times.
- You will also need to be observed by your assessor demonstrating how to maintain clear evacuation routes at all times.

LO8 Be able to implement security measures in the work setting

AC 8.1 Demonstrate use of agreed procedures for checking the identity of anyone requesting access to premises and information

Promoting health and safety at work will also include putting into practice **security** measures. Procedures for checking the **identity** of anyone requesting access to the premises or to information will vary depending on your work role and the setting where you work. There are, however, some general good practice principles that must be followed to keep health and social care settings safe and free from danger.

Key terms

Security means safety or being safe from danger.

Identity is who a person is, their name and designation.

- **Stop and think** – is the visitor known to you or anyone else, has the visitor got an agreed appointment?
- **Use security measures**, such as a spy hole, window or door chain, while checking the identity of the person calling.
- **Check the person's proof of identity**, such as an identity card, and check whether the person looks like the person in the photo and whether the name on the card matches who they say they are.
- **If you are unsure** about the person's identity, do not allow them to enter the premises until you have sought advice from your manager, explaining what your concerns are. It may be necessary to call the police.

As well as keeping health and social care settings safe it is important to ensure that all information about individuals is kept safe and secure, as this will not only ensure the provision of safe and effective care but is also crucial to maintaining trust between you and the individuals with whom you work.

The Data Protection Act 1998 protects how personal information is maintained and used. It is part of your responsibilities to ensure that the individuals with whom you work understand that personal information about them, such as in relation to their care and support needs, will be shared with others who are involved in their care or support. This means it is very important when disclosing information about an individual to others that you check you have the individual's consent to do so. You must also always check who they are and the purpose of their request. You may have to do this in person or by phone or in an email, depending on the nature of the enquiry.

Everyone providing or receiving information about an individual is also required to understand that the personal information being shared is confidential and must remain so. When having to provide information to others without informing the individual, for example in the case of a health emergency, it is good practice to inform the individual afterwards how and why you did so.

Case study

8.1 Damerae

Damarae is the senior support worker on duty this morning and a carer has asked for his advice regarding providing access to a contractor who has arrived on the premises stating that it has been agreed for him to carry out work in the front and back gardens of the premises. The carer explains to Damerae that the pharmacist has also phoned requesting some information about the medication that Bert, one of the individuals who lives in the setting, is taking.

1 What advice should Damerae provide to the carer?
2 How can the identity of the contractor be checked?
3 How can the identity of the caller be checked?

AC 8.2 Demonstrate use of measures to protect own security and the security of others in the work setting

As well as checking the identity of those requesting access to the premises and to information about individuals, different work settings will have in place a range of MEASURES (see Figure 8.8) to protect your security and the security of others, including the following:

M **M**aintenance of buildings and areas within the premises.

E **E**veryday monitoring of working practices to ensure they are effective.

A **A**rrangements for disclosure and barring checks to help employers identify people who may be unsuitable to work with children and vulnerable adults.

S **S**ystems for lone working and for dealing with people who may show aggression, self injure, throw items or run away.

U **U**se of CCTV, visitors' books, swipe cards, passwords and key pads on doors to protect the security of both the premises and the personal information held about individuals.

R **R**ecording and reporting procedures for security emergencies.

E   Everyday vigilance of buildings and areas within the premises.

S   Support, information and training about how to protect your security and the security of others.

Figure 8.8 What security measures are in place in your setting?

Research and investigate

8.2 **Types of security measures**

Research the different types of security measures that are available to health and social care settings.

AC 8.3 Explain the importance of ensuring that others are aware of own whereabouts

As we learned in the previous section, work settings have a number of security measures in place. Ensuring that others are aware of your whereabouts is central to maintaining both your security and the security of others at work. The acronym BE SAFE will help you remember this:

B   **B**eing safe involves making others aware of where you are, when you arrived and when you'll be leaving.

E   **E**ntering and exiting different work settings and locations increases the risk of danger and harm occurring.

S   **S**afe and effective working practices involve keeping others informed of your whereabouts at all times.

A   **A**ccessing help for you or others can only be done if others are aware of your whereabouts.

F   **F**ollowing your work setting's procedures, including informing others of your whereabouts, is part of your role and responsibilities.

E   **E**nsure you comply with your work setting's lone working, staff welfare and health and safety policies and procedures.

Time to think

8.3 **Do others know where you are at work?**

- How do you let others know your whereabouts?
- Why is this important?
- What are the consequences of not doing so?

Evidence activity

8.1, 8.2, 8.3 **Putting security measures into practice**

- Read through your work setting's procedures for checking the identity of anyone who requests access to the premises or to information about those with whom you work. Reflect on how you use these procedures in your day-to-day work activities and the other measures that are available in your work setting to protect your security and the security of others at work.

- Discuss with your manager the importance of ensuring that others are aware of your whereabouts at all times.
- You will also need to be observed by your assessor demonstrating how to use agreed procedures for checking the identity of anyone requesting access to the premises or to information about those with whom you work, and using measures that are available in your work setting to protect your security and the security of others at work.

LO9 Know how to manage stress

We considered in the previous sections of this chapter many different aspects of promoting safety and security in health and social care settings. In this final section we will look at how you can promote your health and well-being by managing stress.

AC 9.1 Describe common signs and indicators of stress

We all face different pressures and tensions in our everyday lives. Identifying when these cause **stress** is an important part of maintaining our well-being and ensuring that the difficulties we experience are managed. As we are all different, the ways in which we experience stress and show that we are stressed will also be different. There are, however, some common **signs** and indicators of stress as shown in Table 8.6.

Physical signs and indicators	• Increase in blood pressure leading to 'palpitations' and fast breathing • Increased sweating • Stiffness and soreness in limbs due to tense muscles • Nausea • Frequent colds • Headaches • Upset stomach
Psychological signs and indicators	• Difficulty concentrating • Poor memory • Feeling confused and anxious
Emotional signs and indicators	• Mood swings • Irritability • Impatience • Feeling low or depressed • Tearful • Loss of confidence and motivation
Behavioural signs and indicators	• Changes in sleeping and eating habits • Increased bouts of sickness • Increased use of substances such as cigarettes, alcohol and drugs

Table 8.6 Common signs and indicators of stress

Key terms

Stress is the result of pressures and tensions, which can have both positive and negative effects. The unit focuses on the latter.

Signs are indicators of stress.

AC 9.2 Describe signs that indicate own stress

Although there are some common indicators of stress, we all behave in different ways when we are stressed. For this reason it is important that you have a good insight into how your behaviour and personality may change when you are stressed so that you can take positive and immediate action to manage your stress effectively and as early as possible.

The signs that indicate your stress may be very different to that which others experience and show, so it is very important for you to be aware of how you are feeling and to be honest with yourself about why you are feeling the way that you do.

AC 9.3 Analyse factors that tend to trigger own stress

Once you have identified that you are stressed you will then need to think about what has caused your stress, as everyone has different stress **triggers**. Figure 8.9 shows some of the most common stress triggers.

Finding out what has triggered your stress may be more difficult than you think, as sometimes stress can be the result of a build-up of a number of different factors that may have occurred in both your work and personal life. Your personality and attitude to life will also affect your stress triggers and your resilience to these when they occur.

Key term

Triggers are the causes of stress.

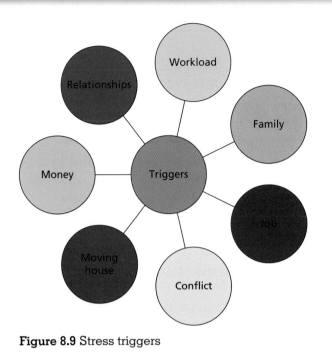

Figure 8.9 Stress triggers

Time to think

9.2, 9.3 Do you know your stress triggers?

- How do you know when you are feeling stressed?
- What changes do you notice in yourself?
- What are the triggers for your stress?
- How do these occur, when and why?

AC 9.4 Compare strategies for managing stress

Managing stress is key to your health and well-being. There are many different ways of doing so positively and effectively depending on your triggers, your personality, your interests and your attitude to life. Some different **strategies** that you can use are shown in Figure 8.10 and include:

- **Keeping your mind and body active** will help you to relax and feel able to think through the difficulties you are having.
- **Staying positive** will help you feel more in control and able to deal with difficult situations.
- **Spending time with others** will not only distract you from your own difficulties but will also provide you with an opportunity to ask others their opinions and views about your situation.

- **Helping others** will provide you with a different purpose in day-to-day life and will also make you feel good about yourself.
- **Learning and developing new skills** will make a real difference to your self-esteem and confidence, as well as providing you with opportunities to meet others.
- **Making time for yourself** will not only help you to think things through calmly, but will also reinforce what the important things in your life are and what matters most to you.
- **Learning to say 'no'** may take some practice but it will stop you feeling so overwhelmed (which adds to the stress triggers in your life), as well as making others aware of your limitations.
- **Managing your time** will enable you to feel more confident in your abilities and skills.
- **Making the decision not to rely on alcohol, drugs, caffeine or food when you are feeling stressed** will not only maintain your health and well-being but will also help you to consider alternative ways to manage your stress, including seeking guidance and advice from a qualified professional such as a counsellor or a psychotherapist.

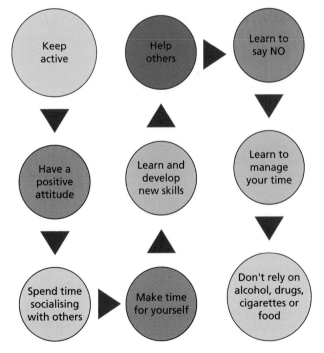

Figure 8.10 Strategies for managing stress

Key term

Strategies are ways to manage stress.

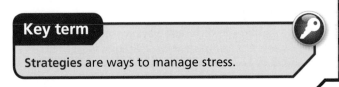

There are many aspects to promoting and implementing health and safety in health and social care settings. It is important that you are aware of your work setting's policies and procedures and of your responsibilities in promoting the health, safety and security of yourself and others with whom you work.

Case study

9.1, 9.3, 9.4 Lucinda

Lucinda is meeting with her manager this morning to discuss her performance at work. Her manager and colleagues have noticed that she has not been her usual self the last few weeks; she seems quite irritable when communicating with others at work, arrives late every day, which is very unusual for her, and is frequently very tearful.

1 Do you think Lucinda is showing signs and symptoms of stress?
2 Why?
3 What do you think may be triggering Lucinda's stress?
4 How can Lucinda's manager assist her to manage her stress?
5 What strategies are there for managing stress and how do these compare?

Research and investigate

9.4 Benefits of managing stress

Find out about the benefits of different strategies for managing stress.

Evidence activity

9.1, 9.2, 9.3, 9.4 Managing stress

- Reflect on your and others' experiences of being under stress and then detail the common signs and indicators of stress, including how these compare to the signs that indicate your own stress.
- Discuss with a colleague the factors that tend to trigger your stress, consider why they are triggers, and what short-term and long-term effects they have on you. Then talk through together the different ways you each manage stress and compare your strategies with theirs.

Legislation

- Control of Substances Hazardous to Health (COSHH) Regulations 2002
- Food Safety Act 1990 and Food Hygiene Regulations 2006
- Health and Safety (First Aid) Regulations 1981
- Management of Health and Safety at Work Regulations (MHSWR) 1999
- Manual Handling Operations Regulations (MHOR) 1992 (as amended 2002)
- Personal Protective Equipment (PPE) at Work Regulations 1992
- Provision and Use of Work Equipment Regulations (PUWER) 1998
- Reporting of Injuries, Diseases and Dangerous Occurrences Regulations (RIDDOR) 1995
- Workplace (Health, Safety and Welfare) Regulations 1992
- Lifting Operations and Lifting Equipment Regulations (LOLER) 1998

Useful resources

Websites

Fire Safety Advice Centre

firesafe.org.uk

Health and Safety Executive

hse.gov.uk

Infection Control Services

infectioncontrolservices.co.uk

Public Health England

publichealthengland.gov.uk

Stress Management Society

stress.org.uk

Publications

Health and Safety Executive (1997) *Successful Health and Safety Management* (guidance booklet). Sudbury: HSE Books.

Health and Safety Executive (2007) *Managing the Causes of Work-related Stress: A step-by-step approach using the management standards* health and safety guidance). Sudbury: HSE Books.

Bateman, M. (2006) *Tolley's Practical Risk Assessment Handbook*. Abingdon: Taylor & Francis.

Unit HSC 038

Promote good practice in handling information in health and social care settings

This unit is worth 2 credits

What are you finding out?

In this unit you will learn about the key requirements for handling information in health and social care settings, including the relevant legislation and codes of practice. Being able to implement good practice in recording, sharing, storing and accessing information is central to carrying out your role effectively.

You will also learn about how to support others – including colleagues and individuals accessing care or support – to handle information,

including furthering their understanding of records and the need for the secure handling of all information.

By the end of this unit you will:

1 Understand requirements for handling information in health and social care settings.
2 Be able to implement good practice in handling information.
3 Be able to support others to handle information.

Links to Level 3 Certificate in Preparing to Work in Adult Social Care

HSC 038 Assessment Criteria	PWC 38
AC 1.1	AC 1.1
AC 2.1	AC 2.3

LO1 Understand requirements for handling information in health and social care settings

AC 1.1 Identify legislation and codes of practice that relate to handling information in health and social care

Health and social care workers have a vital role to play in ensuring that they promote good practice when recording, sharing, storing and accessing information. This includes information presented in a variety of formats, such as paper records, emails, and information shared verbally, both in person and over the telephone.

Legislation

There are a number of key pieces of legislation that govern the recording, sharing, storing and accessing of information in health and social care settings.

- **The Data Protection Act 1998** was implemented in March 2000 and gives individuals a right to access information held about them by organisations such as adult social care providers. It consists of the following eight key principles:
  1 Information must be processed fairly and lawfully.
  2 Information collected must be processed for limited purposes.
  3 Information collected must be adequate, relevant and not excessive.
  4 Information collected must be accurate and up to date.
  5 Information must not be held for longer than is necessary.
  6 Information must be processed in accordance with the individual's rights.
  7 Information must be kept secure.

8 Information should not be transferred outside the European Economic Area unless adequate levels of protection exist.

- **The Computer Misuse Act 1990** was introduced to protect against a range of offences relating to computer records, including those held in health and social care settings. Offences include:
  - unauthorised access to computer material
  - unauthorised access with intent to commit or facilitate a crime
  - unauthorised modification of computer material
  - making, supplying or obtaining anything that can be used in computer misuse offences.
- **The Freedom of Information Act 2000** gives everyone a right of access to all types of recorded information held by public authorities, including publicly funded organisations, local authorities and the NHS.
- **The Human Rights Act 1998** sets out everyone's fundamental rights and freedoms in the UK. In relation to handling information these include the rights to privacy and security, as well as respect for your private correspondence.

Codes of practice

As well as legislation there are a number of codes of practice that set out how health and social care professionals should handle information.

- The **Health and Social Care Information Centre (HSCIC)** provides advice to health and social care organisations under the Health and Social Care Act 2012 on how to handle confidential information. In 2013 it published a code of practice for handling confidential information: *A Guide to Confidentiality in Health and Social Care*.
- The **Caldicott Report** set out a number of general principles that a health and social care organisation should use when reviewing its use of information about individuals.

Figure 9.1 How do you ensure you follow codes of practice for handling information?

- The **NHS Confidentiality Code of Practice** 2003 and the **Records Management NHS Code of Practice** 2006 provide guidance in relation to confidentiality and patients' consent for use of their health records by those who work within or under contract to NHS organisations, including how to protect person-identifiable and sensitive information.
- The **NHS Care Record Guarantee for England**, first published in 2005 and updated in 2011, sets out the rules that govern how patient information is used in the NHS and the control the patient can have over this.

AC 1.2 Summarise the main points of legal requirements and codes of practice for handling information in health and social care

It is important that you are aware of and understand the relevance of all the pieces of legislation and codes of practice covered in AC 1.1 in terms of the requirements and expectations of health and social care workers when handling information.

- Under the **Data Protection Act 1998** an individual must consent to all information collected about them. For health and social care workers this means that they must inform individuals what information is being collected about them and why; they must also support individuals to understand what will happen with their personal information. All information collected must be used only for the reasons given to the individual and only on a need-to-know basis. Ensuring information collected and recorded is accurate and up to date will ensure that individuals' needs are fully met and form part of building a trusting working partnership with individuals.

When storing information you must retain only information that is needed and relevant. This must not be stored overseas unless individuals have provided their consent. Individuals' rights to access the information health and social care workers hold about them must be respected, as must their right to having any inaccurate information that is held about them updated or destroyed. It is health and social care workers' duty to keep secure all information being held about individuals; this includes ensuring that measures are in place to prevent those who are not authorised to access it from doing so.

- Under the **Computer Misuse Act 1990** health and social care workers must ensure that access and updates to computer records are authorised and used only for their required purpose. In addition, **Section 127** of the **Communications Act 2003** requires that those using electronic communications, such as health and social care workers, do so in a professional and respectful manner.
- The **Freedom of Information Act 2000** encourages organisations like health and social care providers to be open and transparent. It allows, for example, individuals who use care and support services to make requests for information.
- The **Human Rights Act 1998** promotes people's rights to privacy; this includes privacy for all types of correspondence and information that health and social care workers may read as part of their day-to-day duties.
- The **HSCIC's 2013 code of practice** for handling confidential information, *A Guide to Confidentiality in Health and Social Care*, sets out five key rules about confidentiality that people can expect will be followed by those who work in NHS care settings and in adult social care services:

1 Confidential information about individuals should be treated confidentially and respectfully.

2 Care teams should share confidential information when it is needed for the safe and effective care of an individual.

3 Information shared for the benefit of the community should be **anonymised**.

4 An individual's right not to consent to information being shared about them should be respected.

5 Organisations should have policies, procedures and systems in place to ensure the confidentiality rules are followed.

- **The Caldicott Standards** are set out in the form of seven principles that health and social care organisations should use when handling information:

1 Justify the purpose for which the information is needed.

2 Only use **person-identifiable information** when absolutely necessary.

3 Use the minimum necessary **personal information**.

4 Access to information should be on a strict need-to-know basis only.

5 Everyone should be aware of their responsibilities to respect individuals' confidentiality.

6 Every use of confidential information must comply with the law.

7 The duty to share information can be as important as the duty to protect individuals' confidentiality.

- The **NHS Confidentiality Code of Practice** provides a framework of good practice required for practitioners using and disclosing confidential personal information. Similarly, the **Records Management NHS Code of Practice** published in 2006 provides guidance about the required standards of practice in the management of records for those who work within or under contract to NHS organisations in England.

The **NHS Care Record Guarantee for England**, published in 2005 and updated in 2011, relates to electronic and paper-based records and includes information about, for example, how people can access their own records, how access to an individual's health record will be kept secure, how to access records in an emergency,

and what happens when an individual is unable to make decisions for themselves.

Summary of key points

Data must be:

- collected with the individual's consent
- used for the required purpose only
- used on a need-to-know basis
- accurate
- up to date
- kept private
- treated confidentially
- treated respectfully
- anonymised
- restricted to who has access to it
- kept safe and secure.

Key terms

Anonymised information is information from which an individual's identity cannot be determined, such as when their name or date of birth has been removed.

Person-identifiable information is information that identifies a person, such as their name, address, date of birth, National Insurance number or photograph.

Sensitive personal information is information about, for example, a person's race, ethnicity, religious beliefs, physical or mental health.

Case study

1.1, 1.2 Silvia

Silvia is a senior residential care worker and as part of her job role she mentors and supervises a small team of residential carers. Silvia's job role includes explaining to new care workers and reinforcing with existing care workers the requirements for handling personal and confidential information at work.

1 What legislation and codes of practice will Silvia explain and reinforce?

2 Why?

3 How do the relevant legislation and codes of practice relate to handling information at work?

Evidence activity

1.1, 1.2 Legislation and codes of practice

- Identify three pieces of legislation and three codes of practice that relate to handling information in health and social care.
- Provide details of the key points for each piece of legislation and code of practice you have identified.

Time to think

1.1, 1.2 Do you understand the requirements for handling information?

- Read through again the legislation and codes of practice discussed for ACs 1.1 and 1.2.
- What do these say about how you must record, share, store and access information?

LO2 Be able to implement good practice in handling information

AC 2.1 Describe features of manual and electronic information storage systems that help ensure security

Having explored the legislation and codes of practice that relate to handling information in health and social care settings, it is important that you are able to implement these and are aware of the key features that help to ensure security when storing information. As part of your day-to-day duties you will be required to store information both **manually** and **electronically**. Figure 9.2 provides details about some of the types of information that you may be required to store.

These records will contain personal information about individuals who live in and staff who work in health and social care settings. As such, the systems used to store these in your work setting will have a number of important features that will enable you to keep the information contained within these secure.

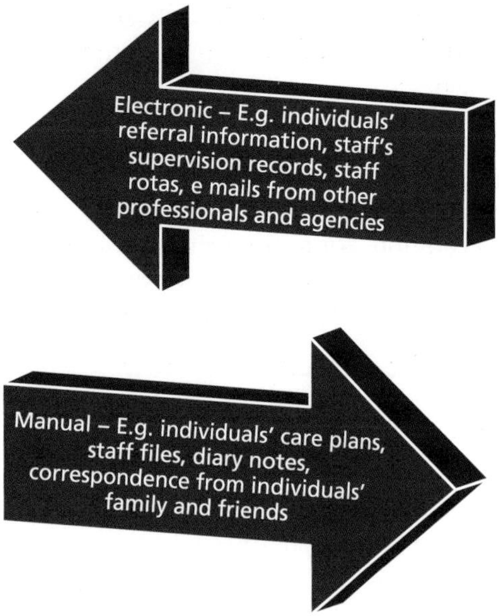
Electronic – E.g. individuals' referral information, staff's supervision records, staff rotas, e mails from other professionals and agencies
Manual – E.g. individuals' care plans, staff files, diary notes, correspondence from individuals' family and friends

Figure 9.2 Some of the types of information that you may be required to store

Key terms

Manual information storage systems are facilities used for storing paper-based records.

Electronic information storage systems are facilities used for storing electronic records.

Manual systems

Filing systems for paper-based records should include procedures for records to be signed out when accessed and signed back in when returned, so that access is limited only to those who have authorisation. Records must be organised in a manner so that they can easily be retrieved; this will reduce the risk of records being misfiled and/or lost. A lockable filing system with a key kept in a secure location, a private and lockable room, as well as a secure filing system so that records cannot be damaged, e.g. due to fire or water, are other essential security features for storing manual information.

Electronic systems

Electronic systems must include secure logins and passwords for staff who need to access documents and files stored on computers. Automatic and password-protected screen savers to protect information that may be displayed on computer screens even for short periods of time are another important security feature for electronic information storage.

AC 2.2 Demonstrate practices that ensure security when storing and accessing information

In addition to being aware of the key security features of manual and electronic information storage systems, you must be able to demonstrate good practice when storing and accessing secure information that may be of a personal or sensitive nature.

To ensure **security when storing paper-based records** you must make sure that you lock all filing cabinets and offices where these are kept so that these remain secure at all times. Returning records to the correct location as soon as they are no longer required will also ensure that these are kept secure and safe. Having a system in place to identify what records have been removed, by whom and when, will provide a means to track records and minimise the chance of them getting misplaced or lost.

To ensure **security when accessing paper-based records** you must ensure that you lock all filing cabinets and offices where these are kept so that these can be accessed only by those who have permission to do so. When completing or reading records it is important that you do this in a private and secure location so that others without authorisation cannot read these. It is also important to recognise that different people

will require different levels of access to records depending on their job role and responsibilities, for example a manager may access an individual's referral information sent by another agency or service, a senior care worker may require access to a staff member's previous supervision meeting notes, a care worker may need to access an individual's care plan. It is therefore necessary for information to be accessed on a **need-to-know basis** only.

When **storing electronic records**, clearly labelled documents and files will allow important information to be retrieved quickly when required and will allow different levels of security to keep information within these secure. Having filing systems in place for storing both paper-based and electronic records will ensure security of information, for example records may be kept alphabetically or numerically or in groups such as in terms of the services or locations they relate to.

When **accessing electronic records** it is important in order to prevent unauthorised access that you keep your login and password details secure and that you do not share these with others. It is also good practice that you do not have just one password for all the documents and files you access, that you do not use short or familiar words for passwords and that you regularly change passwords to avoid others using them to access personal information. When viewing electronic records it is important to consider when and where you do this so that others may not (either deliberately or unintentionally) also view the information these contain. Similarly, when you finish viewing electronic records it is important that you log out of the document, file and application you've been using in order to prevent others accessing these in your absence.

AC 2.3 Maintain records that are up to date, complete, accurate and legible

Maintaining up-to-date, complete, accurate and legible records is crucial to delivering good quality, safe and effective care, as well as to complying with the relevant legislation and codes of practice discussed in ACs 1.1 and 1.2, and can include verbal information obtained over the telephone as well as written information obtained from texts, faxes and emails. Not doing so can result in recorded information not providing a true profile of different individuals and their needs. This may in turn lead to changes in individuals' health and needs going unnoticed and then serious illnesses or even fatalities occurring. In addition, all those who work in health and social care settings have a **duty of care** to the individuals to whom they provide care and support, and maintaining records consistently and to a good standard is required and forms part of workers' day-to-day roles and responsibilities.

Read through Table 9.1, which includes details about some of the key good practice features when maintaining records.

Good practice features of records	Examples of good practices
Up to date	<ul><li>Written as soon as possible, either at the time or after a situation has occurred or a task has been completed.</li><li>Contain only current information.</li><li>Updated regularly.</li></ul>
Complete	<ul><li>Include all the necessary and required information.</li><li>Include the date, time, name and signature of the person recording the information.</li><li>Include the **active participation** of the individual or staff member to which it relates.</li></ul>
Accurate	<ul><li>Contain only information that relates to the facts of what has taken place.</li></ul>
Legible	<ul><li>Written in ink that cannot be erased.</li><li>Written clearly so that others can read and understand the information recorded.</li><li>Include clearly marked alterations, i.e. alterations dated and signed without erasing or removing the original information recorded.</li><li>Written using easy-to-understand language and terminology.</li></ul>

Table 9.1 Good practice features when maintaining records

Key terms

Duty of care is a professional's ethical and legal responsibility to safeguard and protect the well-being of others.

Active participation is a way of working that recognises an individual's right to participate in the activities and relationships of everyday life as independently as possible; the individual is regarded as an active partner in their own care or support, rather than a passive recipient.

Time to think

2.2, 2.3 Do you follow good practice when handling information?

- Ask your manager for feedback on how you store and access information.
- Ask your colleagues for feedback on how you maintain records.
- What could you do differently and why?

Case study

2.1, 2.2, 2.3 Jianyu

Jianyu has worked as a community-based senior carer for more than ten years and leads a team of new and experienced carers, who provide care and support to individuals living in both residential and community-based settings. Jianyu has been asked by his manager to produce a briefing for next week's team meeting about good practice in handling information.

1 What security aspects of manual and electronic information storage systems can Jianyu talk about to the team?
2 What practices can Jianyu discuss with the team for ensuring security across different work settings when storing and accessing information?
3 What guidance can Jianyu provide in relation to maintaining records that are up to date, complete, accurate and legible?

Evidence activity

2.2, 2.3 Following good practice in handling information

- Reflect on your and your colleagues' working practices for ensuring security when you store and access information. Discuss with your manager how you follow good practice when maintaining records by ensuring they are up to date, complete, accurate and legible.
- You will also need to be observed by your assessor demonstrating practices that ensure security when storing and accessing information, as well as maintaining records that are up to date, complete, accurate and legible.

LO3 Be able to support others to handle information

Once you understand the requirements for handling information and are able to implement good practice when storing and accessing information and maintaining records, you will then need to learn more about how to support individuals and your colleagues to understand the importance of keeping information secure, and to understand and contribute to records.

AC 3.1 Support others to understand the need for secure handling of information

Your responsibilities may include supporting others (including colleagues and individuals who access care or support) to understand the need for the secure handling of information. Examples of times when you will need to do this include:

- when meeting with an individual
- at the induction of a new member of staff
- when discussing aspects of performance during a staff member's supervision
- when monitoring staff practices on a day-to-day basis
- when concerns have been raised about a member of staff's practices in relation to keeping information secure.

Figure 9.3 includes some of the different ways to support individuals and colleagues to understand the need for maintaining security when handling information.

For colleagues: set a good example, identify and share good practice, provide information and guidance on relevant legislation and codes of practice and the consequences of not complying with these

For individuals: provide concise and relevant information about their rights and responsibilities, reinforce the need for security when handling information and encourage individuals to be involved

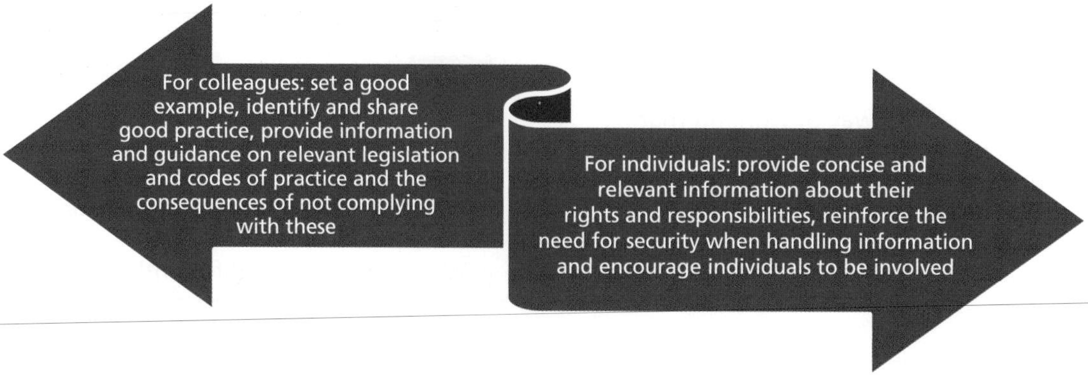

Figure 9.3 Ways of supporting individuals

AC 3.2 Support others to understand and contribute to records

Raising awareness among your colleagues and the individuals with whom you work of the need for secure handling of information is the basis to supporting others to understand and contribute to records, which may be related to them or to the individuals to whom they provide care and support.

- **Supporting individuals to understand records** that have been completed will involve you setting aside some time to talk these through with them; this may involve you preparing records in alternative formats so that they can be understood, such as in large print, **Braille**, using **Makaton** signs and symbols, or using visuals.
- Being able to **support individuals to contribute to records** will involve ensuring they are written using words that individuals use and can understand, with pictures or photographs that they recognise and with them present so that you can check the accuracy and details of what has been recorded with them at the time.

Key terms

Braille is a system of writing and printing for blind or visually impaired people. Varied arrangements of raised dots representing letters and numerals are identified by touch.

Makaton is a visual form of communication for individuals who have learning disabilities and communication difficulties, in which gestures are used in combination with pictures and symbols to communicate messages.

A **protocol** is a procedure, system or agreed way of working.

As discussed in AC 3.1, your colleagues may require support from you from time to time to also understand and contribute to records. There are many ways of doing this:

- When a new way of working is introduced in your work setting it is important that your colleagues understand this and can implement it in their day-to-day practices. This will maintain the consistency of the team's approaches and ways of working; your role in providing information, advice and guidance is therefore crucial.
- Similarly, when there is a change to an individual's medication or health condition it is vital that you are able to instruct and guide your colleagues in understanding what this is, how it may affect the individual and the changes to current ways of working that may need to be implemented, as well as where your colleagues can seek additional information and support if required.

Supporting your colleagues to contribute to records both verbally and in writing involves them being clear about how to contribute, the details to include and the correct **protocol** to follow. It may help your colleagues' learning to see an example of a well-written record that is legible, accurate and contains up-to-date and complete information, or to observe you reporting information about individuals' well-being and support requirements to another colleague at the end of your shift.

As we have explored in this unit you have a vital role to play in understanding, implementing and promoting good practice in recording, sharing, storing and accessing information. Complying with security requirements and making sure you use and understand the systems and procedures in place for maintaining information will ensure that you and staff members you support maintain personal and sensitive information safely and securely.

Case study

3.1, 3.2 Noemie

Noemie is a senior care worker who provides support to a team of care workers as part of her job role. This morning Noemie is meeting with one of the care workers and the individual to whom he provides one-to-one support so that they can prepare for the individual's care review meeting next week.

1 What type of personal and confidential information might they discuss?
2 How can Noemie support the care worker and the individual to understand the need to keep this information secure?
3 How can Noemie support the care worker and the individual to understand and contribute to records?

Time to think

3.1, 3.2 Do you provide good support to others?

- Ask your colleagues and the individuals you support to provide feedback on how you support them to understand and contribute to records.
- What did they say?
- Why?

Evidence activity

3.1, 3.2 Supporting others to handle information

- Explain how you can support others to understand why it is important to handle information securely. Make a list of the different ways you can support them to understand and contribute to records.
- Discuss with your manager two occasions when you supported your colleagues and two occasions when you supported individuals to understand the need for secure handling of information, as well as to understand and contribute to records.

Legislation

- The Data Protection Act 1998
- The Computer Misuse Act 1990
- The Freedom of Information Act 2000
- The Human Rights Act 1998

Useful resources

Websites

The Health and Social Care Information Centre

hscic.gov.uk

Care Quality Commission

cqc.org.uk

Skills for Care

skillsforcare.org.uk

Skills for Health

skillsforhealth.org.uk

Publications

HSCIC (2013) *A Guide to Confidentiality in Health and Social Care: Treating confidential information with respect*. Leeds: HSCIC.

Clark, C. and McGhee, J. (2008) *Private and Confidential?: Handling personal information in social and health services*. Bristol: Policy Press.

Optional
Group B Units

This unit
is worth
3 credits

What are you finding out?

In this unit you will learn about the neurology of dementia, including the causes of dementia syndrome, and about how individuals who have dementia may experience difficulties with their memory and with processing information, as well as changes in their needs and abilities. You will also learn more about how other factors that are unrelated to dementia may be mistaken for dementia.

Having an understanding of the impact on others of early and follow-up diagnosis, as well as the importance of recording and reporting possible signs or symptoms of dementia, is central to providing support to individuals who have dementia and to their families and friends.

This unit will also help you to explore in more detail the role of person-centred approaches and techniques in supporting individuals who have dementia, and to consider how myths and stereotypes related to dementia may affect individuals and their carers, including the different support available to help them overcome any fears that they may have.

By the end of this unit you will:

1 Understand the neurology of dementia.
2 Understand the impact of recognition and diagnosis of dementia.
3 Understand how dementia care must be underpinned by a person-centred approach.

LO1 Understand the neurology of dementia

AC 1.1 Describe a range of causes of dementia syndrome

Dementia syndrome describes brain damage that affects functioning, in areas such as memory, thinking skills, reasoning, language, communication skills, balance and co-ordination, to such a severe extent that an individual's ability to do everyday tasks is impaired. Dementia is caused by a combination of conditions and this is sometimes called a mixed dementia. According to current research it is predicted that in 2015 there will be 850,000 people living with dementia in the UK; this number could exceed 2 million by 2051.

(Source: Dementia 2014 infographic, Alzheimer's Society)

Dementia and the human brain

To understand the causes of dementia and how the brain is affected, we must first learn more about how the human brain works. The brain is divided into four parts:

- the cerebral cortex
- the limbic system
- the cerebellum
- the brain stem.

The **cerebral cortex** is divided into two cerebral hemispheres. Each of these contains four different parts or lobes:

- the frontal lobe
- the parietal lobe
- the temporal lobe
- the occipital lobe.

Each of these lobes is responsible for different functions:

- the frontal lobe controls our decision-making and planning processes
- the parietal lobe processes information received from different parts of the body
- the temporal lobe controls our emotions, memory and use of language
- the occipital lobe controls our vision.

The second part of the human brain, the **limbic system**, controls our learning and memory.

The third part, the **cerebellum**, controls our balance and co-ordination.

The fourth part, the **brain stem**, controls the main physical functions of the body, such as our breathing and heartbeat. Figure 10.1 provides an overview of the key parts of the human brain.

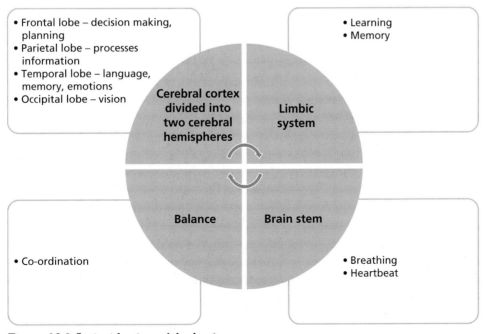

Figure 10.1 An inside view of the brain

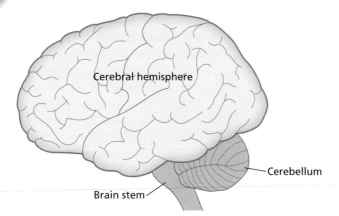

Cerebral hemisphere

Cerebellum

Brain stem

Figure 10.2 The human brain

The brain is made up of nerve cells (also known as neurons); there are 100 billion nerve cells in the brain (see Figure 10.2). We will learn more about these in AC 1.3, but some key information points about nerve cells are:

1 The human brain is made up of billions of nerve cells.
2 Nerve cells require oxygen and nutrients.
3 Nerve cells are interconnected.

Research and investigate

1.1 The brain and dementia
Research how the brain works and the neurology of dementia.

4 These connections are used to pass messages within and out from the brain.
5 Without nerve cells our brains would not work.
6 If nerve cells do not have the oxygen and nutrients they require they will die.

Dementia can occur if something happens that stops parts of the brain or the nerve cells in the brain from working properly. The causes of dementia syndrome therefore can vary; it may result from specific diseases, from damage to the brain or from other conditions. Dementia may be caused by a combination of conditions, sometimes called a mixed dementia. Table 10.1 presents the key information points about the causes of dementia syndrome.

See unit DEM 312 for more information on the conditions described above.

Causes	Examples	How these cause dementia syndrome
Specific diseases	• **Alzheimer's disease**	• Sixty-two per cent* of people living with dementia have Alzheimer's disease. • Alzheimer's causes brain cells to die. • Alzheimer's causes nerve cells to stop working.
	• **Parkinson's disease** • **Dementia with Lewy bodies**	• Five per cent* of people living with dementia are affected by diseases such as Parkinson's disease. • Four per cent* of people living with dementia have dementia with Lewy bodies. • Deposits known as Lewy bodies in nerve cells cause difficulties in how the brain works.
	• **Creutzfeldt-Jakob disease (CJD)**	• Five per cent* of people living with dementia are affected by diseases such as CJD. • Proteins in the brain called prions cause brain cells to die.
Lack of oxygen to the brain	• **Strokes**	• Seventeen per cent* of people living with dementia have vascular dementia, which is caused when the brain is damaged due to lack of oxygen. • This damage causes different parts of the brain to be deprived of blood containing oxygen.
Other conditions	• **Fronto-temporal dementia**	• Two per cent* of people living with dementia have fronto-temporal dementia, which presents itself in people under age 65. • Nerve cells in the frontal and temporal lobes of the brain die. • The connections between the nerve cells deteriorate.

Table 10.1 The causes of dementia syndrome

* Source: Dementia 2014 infographic, Alzheimer's Society

AC 1.2 Describe types of memory impairment commonly experienced by individuals with dementia

The term 'memory' refers to how the human brain stores, retains and retrieves information. As you read in AC 1.1, dementia can occur when parts of the brain are damaged; **memory impairment** is one common feature experienced by individuals who have dementia. Before we learn more about the different types of this memory impairment, let us first think more about how our memory works.

The memory process

The memory process involves the following three important steps:

1 **Storing information** – during this first stage of the memory process, the brain logs the information it receives.
2 **Retaining information** – during this second stage, the brain stores the information it has received until it is needed again.
3 **Retrieving information** – during this final stage, the brain finds or retrieves the information it has stored.

If any of these steps of the memory process is missed out or does not take place, the memory process will not work effectively. Dementia syndrome can affect any or all of these steps, depending on what part of the brain and what type of memory is affected by the dementia.

Types of memory

The memory process also includes three different **types** of memory:

1 **Sensory memory** – our five senses (vision, hearing, smell, touch and taste) are connected to our nervous system and brain, and are constantly receiving and processing information. This happens very quickly, in a fraction of a second. The part of sensory memory that is responsible for processing visual information is referred to as iconic memory; that responsible for processing auditory information is referred to as echoic memory.

2 **Short-term memory** – this type of memory, also sometimes referred to as 'working memory', is responsible for storing information for a short period of time (usually thought to be ten to fifteen seconds), and determining whether this information can be disregarded or should be retained in the long-term memory. If the memory is not passed on to the part of the brain that retains long-term memories then it will be lost.

3 **Long-term memory** – this type of memory is responsible for storing processed information for a long period of time – this could be anything from a few minutes or a few days to many years – and this information is processed and stored in different parts of the brain. There are two main types of long-term memory: explicit and implicit. Explicit (or episodic) memories are those that you consciously remember in your life, such as an individual's date of birth, and implicit (or procedural) memories are those that you remember without thinking about (you 'just know' them), such as riding a bicycle.

Memory loss

In addition to affecting any of the steps of memory, dementia can affect any of these three different types of memory. Just as each individual is unique, their experience of dementia – including the type(s) of memory loss they experience – will also be unique.

- Individuals who have dementia commonly experience impairment with **remembering new information** if the part of the brain for processing new information has been damaged.
- Individuals who have dementia may also experience difficulties with **remembering recent information**. This is because our most recent memories are stored on the surface of the brain lobes, while past memories are stored much deeper in the brain lobes. This is why, for example, an individual who has dementia may not be able to remember having a conversation with someone five minutes ago (this memory is still in the short-term memory), but can remember the exact date, time and location

Key term

Memory impairment is memory loss caused by damage to the brain.

they met with someone 20 years ago (this memory is stored in the long-term memory). In Alzheimer's disease, for example, the hippocampus which is the part of the brain that is responsible for converting recent memories into stored memory is one of the first parts of the brain that will suffer damage.

- Losing the ability to **recognise people, places and objects** can also occur in individuals who have dementia if the part of the brain responsible for these functions has been damaged and no longer works effectively. This is why, for example, an individual who has dementia may no longer be able to recognise their close family and friends. This can be utterly devastating for not only the individual but also their family and friends.
- Finally, individuals who have dementia may also experience difficulties with **determining what is real and true from what is fictitious and imagined** if damage has occurred to the part of the brain that controls our thoughts, feelings and perceptions. This is why, for example, an individual who has dementia may believe that someone has stolen their purse when they cannot remember where they have placed it.

AC 1.3 Explain the way that individuals process information with reference to the abilities and limitations of individuals with dementia

The brain first starts processing information through our five sensory organs, which transform what we see, hear, smell, touch and taste into **electrochemical signals**. In order for the brain to be able to process information it must first be stored and then maintained. As we learned in AC 1.2 this process involves three different types of memory: sensory, short-term and long-term.

The brain is made up or nerve cells or neurons that send signals to and from your brain along your spinal cord. These enable your brain to regulate for example your digestion and breathing as well as allow you to think and learn. The way in which the brain processes information is complex. Each neuron passes messages to other cells by electrical impulses and chemical signals referred to as neurotransmitters. Each neuron passes messages to other cells using electrical impulses and chemical signals. The part of the neuron that passes on these electrical impulses is the **axon** and the part of the neuron that communicates with other cells is referred to as the **dendrites** or more commonly the **nerve endings**. Chemicals referred to as **neurotransmitters** are released from the end of the axons. The nerve cells of individuals who have dementia are damaged, meaning messages by electrical impulses and chemical signals are not sent out or passed on to other cells, thus causing individuals to have difficulties with processing information. For example, research has shown that individuals who have Alzheimer's disease have low levels of the neurotransmitter (chemical) **acetylcholine**; increasing the levels of acetylcholine in the brain improves individuals' thinking and memory skills.

The chemical **Dopamine** affects the brain's functions that control movement and emotional responses; insufficient levels of Dopamine in the brain will mean that individuals will have difficulties with controlling their movements and understanding emotions such as pleasure or pain, i.e. as individuals who have Parkinson's disease experience. The chemical **Serotonin** is responsible for controlling various functions including sleep, appetite and mood balance; a decrease in Serotonin levels can lead to individuals becoming depressed, anxious and angry and can be experienced by individuals who have Vascular Dementia. The chemical **Glutamate** is responsible for learning and memory functions; a decrease in Glutamate can lead to memory difficulties, i.e. as individuals who have Alzheimer's disease, experience.

As stated previously, it is also important to understand that the brain's cerebral cortex is divided into two cerebral hemispheres: the left side and the right side. Each cerebral hemisphere is responsible for different functions in the body. The left hemisphere controls language and the right hemisphere controls thinking skills. If an individual who has dementia has damaged nerve cells on the right side of the brain this can lead to difficulties with cognitive functioning and communication, such as difficulties learning new information and skills, remembering or recalling information such as people's names and important events, and taking part in and following a conversation with someone else. When working with individuals who have dementia it is important to know what areas of the brain have been damaged so that you and other professionals can develop an effective range of techniques and **agreed ways of working** to support the individual to improve their communication skills and **cognitive abilities**.

It is also important to remember that although some areas in the brain may have been damaged, others may not have been. This means individuals may continue to retain their abilities and strengths;

Key terms

Acetylcholine or Ach controls activity in the areas of the brain that are responsible for learning, attention and memory.

Dopamine controls activity in the areas of the brain that are responsible for controlling movement and emotional responses.

Serotonin controls activity in the areas of the brain that are responsible for sleep, appetite and mood balance.

Glutamate controls activity in the areas of the brain that are responsible for learning and memory.

Agreed ways of working means complying with workplace procedures and guidelines.

Cognitive abilities are abilities to learn, remember, problem-solve and pay attention.

Person-centred working is a way of working that recognises what is important to individuals and helps them to live the life they choose.

Cognitive abilities are abilities to learn, remember problem solve and pay attention.

Research and investigate

1.3 Definitions
Look at some of the terms you are unfamiliar with and research these further.

focusing and building on these will be crucial to **person-centred working**, an area we will explore in more detail later on in the unit.

AC 1.4 Explain how other factors can cause changes in an individual's condition that may not be attributable to dementia

When an individual has been diagnosed with dementia it is all too easy for this 'label' to become attached to the person and for any difficulties or changes they show in their condition to be attributable to dementia. There may, in fact, be other reasons for these changes. It is important when an individual's condition changes that all possible reasons for this are explored in full so that the individual can access the correct care, treatment or support as quickly as possible.

Time to think

1.4 Changes in Individuals' Conditions
Read through Table 10.2 and consider how each of the factors presented may cause changes in an individual's condition that may result in signs and symptoms that may be mistaken for dementia. Can you think of any others?

AC 1.5 Explain why the abilities and needs of an individual with dementia may fluctuate

It is not uncommon for individuals who have dementia to have variable abilities and needs; for example being able to complete a task such as combing their hair independently in the morning and then not knowing how to do the same again in the evening. It is not fully understood why this happens but it may be attributable to a variety of reasons. For example, could it be related to the individual feeling tired in the evening and therefore expressing a lack of desire to comb their

Factors that can present as dementia	Signs and symptoms that can be mistaken
Infections	Urinary tract infections, for example, can make individuals feel confused, unsteady and disorientated.
Stroke	A stroke can result in individuals appearing confused and having difficulties with understanding what others are saying.
Head injuries	Head injuries as a result of a fall for example can result in individuals having difficulties with their memory, speech and language skills.
Brain tumour	Brain tumours can occur in different parts of the brain and can result in individuals experiencing memory loss and difficulties with planning and organising as well as changes to their personality.
Huntington's disease	Huntington's disease can cause individuals to have memory lapses and have difficulties with communication, thinking and perception.
Multiple sclerosis	MS can cause individuals to have problems with their memory and thinking processes.
Parkinson's disease	Parkinson's can cause individuals to have difficulties with their speech and communication.
Myalgic Encephalomyelitis (ME)	ME can cause confusion, memory loss and difficulties with concentrating.
Encephalitis	Encephalitis can lead to confusion and agitation in individuals.
Hydrocephalus	Hydrocephalus can cause changes in personality and difficulties with memory, concentration and co-ordination.
Lyme disease	Lyme disease can cause individuals to experience difficulties with their memory, concentration as well as changes in their personality.
Depression	Depression can make individuals feel overwhelmed and can affect their levels of concentration and memory.
Side effects of medication	Some types of medication can cause individuals to become confused and disorientated.
Stress	Stress caused by, for example, moving into a new home or working with a new care team or receiving some sad news can cause individuals to be confused and to feel depressed.
Diet and dehydration	Dehydration can affect an individual's mental and physical well-being; they may become confused and disorientated, and feel depressed.
Lack of sleep and/or insomnia	Insufficient sleep and/or insomnia can lead to individuals having difficulties with concentration and their memory as well as an increase in irritability.
Abuse of drugs and/or alcohol	Abuse of drugs and alcohol can lead to individuals experiencing confusion, lapses in memory and difficulties with concentration.

Table 10.2 Other factors that may cause changes in an individual's condition

hair? Or because a different carer is supporting the individual in the evening, who uses a different approach? Or because the individual is combing their hair at a different time of day and this does not feel comfortable to them? Or because the individual has received some sad news during the day?

Whatever the reasons, what is important is that you understand that it is likely that the abilities and needs of individuals who have dementia will fluctuate from time to time in order that you can respond to them effectively. As time goes on and an individual's dementia progresses the individual may require even more support from you and others. This may include both practical support with daily living activities that they are unable to carry out any longer themselves and emotional support with the changes they are having to come to terms with in view of how they live their life. Spending time getting to know the individual

who has dementia will help you and others to work with the individual and build up a picture of who the individual is, what their strengths and limitations are, as well as the key factors that may affect their physical and emotional well-being.

Figure 10.3 It is important to find out what an individual's support needs are

Case study

1.1, 1.2, 1.3, 1.4, 1.5 Shelley

Shelley is a senior community carer and provides support and supervision to a large team of carers who provide support to individuals who have dementia and wish to remain living in their own homes. As part of Shelley's professional practice supervisions she plans to assess the level of understanding each team member has of the neurology of dementia, with a view to identifying current and future training needs.

1 What causes of dementia syndrome and types of memory impairment would Shelley expect each team member to know about?

2 What are the key points that team members would need to explain are relevant to the abilities and limitations of individuals who have dementia when they process information?

3 What other factors that can cause changes in an individual's condition might the team mistake for dementia?

4 What are the key reasons that team members would need to include when explaining why the abilities and needs of an individual who has dementia may fluctuate?

Evidence activity

1.1, 1.2, 1.3, 1.4, 1.5 The neurology of dementia

- Provide details about three causes of dementia syndrome. For each, detail with examples how it causes dementia syndrome. Provide details about the different types of memory impairment that are commonly experienced by individuals who have dementia.
- Make a poster of the different parts of the brain and their functions. Then provide an explanation

of how the brain processes information, and include the abilities and limitations of individuals who have dementia in doing so.

- Discuss with a colleague other factors that may cause changes in an individual's physical and emotional condition that are not attributable to dementia, as well as why the abilities and needs of an individual who has dementia may fluctuate. Include examples and details of reasons why in your discussions.

LO2 Understand the impact of recognition and diagnosis of dementia

AC 2.1 Describe the impact of early diagnosis and follow up to diagnosis

Recognising the signs of dementia can affect individuals, their families and others involved in their lives in different ways. Read through the comments below made by individuals who have dementia and their families.

These comments include a mixture of positive and negative reactions, depending on the levels of understanding of what dementia is and when they were diagnosed, as well as the speakers' individual personalities and current support networks.

Diagnosing that an individual has dementia and what type of dementia they have is important for ensuring that the individual receives effective care, support and treatment, as well as access to a range of information, advice and support services and specialist professionals such as health visitors, dementia nurses, counsellors, financial advisors and memory clinics. An early diagnosis can also help individuals and their families make plans for the future and adapt to the changes that will occur in their lives over a period of time, such as putting

their finances in order, making a will and the adaptations that will be necessary to their home. Being able to do this can reduce anxiety and stress, as well as bring an enormous sense of achievement and relief to all concerned.

After diagnosis

After diagnosis it is important that the individual who has dementia is able to express their own desires for how they wish to live, for example one individual may choose to go and live in a residential care setting as they may not want to be a burden to their family, another individual may feel they want to spend every moment they can with their close family and friends by retiring early from work or moving closer to them.

Following diagnosis it is also very important that the individual who has dementia continues to be an **active participant** in discussions about their life and future; **advance care planning** and setting up a **power of attorney** if the dementia is progressive will enable the individual to retain a sense of ownership and control over their life and what's important to them.

> ### Comments made by individuals who have dementia and their families
>
> 'I was shocked to find out I had dementia, I never thought it could happen to me.'
>
> 'What happens now that I know she's got dementia?'
>
> 'Will I have to go into a home?'
>
> 'How will we manage?'
>
> 'I prefer knowing, I knew there was something wrong.'
>
> 'It's a relief to have a diagnosis, we can now prepare ourselves.'
>
> 'Being diagnosed meant I could get my life in order.'

> ### Key terms
>
> **Active participant** means the individual is regarded as an active partner in their own care or support, rather than a passive recipient, and has a right to participate in the activities and relationships of everyday life as independently as possible.
>
> **Advance care planning** is a way of working that improves the planning and provision of care for an individual and recognises the individual's right to live their life as they wish.
>
> **Power of attorney** is when you give someone who you trust the power to make decisions about you if you are unable to.

AC 2.2 Explain the importance of recording possible signs or symptoms of dementia in line with agreed ways of working

As stated previously individuals who have dementia may display a range of common and noticeable signs and symptoms. These may include difficulties following conversations, repeating themselves over and over when speaking with others, forgetting what they have seen and read, and/or forgetting the names of relatives and friends. Identifying these changes in an individual and then recording them accurately and fully is very important. Look at Figure 10.4, which shows the different ways of recording possible signs or symptoms of dementia.

Recording possible signs or symptoms of dementia is important and part of your duty of care. This may involve recording changes that you notice in relation to their memory including how often they occur or changes to their personality such as increased irritability, anxiety, depression.

Doing so will benefit the individual, their partner, family, friends, neighbours, and others who work with the individual such as carers, advocates, GP, consultant or neurologist.

- The **individual** will feel reassured that any signs or symptoms of dementia they may be experiencing are being monitored and taken seriously.
- Involving the **individual's family** will make them feel they are helping and ensure they continue to feel involved and consulted in the individual's life.

Figure 10.4 Methods of recording possible signs or symptoms of dementia

> ## Key term
>
> **Level and type of care and support** is the care and support an individual requires for their needs to be met, such as a prompt (low-level support) or physical assistance (high-level support).

- For all those **others** who work with the individual it is crucial that any possible signs or symptoms of dementia are recorded in full to comply with agreed ways of working, to build up a picture of and monitor the individual's physical and emotional well-being, and to determine and plan for the **level and type of care and support** needed both now and in the future.

AC 2.3 Explain the process of reporting possible signs of dementia within agreed ways of working

Once information has been gathered and recorded about an individual's possible signs or symptoms of dementia they will then need to be reported in line with your work setting's agreed ways of working. Although procedures will vary depending on the work setting and your role within it, there are three important steps that must be followed and that apply to all work settings:

1 Do not ignore possible signs of dementia.
2 Report these as soon as possible to someone in a more senior position to you, i.e. your manager or co-ordinator. Provide full details of the signs you have observed; give a factual verbal account only and try to avoid including your opinions or judgements. Be clear and concise.
3 Ensure you document in full and as accurately as possible the verbal account that you have provided. Include the date and time and the details of the possible signs of dementia that you reported, including to whom you reported these.

After reporting the possible signs of dementia you may be asked to continue to monitor the individual concerned using agreed procedures or to provide more specific information to other health professionals about the signs you have reported. This may include the use of digital media to capture visual changes or charts and graphs that capture the dates and times of changes. The person in your work setting to whom you have reported the signs may then decide to seek further advice and information from the individual's GP, who may then refer the individual to a consultant for further assessment and/or tests such as the **Mini Mental State Examination** (MMSE).

It is important that you find out what your work setting's process is for reporting possible signs of dementia and ensure you understand how to follow it correctly, including to whom reports must be made, when and how.

Key term

The **Mini Mental State Examination (MMSE)** is a tool comprising a series of questions and tests, used by health professionals to diagnose and assess dementia.

Research and investigate

2.2, 2.3 Recording and reporting procedure
- Find out how the procedures for recording and reporting possible signs or symptoms of dementia in your work setting compare to those in other services or settings.
- Research the NICE Guidelines 'Supporting people with dementia and their carers in health and social care'. What do they say about the processes for diagnosing and referring individuals who have dementia? What do they say about how families and friends should be included?

Evidence activity

2.2, 2.3 Recording and reporting signs or symptoms of dementia
Reflect on the policies, procedures and guidance available to you in your work setting and then consider how you must record and report signs or symptoms of dementia for two different individuals with whom you work.

AC 2.4 Describe the possible impact of receiving a diagnosis of dementia on the individual and their family and friends

As you read in AC 2.1, the impact of receiving a diagnosis of dementia can vary both for individuals and their families and carers; understanding this is central to the care and support you provide.

- **For individuals who show a positive reaction**, such as viewing their diagnosis as an opportunity to put their life in order: be prepared to spend time with the individual, listening to their desires and talking through with them the goals they would like to achieve.
- **For individuals who show a negative reaction**, such as feeling overwhelmed or fearful or depressed: it is important that they feel they can approach you and share with you in confidence how they are feeling. They may be able to be more honest with a professional than with a relative, whom they may not want to burden or upset. Depending on the nature of individuals' negative reactions you may need to report these to your manager or provide the individual with information about the range of additional support and services available to them in their local community.
- **For individuals' families and friends who show a positive reaction**, such as viewing their relative's diagnosis as a confirmation of the changes they have observed but could not explain: it is important that they are made aware of the services and organisations they can approach for information and answers to their questions, as well as for practical, emotional and financial support.
- **For individuals' families and friends who show a negative reaction**, such as feeling guilty, angry, fearful or worried about the future and how they will manage: provide information and support them to talk through what dementia is and what dementia is not. This will enable them to understand more about how dementia will affect their relative, including the care, support and treatments

available. Depending on your role and your work setting's policies and procedures, this may take place with you or with another trained professional. Services and organisations that provide practical, financial and emotional support will have a large role to play, as will you. You may very often be the first, only and/or most regular professional they know and with whom they meet.

LO3 Understand how dementia care must be underpinned by a person-centred approach

AC 3.1 Compare a person-centred and a non-person-centred approach to dementia care

It is very important to ensure that individuals who have dementia remain in control of their lives and that their unique strengths, abilities and interests are the focus of all care and support planned and implemented. These ways of working in dementia care are often referred to as 'person-centred approaches'; as the name suggests, the focus is on the individual and who they are, not on their dementia.

There are four key components to person-centred approaches to dementia care:

1 **Valuing the individual for who they are** – finding out as much as you can about the individual – their strengths, their interests, their background, their wishes, their preferences, their needs – helps to ensure that the **plan of care** (see page 180 for definition) that is put in place happens with the individual and reflects how they want to live their life.
2 **Understanding that each individual is unique** – we are all different and this is true

Evidence activity

2.1, 2.4 Early diagnosis and follow-up to diagnosis
Reflect on an individual with whom you work and think about how early diagnosis and follow-up to diagnosis could impact on their life and on others involved in their lives, including their family and friends.

Time to think

2.1, 2.4 Do you understand the impact of recognising and diagnosing dementia?
- How would you feel if you or someone close to you received a diagnosis of dementia?
- Why?
- What do you think are the benefits of being given a diagnosis?

Case study

2.1, 2.2, 2.3, 2.4 Akim
Akim has been living on his own since his wife died three years ago. Akim enjoys living independently and does not like to rely on others or burden others too much with his concerns. Daya is Akim's support worker and he visits Akim every lunchtime to provide him with some company and to assist him with small household tasks. Daya has noticed some unusual changes in Akim over the past week, including him forgetting Daya's name and the purpose of his visit, and not changing his clothes from one day to another. Daya is aware that Akim

is feeling anxious about his wedding anniversary next week and has also recently started taking a new course of antibiotics.

1 What do you think Daya should do? Why?
2 Explain why it is important to record possible signs of symptoms of dementia.
3 Explain the process that Daya should follow for reporting these.
4 Provide details of the possible impact on Akim, his family and friends of receiving an early diagnosis of dementia and follow-up to diagnosis.

for individuals who have dementia too. Recognising this and ensuring that the plan of care reflects an individual's choices and personal preferences is essential.

3 **Respecting the individual's feelings** – showing **empathy** when supporting an individual who has dementia with their care or support is essential, in particular when providing support with activities that the individual used to be able to complete independently, such as personal care or shopping.

4 **Respecting the individual's rights** – respecting that an individual who has dementia has the same rights as all of us is important. This includes the right to choice, dignity, privacy, independence, respect, individuality and working in partnership as an active partner in their care or support.

Working in this person-centred way with individuals who have dementia ensures that they continue to be fully involved in all aspects of their lives even as the dementia progresses and that a care plan is drawn up once an individual's needs have been identified. Non-person-centred approaches to dementia care disable the individual further by focusing on the dementia and on the tasks that require completion, rather than on the individual. Look at Figure 10.5, which includes some of the consequences of non-person-centred approaches to dementia care. Which approaches do you think are the best to use for the delivery of safe, personalised and effective dementia care?

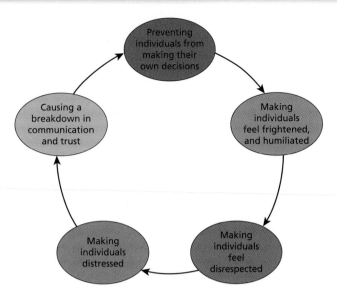

Figure 10.5 Consequences of non-person-centred approaches to dementia care

AC 3.2 Describe a range of different techniques to use to meet the fluctuating abilities and needs of the individual with dementia

As we explored in the previous section, working in a person-centred way involves dementia care that is unique to the individual; this includes ensuring it is also flexible so that individuals' variable abilities and needs are met.

There is a range of different ways of working that can be used to meet the fluctuating abilities and needs of individuals who have dementia. Not all techniques will be suitable for all individuals and so it is important that you choose the right technique for the right individual; you can do this only if you know the individual with whom you are working.

- **Care or support plan** – by ensuring this reflects who the individual is and how their abilities and needs may change, everyone who works with the individual can use this information to inform their working practices.
- **Life history and reminiscence work** – encouraging the individual and others who are important to them to share information with you about their past and background will

> ### Key terms
>
> An individual's **plan of care** is the document where day-to-day requirements and preferences for care and support are detailed. It may be known by other names, e.g. support plan, individual plan or care delivery plan.
>
> **Empathy** is the ability to understand and share how someone else may be feeling.

make them feel valued, and will help you and the team find out how best to work with an individual's fluctuating abilities and needs.

- **Creating a person-centred environment** – ensuring that the individual's living environment is homely, personalised with what is important to them and includes activities they can take part in will make them feel secure, more likely to retain their independence and promote their individuality, particularly when their needs and abilities vary from day to day. When working with individuals who have dementia, it is important to maintain familiarity and regularity in the setting, for example with regular staff and routines and a familiar environment. When thinking about the environment, also consider that people with dementia may tend to feel restless and walk about a lot and so having an area where they can go and walk about safely can be a good source of stimulation for them. Individuals can be distracted from repetitious questioning and actions where environments include a range of different activities that they may like to try.

- **Use of therapies** – using therapies such as **validation therapy** and **behavioural therapy** in everyday working practices can improve individuals' sense of well-being, make individuals feel valued and reduce feelings of confusion and distress.

Key terms

Validation therapy is a way of working that involves acknowledging how an individual who has dementia thinks and feels.

Behavioural therapy is a way of working that involves finding out the reasons for difficult behaviours, e.g. individuals who have dementia may display behaviours such as wandering, repetitive actions and questions, or inappropriate sexual behaviours.

Evidence activity

3.1, 3.2 Person-centred approaches and techniques

- Reflect on an individual with whom you work and think about the person-centred approaches to dementia care that are used and how these differ from non-person-centred approaches.
- Provide details of at least three techniques that are used to meet this individual's fluctuating needs and abilities, including how and why these work.

Research and investigate

3.2 Dementia care therapies

Research how validation therapy and behavioural therapy can be used in dementia care.

AC 3.3 Describe how myths and stereotypes related to dementia may affect the individual and their carers

Enabling person-centred approaches will also involve understanding the impact that **myths** and **stereotypes** (see page 182 for definition) can have on individuals and their carers. As you have read, individuals who have dementia have unique characteristics, strengths, abilities and needs; myths and stereotypes about dementia make all individuals the same, which is incorrect.

Myths and stereotypes are created by the media, by organisations and by people. Negative images and stories about individuals who have dementia can adversely affect the self-esteem of individuals who have dementia and people's perceptions of what dementia is. This may result in individuals and their carers being discriminated against, being fearful of what dementia is, and feeling depressed and alone.

Time to think

3.3 The effects of stereotyping
- How would you feel if someone close to you was discriminated against because they had dementia?
- Why?
- What would you do?

AC 3.4 Describe ways in which individuals and carers can be supported to overcome their fears

Working together in person-centred ways involves enabling individuals and their carers (including partners, families, friends and neighbours) to overcome their fears about dementia and dementia care. Gathering as much information as we can about what dementia is and what dementia care involves, as well as talking about dementia using positive language, can help address some of these fears that have been created by inaccurate myths and stereotypes.

Involving individuals and their carers from the outset when they first receive a diagnosis of dementia and ensuring that they are fully aware of the type of dementia the individual has will help to support them to manage and overcome their fears. It will also help them to overcome their fears to know its prognosis and the care and support services available, as well as the range of information, advice and support that can be accessed on a range of topics from both professionals and organisations. They can also encourage them to plan for the future.

Time to think

3.3, 3.4 Myths and stereotypes

Discuss with a colleague and make a list of all the myths and stereotypes you have heard, seen or read about in relation to dementia. Discuss the effects that these have on individuals who have dementia and on their carers. Discuss ways in which you and others can support individuals who have dementia and their carers to overcome their fears in relation to dementia.

Case study

3.1, 3.2, 3.3, 3.4 Alan and Gary

Alan and his partner Gary are meeting with senior carer Maria to find out more about the dementia care services that are available to support them to continue to live together at home in the way that they choose. They worry that this type of support does not exist.

1 Why might Alan and Gary feel this way?
2 How can Maria help Alan and Gary to overcome their fears?
3 What details about person-centred approaches could Maria share with them?
4 What specific techniques could Maria discuss with them to meet their varying abilities and needs?

Legislation

- The Equality Act 2010
- The Health and Social Care Act 2012
- The Human Rights Act 1998
- The Mental Capacity Act 2005

Useful resources

Websites

Advisory, Conciliation and Arbitration Service

www.acas.org.uk

Alzheimer's Society

alzheimers.org.uk

Alzheimer's Research UK

alzheimersresearchuk.org

Creutzfeldt-Jakob Disease Support Network

cjdsupport.net

Huntington's Disease Association

hda.org.uk

Parkinson's UK

parkinsons.org.uk

Publications

Alzheimer's Society (2001) *Quality Dementia Care in Care Homes: Person-centred standards.* London: Alzheimer's Society.

Kitwood, T. (1997) *Dementia Reconsidered: The person comes first.* Buckingham: Open University Press.

Stokes, G. (2003) *Challenging Behaviour in Dementia: A person-centred approach.* London: Speechmarks Publishing.

The principles of infection prevention and control

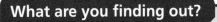

This unit is worth 3 credits

What are you finding out?

Infection prevention and control are key to the work of health and social care workers and employees, who have a responsibility to work to legislation, regulatory and professional body standards. Health and social care employees also have a responsibility to adhere to infection control and risk assessment procedures, of personal protective equipment (PPE) and of maintaining good personal hygiene.

In this unit you will learn about how to prevent and control infection, your roles and responsibilities and those of your employer. You'll also find out about legislation, policies and procedures. You'll consider the potential risks of infection within the workplace, how to use personal protective equipment to control infections as well as understand the importance of good hygiene and practices such as effective handwashing.

By the end of this unit you will:

1 Understand roles and responsibilities in the prevention and control of infections.
2 Understand legislation and policies relating to prevention and control of infections.
3 Understand systems and procedures relating to the prevention and control of infections.
4 Understand the importance of risk assessment in relation to the prevention and control of infections.
5 Understand the importance of using personal protective equipment in the prevention and control of infections.
6 Understand the importance of good personal hygiene in the prevention and control of infections.

LO1 Understand roles and responsibilities in the prevention and control of infections

What is an infection?

Infection is caused by **pathogens**. All infectious diseases are transmissible but some, such as **influenza**, **MRSA**, *C. difficile* and **norovirus**, have the potential to spread from one person to another. Understanding how pathogens behave and spread is crucial to their prevention and control. This unit will enable you to understand the principles of infection prevention and control.

Users of health and social care services are physically and emotionally vulnerable to infection:

- Influenza vaccination is recommended for all elderly people in the UK aged 65 and over, as well as people in at-risk groups, such as those suffering from respiratory problems like asthma and COPD (chronic obstructive pulmonary disease).

- During the year to March 2013, just under half of reported cases, 43 per cent, of MRSA and *C. difficile* in England and Wales were contracted by patients while in hospital.

For the most upto date information, go to https://www.gov.uk/government/organisations/public-health-england

Experts state that during 2012–2013 there were more cases of Norovirus than usual. The figures show there were 4,140 laboratory confirmed cases, a 63 per cent higher figure than the number reported at the same point in 2011–2012.

Many infectious diseases can spread very rapidly and have dire effects within health and social care settings. Infection is a major cause of illness and hospitalisation among people living in residential care homes, and **healthcare-associated infections** (HCAIs) may be serious, even life threatening. Many of these infections can worsen underlying medical conditions, and some HCAIs are resistant to antibiotics. For these reasons, both employers and employees have very clear roles and responsibilities in ensuring the prevention and control of infections.

Infection prevention and control is therefore key to the work of health and social care employers and employees, who have a responsibility to comply with the relevant legislation and regulatory and professional body standards. Health and social care employees also have a responsibility to understand the importance of infection control and risk assessment procedures, of personal protective equipment (PPE) and of maintaining good personal hygiene.

(Sources: www.rcn.org.uk; www.healthcarerepublic.com; www.dailymail.co.uk)

Key terms

A **pathogen** is a bacterium that can produce disease, fungus, virus, infestation.

Influenza is a contagious viral infection of the respiratory passages which can for example cause fever, severe aching.

MRSA (*methicillin-resistant staphylococcus aureus*) is a bacterial infection that is resistant to antibiotics

C difficile or *Clostridium difficile* are bacteria can affect the digestive system; symptoms can range from diarrhoea to serious and even fatal inflammation of the colon.

Norovirus are a group of viruses that can cause food poisoning and acute gastroenteritis.

Superbug is a strain of bacteria that is resistant to antibiotics.

Healthcare-associated infection (HCAI) is an infection that has been acquired from being in a healthcare setting.

Research and investigate

LO1 Superbugs

Research the press and the internet for news items relating to superbugs that have threatened health around the world recently. In what ways have they affected the people you support?

AC 1.1 Explain employees' roles and responsibilities in relation to the prevention and control of infection

As a health and social care worker you have roles and responsibilities in relation to infection prevention and control (see Table 11.1), including:

- to co-operate with your employer in preventing and controlling infection
- to know and understand your organisation's infection prevention and control policies and procedures
- to follow infection control procedures and apply standard infection control principles to all situations all of the time
- to know how to get advice on the prevention and control of infection and to stay up to date in your knowledge and understanding of the subject
- to make your manager aware of any difficulties you have in following procedures
- to report breaches in good practice and take corrective action as appropriate.

You also have a responsibility to be on your guard for potential outbreaks of infection or resistance to antibiotics and to inform your employer if you have any concerns.

You should also refer to the Health and Safety at Work etc. Act 1974 for more information on your role and responsibilities in relation to health and social care – see Table 11.1 and Figure 11.1.

Evidence activity

1.1 Your roles and responsibilities regarding infection prevention and control

What are your roles and responsibilities in relation to infection prevention and control? Why is it important that you fulfil your roles and responsibilities in your work?

AC 1.2 Explain employers' responsibilities in relation to the prevention and control of infection

Policies, procedures and sharing information

Policies set out the arrangements that an organisation has for complying with legislation. Employers must have written policies describing the measures they take to prevent and control infection in order to uphold the law.

Procedures describe the activities that need to be carried out for policies to be implemented. Employers should have accessible (easily located, understandable, straightforward and manageable) infection prevention and control procedures that ensure a safe environment and safe working practices. They should also have a system for ensuring that you understand and follow those procedures. Failure by your employer to minimise the risk of infection and to protect you, your colleagues, the individuals you support and their

Prevention of infection: your roles and responsibilities	Control of infection: your roles and responsibilities
Co-operate with your employer in preventing and controlling infection	Follow infection control procedures and apply standard infection control principles to all situations all of the time
Know and understand your organisation's infection prevention and control policies and procedures	Know how to get advice on the prevention and control of infection and to stay up to date in your knowledge and understanding of the subject
Report breaches in good practice and take corrective action as appropriate	Make your manager aware of any difficulties you have in following procedures

Table 11.1 Prevention and control of infection – your roles and responsibilities

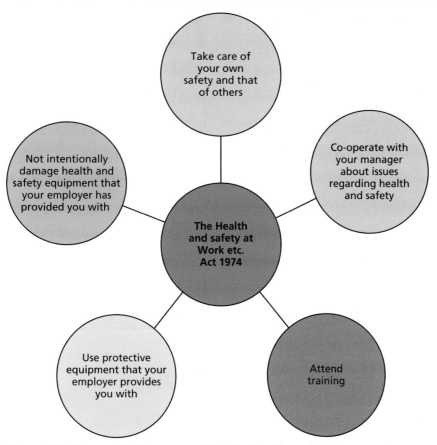

Figure 11.1 Responsibilities covered by the Health and Safety at work etc. Act 1974

family and friends against infectious disease means neglect.

Employers have a responsibility to produce regular infection prevention and control reports that describe:

- the policies and procedures that are in place and how they are monitored
- any outbreaks of infection that have taken place and the actions taken to rectify problems
- the education and training that have taken place
- planned improvements.

The purpose of infection prevention and control reports is to reduce infections and ensure improvements in infection prevention and control.

Employers have a responsibility to obtain and share with staff up-to-date advice and information about infection prevention and control from

suitably qualified and competent individuals. People who can offer advice include:

- general practitioners (GPs)
- health protection nurses (HPNs)
- **Royal College of Nursing (RCN)** nurse advisors for infection prevention and control
- community infection control nurses (CICNs)
- environmental health practitioners (EHPs).

For more information see www.rcn.org.uk and www.cieh.org.

General responsibilities

General responsibilities include providing and maintaining a safe place of work, organising the necessary training, providing personal protective equipment (PPE) and maintaining the cleanliness of the work setting.

Reporting outbreaks of infection

Employers have a responsibility to report suspected outbreaks of infection, changes in resistance to antibiotics and occurrences of notifiable diseases to the local Health Protection Unit (HPU). Typical characteristics of a notifiable disease include:

- it is potentially life threatening
- it spreads rapidly
- it cannot easily be treated or cured, for example there is no vaccine or antibiotics available.

* Note that Public Health England (PHE), which has responsibility for dealing with public health issues such as infectious diseases, is an executive agency, sponsored by the Department of Health.

Employers have a responsibility to ensure that people with infectious disease are nursed in **isolation**.

Immunisations

Employers also have a responsibility to ensure that their staff are immunised against infectious disease; that they receive ongoing training in the prevention and control of infection; and that their personal development plan shows what training they have completed and what they need to do.

(Source: 'Infection control guidance for care homes', Department of Health, 2006; https://www.gov.uk/.../Care-home-resource-18-February-2013.pdf)

Notifiable diseases

These include:
- acute encephalitis
- acute poliomyelitis
- anthrax
- cholera
- diphtheria
- dysentery (amoebic or bacillary)
- food poisoning
- leprosy
- leptospirosis
- malaria
- measles
- meningitis
- meningococcal septicaemia (without meningitis)
- mumps
- ophthalmia neonatorum
- paratyphoid fever
- plague
- rabies
- relapsing fever
- rubella
- scarlet fever
- smallpox
- tetanus
- tuberculosis
- typhoid fever
- typhus
- viral haemorrhagic fevers
- viral hepatitis
- whooping cough
- yellow fever

Time to think

1.2 Immunisation
Against what diseases are you immunised? Are your immunisations up to date? What could happen if you failed to be immunised properly?

Evidence activity

1.2 Employers' roles and responsibilities regarding infection prevention and control
What are your employer's responsibilities in relation to infection prevention and control? Why is it important that your employer fulfils these responsibilities? How do they contribute to the prevention and control of infection?

Key terms

The **Royal College of Nursing (RCN)** represents nurses and nursing, promotes excellence in practice and shapes health policies.

Isolation nursing is the physical separation of an infected patient from others.

LO2 Understand legislation and policies relating to prevention and control of infections

AC 2.1 Outline current legislation and regulatory body standards relevant to the prevention and control of infection

Regulatory bodies
Regulatory bodies are organisations set up by the government to establish national standards for qualifications and best practice and to

Key term

Cross infection is the spread of pathogens from one person, object, place or part of the body to another.

Legislation	Purpose of the legislation
Health and Safety at Work etc. Act (HASAWA) 1974	Ensures the health and safety of everyone who may be affected by work activities.
Management of Health and Safety at Work Regulations (MHSWR) 1999	Require employers and managers to carry out risk assessments to eliminate or minimise risks to health and safety, including from **pathogens**.
Personal Protective Equipment at Work Regulations (PPE) 1992	Minimise the risks to health and safety associated with **cross infection**.
The Health Act 2006	Aims to prevent and control healthcare-associated infections (HCAIs).
The Health and Social Care Act 2012	Aims to protect public health by preventing and controlling the spread of infectious diseases.
The Reporting of Incidents, Diseases and Dangerous Occurrences (Amendment) Regulations (RIDDOR) 2013	Require that certain work-related injuries, diseases and dangerous occurrences are reported to the HSE or local authority.
Public Health (Control of Disease) Act 1984 Public Health (Infectious Diseases) Regulations 1988	Require that outbreaks of infection, changes in resistance to antibiotics and notifiable diseases are reported to the HPU so that they can be managed to prevent their spread.
Food Safety Act 1990 Food Hygiene Regulations 2006	Minimise the risks to health and safety associated with food handling.
Control of Substances Hazardous to Health Regulations (COSHH) 2002	Minimise the risks to health and safety from the use of hazardous substances, including pathogens.
Hazardous Waste Regulations 2005	Require that waste is dealt with so as to avoid putting health at risk.
The Waste (England and Wales) Regulations 2011	Require that waste, including contaminated waste, is properly stored and packaged while awaiting removal from the premises as well as collected and recorded.

Table 11.2 Legislation relevant to infection prevention and control

ensure that these standards are consistently observed. They include:

- The Care Quality Commission in England, which regulates health and social care provided by the NHS, local authorities, private companies and voluntary organisations. Its standards of quality and care state that people can expect to be cared for in a clean environment where they are protected from infection. For more information see www.cqc.org.uk
- The General Social Care Council in England (GSCC), Care Council for Wales, Scottish Care Council and Northern Ireland Social Care Council introduced codes of practice that dictate the standards of practice and conduct that social care

workers and employers should meet, including protecting individuals from danger or harm. Following the closure of the GSCC in 2012, Skills for Care is housing the codes of practice until a new joint code of conduct and minimum training standards for healthcare support workers and adult social care workers in England is agreed. For more information see www.skillsforcare.org.uk/Standards/National-minimum-training-standards/National-minimum-training-standards.aspx; www.ccwales.org.uk; www.sssc.uk.com; www.niscc.info

- The guides and strategies for improvement of the General Medical Council (GMC) shape the role of healthcare professionals with regard to infection prevention and control. For more information see www.gmc-uk.org

- The code or 'Standards of conduct, performance and ethics for nurses and midwives' of the Nursing and Midwifery Council (NMC) is a key tool in protecting and promoting health and well-being, requiring nurses and midwives to manage risks, including risk of infection. For more information see www.nmc-uk.org

- The Health and Care Professions Council (HCPC) 'Standards of conduct, performance and ethics' require **allied health professionals** to deal safely with risk of infection by taking precautions to protect everyone, including themselves, from cross infection. For more information see www.hpc-uk.org

- The Office for Standards in Education, Children's Services and Skills (Ofsted) regulates and inspects care service provision for children and young people. For a care provider to meet Ofsted's standards and regulations, it has to demonstrate that children and young people are not at risk from cross infection due to low standards of hygiene. For more information see www.ofsted.gov.uk

- Some occupations are not covered by regulatory standards or codes of practice, for example healthcare assistants in England and Wales. Instead, national occupational standards (NOS) set out the **competences** that apply to their job roles and level of experience. NOS for workers in the health and social care sectors are written by the National College for Teaching and Leadership (NCTL), by Skills for Health and by Skills for Care. For more information see www.gov.uk/government/organisations/national-college-for-teaching-and-leadership; www.skillsforhealth.org.uk; www.skillsforcare.org.uk

Evidence activity

2.1 Legislation and regulatory body standards

Summarise the Acts and Regulations, regulatory body standards and national occupational standards that are relevant to your responsibilities in relation to infection prevention and control.

AC 2.2 Describe local and organisational policies relevant to the prevention and control of infection

Policies set out the arrangements an organisation has for complying with legislation (see Figure 11.2). Infection prevention and control policies describe the measures that organisations take to comply with the legislation listed in Table 11.2.

Local authorities and health trusts produce **evidence-based policies** that guide health and social care settings within their districts and regions to comply with legislation while taking account of local needs. National initiatives and campaigns also help to shape how local health and social care providers can minimise and prevent the spread of infection. For example, the RCN 'Wipe it out' campaign is aimed at reducing the **prevalence** of HCAIs, as are its booklets 'Good practice in infection prevention' and 'Guidance on uniforms and work wear'.

Organisational policies include accident and incident reporting and personal hygiene requirements (see Figure 11.2). It is important to know what these policies need you to do as they form a vital part of your work role.

Key terms

Allied health professionals are clinical healthcare professionals, distinct from medicine, dentistry and nursing, who work in a team to make the healthcare system function.

Competence is the ability to do something (e.g. your job) successfully due to having the right knowledge, understanding and capabilities.

Evidence-based policies are policies that have been proven to work.

Prevalence is the proportion of individuals in a population who have a particular disease.

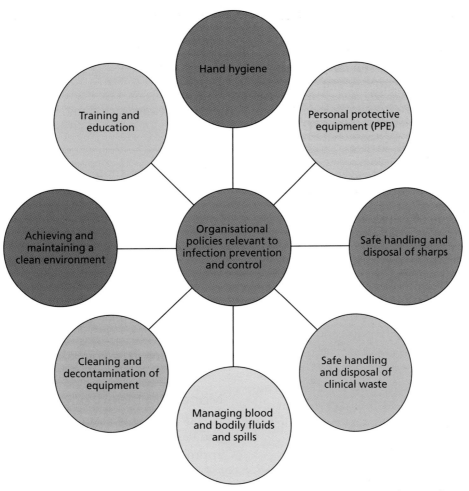

Figure 11.2 Organisational policies relevant to infection prevention and control

The Department of Health has produced a number of documents addressing infection prevention and control at a local level, such as:

- 'Essential steps to safe, clean care: reducing healthcare-associated infections', which guides local health and social care providers in the use of best practice to prevent and manage the spread of infections.
- 'A matron's charter: an action plan for cleaner hospitals', which explains how staff, patients and visitors can make their local hospital a cleaner and safer place.
- 'Prevention and control of infection in care homes: an information resource', which describes how everyone involved in providing residential care can protect residents and staff from acquiring infections.

The Health Protection Agency provides support and advice to, for example, local authorities and health and emergency services. Its 'Guidance on infection control in schools and other childcare settings' describes the importance of immunisation, personal hygiene and a clean environment.

Evidence activity

2.2 Local and organisational policies

- Describe infection prevention and control policies written for your workplace. What is the purpose of each?
- Describe infection prevention and control policies written for health and social care organisations in your locality. Which organisations produced them? Why was it necessary for them to be produced?

LO3 Understand systems and procedures relating to the prevention and control of infections

AC 3.1 Describe procedures and systems relevant to the prevention and control of infection

While policies set out the arrangements an organisation has in place for complying with legislation, procedures describe the activities or practices that need to be carried out for policies to be implemented. Figure 11.2 introduced you to a range of policies that is relevant to infection prevention and control. The following checklist summarises routine safe practices or **standard precautions** that protect not only the individuals with whom you work but also you and your colleagues. Note that this checklist is not a substitute for your workplace's procedures and you should follow it in relation to the people you are supporting and to the setting you work in. Policies cannot be applied in exactly the same way to all settings and people.

Safe handling and disposal of sharps, for example needles, scalpels, stitch cutters and glass ampoules

- Do not attempt to handle or dispose of sharps until you have had the appropriate training.
- Keep handling to a minimum and do not pass directly from hand to hand.
- Never re-sheath needles and do not use broken or bent needles.
- Do not dismantle syringes or needles – dispose of them as a single unit.
- Dispose of sharps in the designated container at the point of use, i.e. where you are working.
- Do not fill containers more than two-thirds full and store them in an area away from the public.
- Sharps can cut you but they can also carry and cause infection, so dispose of them properly.

> **Key term**
>
> **Standard precautions** are intended to minimise exposure to and transmission of a wide variety of micro-organisms.

Safe handling and disposal of clinical waste

Clinical waste is any waste that poses a threat of infection, for example: body fluids, such as blood; body waste, such as urine, faeces, vomit; soiled swabs, dressings; clothing, bed linen; sharps. Safe handling and disposal of clinical waste requires that you:

- have had the appropriate training
- wear appropriate PPE and maintain good hand hygiene
- dispose of body fluids and waste down the sluice, or bag as follows:
  - yellow bag – infected waste and used swabs and dressings, to be incinerated
  - clear alginate bag inside a red plastic bag – soiled and infected clothing and linen, to be laundered
- report any dangerous handling and disposal of clinical waste to your manager.

Managing blood, body fluids and spills

Do not attempt to clean up spills or collect and handle specimens until you have had the appropriate training.

Collecting and handling specimens

- Wear appropriate PPE.
- Make sure containers are suitable, sterile and leak-proof.
- Label containers with relevant information and complete any accompanying forms.
- Send specimens to the lab as soon as possible – never leave them lying around.
- Enter test results into patient records as soon as you receive them and highlight any abnormal results to the appropriate person.

Spills

- Wear appropriate PPE.
- Clean up as soon as you can, using cleaning materials and disinfectants that are appropriate to the type of spill and the surface that has been spilled on.

Decontamination of equipment

Do not attempt to use decontamination techniques and equipment until you have had the appropriate training. Always follow the manufacturer's instructions and do not use any equipment if you are not confident that it has been installed and maintained properly.

- **Single-use equipment**, for example nebulisers and disposable catheters, should not be decontaminated and re-used. Dispose of it as appropriate. Re-usable equipment, such as bed pans and surgical instruments, must be decontaminated before re-use through a process of cleaning and disinfection, or cleaning and sterilisation. If equipment is not correctly decontaminated it can cross infect and cause illness as a result.
- Cleaning, using hot water and detergent, removes visible contamination but may not destroy pathogens. It is suitable for environmental cleaning.
- Disinfection uses chemicals or heat to reduce the number of **viable** pathogens. Washer-disinfectors and ultrasonic baths use very high temperatures to disinfect equipment that would be damaged by chemicals. Chemicals, such as **formaldehyde** and **peroxide**, are used when heat is insufficient.

- **Sterilisation** ensures that an object is totally free from pathogens. You may have access to a **sterile services department** (SSD), or you could use a bench-top vacuum steam steriliser.
- Low-risk equipment that does not touch broken skin or **mucous membranes**, or is not in contact with patients, such as wheelchairs and bedframes, must be cleaned and/or disinfected after every use.
- Medium-risk equipment that touches intact skin or mucous membranes, for example bed pans, must be cleaned and sterilised after every use but does not need to be sterile when being used.
- High-risk equipment that touches a break in the skin, enters the skin or body, must be cleaned and sterilised after each use and be sterile when used.

Achieving and maintaining a clean environment

A dirty environment holds a risk of infection. Dust and dirt, body fluids and waste, and household waste such as leftover food, provide conditions that support the growth and reproduction of a variety of pathogens. Health and social care settings should therefore have:

- fixed schedules for thorough cleaning of all areas, using properly maintained cleaning equipment that is appropriate to the surface being cleaned
- appropriate and clean facilities for the disposal of non-clinical, household waste.

Key terms

Single-use equipment is items that can be used only once.

Viable means it is alive and able to reproduce.

Formaldehyde is an organic compound used for disinfecting.

Peroxide is used as a disinfectant.

Sterilisation is a process that removes transmissible agents such as bacteria or viruses that may be present on a surface, in a fluid or medication for example.

Sterile service department carries out sterilisation and other actions on medical devices and equipment.

Mucous membranes are mucous-secreting membranes lining the body cavities and canals that connect with the outside air, such as the alimentary canal and respiratory tract.

Evidence activity

3.1 Procedures and systems for the prevention and control of infection

Describe infection prevention and control procedures or standard precautions that:

- you are required to follow in your work
- a colleague who has a different job role from you has to follow in their work.
- What actions should you take in order to ensure equipment is cleaned and decontaminated?

AC 3.2 Explain the potential impact of an outbreak of infection on the individual and the organisation

Minor outbreaks of infection are characterised by close neighbours, for example in a ward, classroom or adjacent rooms in a residential care home, developing similar signs and symptoms over a period of days or weeks. Minor outbreaks of infection are usually easily managed.

A serious outbreak is characterised by 20 or more people throughout a health or social care setting developing signs and symptoms within 24 hours of each other. Serious outbreaks are dealt with using serious outbreak procedures.

An outbreak can have a serious impact not only on the business but on people accessing it or living there. For example, the employer's reputation could be affected, they will have to deal with any expenses for example related to cleaning issues, staff may be affected by illness, and in more serious cases they may face fines or even imprisonment.

Control measures and actions to take

It is important to recognise potential outbreaks promptly so that prevention and control measures can be put in place as soon as possible. You read about the characteristics of a possible outbreak in AC 1.2. It is also important to report without delay suspicions of infection or an actual outbreak to the individual in your setting who has responsibility for managing infection control.

When a suspected outbreak has been reported, the individual or team responsible for managing infection will assess the situation and decide what action to take. This could include:

- isolating the individual or group of people, including staff, who are infected and restricting staff movement in order to minimise exposure to the source of infection

- ensuring that staff who are exposed to the infection use appropriate PPE and have a sufficient supply of alcohol gel
- ensuring that appropriate antibiotics are available
- restricting visitors or closing the affected ward, department or setting
- informing the local Health Protection Unit (HPU) if the infection is a notifiable disease
- keeping residents' relatives and friends informed
- employing additional staff to cover for those who are sick or whose time is devoted to isolation nursing.

When the outbreak has been controlled, the environment and any equipment used during the outbreak should be thoroughly decontaminated, and an audit carried out to check:

- the effectiveness of infection prevention and control procedures
- whether staff followed procedures to the letter
- whether there were any barriers to following procedures, for example time constraints, staff shortages and lack of resources
- the need for further training.

Impact

The impact of an outbreak of infection on an organisation can be significant (see Figure 11.3). For example:

- Hospital-based infections, such as *C. difficile* and MRSA, are the focus of huge amounts of attention from the media, impacting on the reputation of the hospitals affected and staff morale.
- Having to buy in additional resources, such as staff, impacts on finances.
- Discontinuity of care due to using agency staff affects the emotional well-being of patients.
- The additional work involved in dealing with an outbreak of infection is time consuming and can jeopardise job satisfaction and the day-to-day running of the organisation.

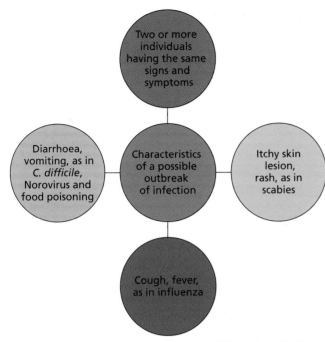

Figure 11.3 Characteristics of a possible outbreak of infection

LO4 Understand the importance of risk assessment in relation to the prevention and control of infections

AC 4.1 Define the term risk

A hazard is anything with the potential to cause harm, and a risk is the likelihood that a hazard will cause harm. For example, a broken paving stone is a hazard – it has the potential to cause someone to trip, fall and break a leg. But the likelihood or risk of this happening depends on factors such as the person's age and ability. An able-bodied child is less likely to fall and break a bone than a frail older person or an adult with visual impairment.

Figure 11.4 How do you manage risk within your setting?

Evidence activity

3.2 The potential impact of an outbreak of infection

Talk with your manager about an outbreak of infection at your workplace. How was the outbreak dealt with? How did it affect the people and the organisation? Why did it have these effects? What steps were taken subsequent to the outbreak? Has there been a further outbreak of the same infection? If so, why?

Case study

4.1 Care in the community

Sevenside Community Centre is situated on a busy main road. It is an old house on three floors and the front door opens straight on to the pavement. Its ground floor kitchen/dining room, which is open plan and freely accessible, is much in need of a makeover, as are the two toilets, which are both on the second floor and lack adequate disabled facilities. There is a lounge on the first floor and a TV and games room on the second floor. The garden is grassed.

The community centre is used by groups of children, young people, mothers and toddlers, elderly people, and people with learning and physical difficulties including sensory impairments.

1 What hazards can you identify at Sevenside Community Centre? How does the risk to health and safety vary within the different groups of people using the centre?

The expression 'at risk group' is used to describe a group of people who have a higher-than-average risk of being harmed by hazards, for example because of their age, lifestyle, existing health status or genetic inheritance. If a risk is identified it is important to consider how high the risk is, how severe the hazard is and who will be at risk. See Figure 11.4.

AC 4.2 Outline potential risks of infection within the workplace

Infection can occur anywhere where pathogens are present (see Table 11.2). Failure to prevent pathogens being brought into health and social care settings, for example by patients, staff and visitors, or to control outbreaks of infection once they are established, can have dire effects on vulnerable at risk groups.

Healthcare-associated infections
Healthcare-associated infections (HCAIs) are infections acquired in hospital or brought into hospital by people already infected. They include:

- MRSA (methicillin-resistant *Staphylococcus aureus*), a bacterium that is resistant to the antibiotic methicillin. Many of us carry *Staph aureus* (SA) on our skin without developing an infection, but if it enters the body it can cause blood poisoning and infections such as boils, abscesses and impetigo. It is spread by direct contact with infected patients, and also indirectly by touching contaminated

> **Key terms**
>
> An **in-dwelling device** is a device that is inserted into the body.
>
> A **catheter** is a plastic tube inserted into the body to drain fluid.

sheets, towels, clothes and dressings. At risk groups include people who take frequent courses of antibiotics, are already in poor health, have an open wound or skin condition such as psoriasis, or have an **in-dwelling device** such as a **catheter** or intravenous drip.

- *Clostridium difficile* (*C. difficile*), a bacterium present in the large bowel that does not usually cause problems in healthy people. It is spread in the same way as MRSA, but contaminated surfaces are more likely to be bedpans and toilets. Symptoms include stomach ache, diarrhoea, inflammation and bleeding of the bowel, blood poisoning and fever. It can also be fatal. At risk groups include elderly people and people in hospital, particularly if they are taking antibiotics, which destroy the bacteria that prevent *C. difficile* causing problems.

Head lice
The head louse is a tiny, wingless parasitic insect that lives among human hairs and feeds on blood from the scalp. They are very common and their

Main route of spread of infection	Examples of pathogenic infections
Skin – direct contact is skin-to-skin contact between two people. Indirect contact is touching things that another person has used and contaminated	- Bacterial infections, such as MRSA and *C. difficile* - Infestations, such as lice - Fungal infections, such as ringworm
Airways (inhalation)	- Bacterial and viral infections, such as influenza, pneumonia, bronchitis and tetanus
Digestive tract, when consuming food and drink	- Bacterial and viral infections, such as *E. coli*, Salmonella, rotavirus and norovirus
Use of healthcare instruments, such as sharps	- Viral infections, such as HIV/Aids and hepatitis B

Table 11.2 Routes of the spread of infection

bites cause the scalp to itch; these bites, if scratched, can become infected. While they cannot fly or jump, lice have claws that allow them to cling firmly to hair. They spread mainly through head-to-head contact, but also indirectly when clothing and hair equipment are shared. At risk groups are people who have close contact, especially children.

Ringworm

Ringworm is caused by the dermatophyte fungus that lives on dead skin, hair and nails. When it affects the skin between the toes, it is known as athlete's foot, and appears as red, scaly patches. Ringworm of the scalp starts as a small sore that becomes scaly, causing hair to fall out or break into stubbles. Ringworm of the nails causes them to become thick, discoloured and brittle. It is spread directly and indirectly, for example from damp clothing and wet floors and surfaces. At risk groups include people who use changing room facilities and swimming pools, and people in hospitals and residential care who share bathrooms.

Influenza

Influenza is a highly infectious illness caused by a flu virus. It infects the respiratory system, causing fever, aches and pains, dry cough, nausea and loss of appetite. Like the common cold, it is spread by inhaling small droplets of virus-containing saliva that are coughed or sneezed into the air by an infected person. It is also spread by indirect contact, for example when an infected person touches a surface, such as a door handle, with unwashed hands. At risk groups include elderly people and people with weak immune systems, such as cancer and Aids patients.

Pneumonia and bronchitis

Pneumonia is a bacterial or viral infection of the lung tissue, and bronchitis is a bacterial infection of the **bronchi**. They can occur together as broncho-pneumonia and are spread in the same way as influenza. Symptoms include aches and pains, fever, chest pain, cough, breathlessness, and yellow/green, sometimes bloodstained, sputum. At risk groups include people who are frail, elderly and already in poor health, for example with a chest disease. Pneumonia is a common cause of death in people who are already in poor health, for example people in the late or terminal stages of a cancer.

Key terms

The **bronchi** are the large airways that carry air from the trachea into the lungs.

A **spore** is a temporary, dormant structure that a bacterium changes into when conditions for its survival become hazardous.

Tetanus

Tetanus is caused by the bacterium *Clostridium tetani*, which is found in soil and animal manure. If the bacterial **spores** get into a wound they release a toxin that attacks the nervous system and causes problems such as muscle spasm, as in lockjaw. At risk groups include people who work with soil and animal manure, children who play outdoors, and people in health and social care settings where cleanliness is not maintained.

Food poisoning

Food poisoning is caused by poor standards of personal hygiene, poor hygiene in food storage, preparation and eating areas, and incorrect storage and cooking temperatures. Food poisoning bacteria include *Escherichia coli* (*E. coli*) and Salmonella, and viruses such as rotavirus and norovirus. In addition to growing and reproducing in food, these bacteria are carried by people on their bodies and clothes; by animals in their urine and faeces; and on kitchen surfaces and equipment. Signs and symptoms include nausea, stomach ache, diarrhoea and vomiting. At risk groups include babies, children, elderly people and people with pre-existing health problems.

Hepatitis B

Hepatitis B is a highly infectious virus that damages the liver. It is fifty to a hundred times as infectious as HIV (human immunodeficiency virus) and, like HIV, is carried in body fluids such as blood, saliva, semen and vaginal fluid. At risk groups are drug users who use contaminated needles, patients exposed to contaminated equipment and blood, for example during transfusions, and people who have unprotected sex. Hep B is also an important complication of accidental **needle stick injuries** and therefore a

Key term

A **needle stick injury** is a skin puncture by a syringe, needle or other sharp object.

Evidence activity

4.1, 4.2 Potential risks of infection within the workplace

In your own words, explain what is meant by the term 'risk'.

Bearing in mind the type of setting in which you work, the care that is provided and the characteristics of the people you support – for example their age, lifestyle and existing health status – outline potential risks of infection within your workplace.

Time to think

4.2 Risk assess or risk averse?

Do you think 'risk assessment' as you carry out your activities? Or are you blind to things that could go wrong? Can you see the benefit of being on the alert for potential hazards and associated risks?

risk factor for unvaccinated healthcare and body art workers.

(Sources: www.patient.co.uk; www.nhs.uk; http://kidshealth.org; www.bupa.co.uk; www.bbc.co.uk)

Factors to consider

A person is more at risk from infection if they are older, have low immunity, poor nutrition, are not well or have an open wound. An open wound could be due to surgery, drug therapy or invasive therapy.

AC 4.3 Describe the process of carrying out a risk assessment

According to the HSE, there are five steps to a risk assessment. In relation to risk assessment of the prevention and control of infections, these are:

Step 1: Identify hazards

- Inspect the cleanliness and hygiene of people, equipment and the working environment.
- Check that facilities for maintaining cleanliness and hygiene are in good repair.
- Check that infection prevention and control procedures are understood and followed to the letter.
- Check that systems are in place for monitoring the use of procedures, educating everyone concerned about the importance of following procedures, and supervising them to ensure that they put their learning into practice.
- Review records relating to infectious outbreaks to check that they were appropriately dealt with.

Step 2: Decide who might be harmed and how

Harm in relation to prevention and control of infections is exposure to infection and the consequences of infection. The people who might be harmed are the people you support, you, your colleagues and any visitors.

Step 3: Assess or evaluate the risks

This means you must assess or evaluate the risks arising from the hazards and decide whether the existing precautions are adequate or if more should be done. If something needs to be done, take steps to eliminate or control the risks.

As you know, a hazard is anything with the potential to cause harm to a person, but the risk that it will cause harm depends on a variety of factors, including the person's age, health status and so on. Because of the vulnerability of the people you support, the physical proximity that you share with them and the fact that the setting where you work is accessed frequently by the visiting public, the chances are that your evaluation of the risks will be that all the hazards you identify could have dire consequences for the health of everyone concerned.

4.3 Carrying out a risk assessment

1 Identify an infection hazard, for example that colleagues aren't washing their hands as often as they should.
2 Who might be harmed and how?
3 What are the risks to health caused by the hazard? What can be done to eliminate or control these risks?
4 How could you make people aware of changes that need to be made to eliminate or control the risks?
5 When do you think you should review the effectiveness of the changes?

4.4 Explain the importance of carrying out a risk assessment

Identify a couple of activities that you carry out and that have been risk assessed, for example preparing food and helping someone use the toilet. Why do you think these activities have been risk assessed? Why is it important that you follow procedures for these activities to the letter?

Are existing precautions adequate? Can you eliminate the hazards? Can you control associated risks?

Step 4: Record the findings and say how the risks can be controlled to prevent harm

Inform everyone about the outcome of the risk assessment, as everyone will be involved in controlling the risk.

It is very important to let everyone know the upshot of your risk assessment. Risks will remain unless you let people know how they must adapt their work practices.

Step 5: Review the assessment from time to time and revise it if necessary

Review is similarly important. Unless you review the effects of changes to work practices, you won't know if they are working! Also, you may be asked to use new equipment, materials and procedures, which could lead to new hazards. So do not be afraid to suggest further changes if necessary. While you do not want to continually re-invent the wheel, there is an argument for never standing still, that things can only get better!

(Source: www.hse.gov.uk)

AC 4.4 Explain the importance of carrying out a risk assessment

Managing the risk of infection by carrying out a risk assessment helps to maintain your health and that of the people you support, your colleagues and members of the public. Because ill health harms lives, you have a moral obligation to help manage risk. Ill health also harms the reputation and financial standing of an organisation, which in turn would affect your employment status. There is, in addition, a legal requirement to carry out risk assessments.

A risk assessment should also alert you to your standard of work practice, and whether you are enacting your duty of care to the health of everyone affected by your actions, including yourself.

(Source: www.hse.gov.uk)

It is a legal requirement to undertake a risk assessment so failure to do so is breaking the law and putting the health and safety of people at the setting at risk.

LO5 Understand the importance of using personal protective equipment in the prevention and control of infections

AC 5.1 Demonstrate correct use of PPE

Personal protective equipment or PPE is equipment that is intended for use by workers to protect them against risks to their health or safety. It must be used wherever there are risks to health and safety that cannot adequately be controlled in other ways. PPE must come with instructions on how to use it safely, and people who use it must be trained in its use and supervised to make sure they use it correctly. AC 5.7 describes the correct practice in putting on and taking off PPE; and AC 5.8 describes the correct procedure for its disposal.

5.1 Correct use of PPE

Ask an experienced colleague to observe you using PPE, including putting it on, taking it off and disposing of it. Are you both confident that you use it correctly?

AC 5.2 and AC 5.3 Describe different types of PPE and Explain the reasons for use of PPE

There are different types of PPE, each helping prevent the spread of pathogens from one person, object, place or part of the body to another.

Body protection

Some procedures involve contact with blood, body fluids and waste. If there is a risk of extensive splashing to your skin and clothing, you should wear a full-body fluid-repellent gown. If the risk of splashing is restricted to your trunk area, or you are carrying out procedures that involve contact with skin lesions and mucous membranes, a disposable, single-use apron is more suitable.

You should also wear a disposable apron when you are handling food, cleaning, making beds, disposing of waste and decontaminating equipment. Do not wear an apron all the time 'just in case', but do wear one where there is a possibility of risk, not just to protect you against any potential infection but also to protect others against any pathogens you may be harbouring in your clothes. You may also be required to wear protective hats and shoes. Any uniform you wear should be carefully removed before you leave the setting.

Face protection

Some cleaning materials can cause breathing problems, such as asthma. Dirt and dust,

which may contain bacterial spores, can also be inhaled during cleaning. And, as you know, some infections are caught by inhaling the small droplets coughed or sneezed into the air by an infected person. To protect your airways and lungs against inhalation hazards, use PPE that covers your nose and mouth, such as a face mask or disposable filtering face piece. See Figure 11.5.

Gloves

Single-use, disposable gloves are absolutely vital for protecting you and the people with whom you work against infection. You should use them for all procedures that involve contact with:

- people suspected or known to have an infection
- anything that may have been touched or used by someone who has an infection
- body fluids and waste, including soiled linen and clothing
- skin lesions and mucous membranes
- sterile instruments
- hazardous chemicals.

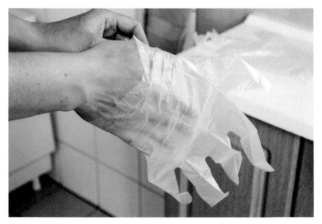

Figure 11.5 PPE: what standard precautions do you take in preventing and controlling infections?

Eye protection

Chemicals, body fluids and waste are splash hazards. Wear PPE such as visors and safety goggles to protect your eyes.

Evidence activity

5.2, 5.3 Different types of PPE and the reasons for their use

Complete Table 11.3 to show that you know when to use PPE, what PPE to use and why you should use it.

Items of PPE	When I wear it	Why I must wear it

Table 11.3 Items of PPE

AC 5.4 and 5.6 State current relevant regulations and legislation relating to PPE and Describe employer's responsibilities regarding the use of PPE

Relevant legislation and regulations	Responsibilities of your employer
Personal Protective Equipment at Work Regulations (PPE) 2002	To provide you with PPE that: • is appropriate and suitable • is properly maintained and stored • has instructions on safe usage • you can use correctly.
Health and Safety at Work etc. Act (HASAWA) 1974	To write health and safety policies and procedures regarding the use of PPE and make you aware of them.
Management of Health and Safety at Work Regulations 1999	To carry out risk assessments to eliminate or reduce risks to health and safety, including using PPE, and provide you with clear information, supervision and training in how to use PPE.
Provision and Use of Work Equipment Regulations (PUWER) 1998	To make sure suitable replacement PPE is always readily available and that it is well looked after and properly stored when not being used, for example in a dry, clean cupboard, or in its box or case.
Control of Substances Hazardous to Health Regulations (COSHH) 2002	To carry out risk assessments on activities that involve exposure to hazardous substances and to write procedures for their correct and safe use, including using PPE.
Health and Social Care Act (2014)	To make sure PPE is clean and fit for purpose, to minimise the risk of HCAIs. →

Table 11.4 Regulations and legislation relevant to PPE

Department of Health (2004) 'Standards for better health' (England only)	To maintain the safety of patients, staff and visitors by having systems that ensure a reduced risk of infection for patients, including using PPE.
Food Safety Act 1990 Food Hygiene Regulations 2006	To make sure that food safety hazards are controlled, including using PPE.
Hazardous Waste Regulations 2005	To make sure that hazardous waste, including used PPE, is dealt with so as to avoid putting health at risk.
The Waste (England and Wales) Regulations 2011	To make sure that waste, including used PPE, is properly stored and adequately packaged while awaiting removal from the premises as well as collected and recorded.

Table 11.4 (Continued)

Evidence activity

5.4, 5.6 Regulations and legislation relevant to PPE and your employer's responsibilities

Make a list of the Regulations and Acts of Parliament that are relevant to your work with regard to infection prevention and control, and describe how this legislation affects your employer's responsibilities regarding the use of PPE.

Research and investigate

5.5 Responsibilities

Find out what could happen if you failed to:

- comply with requests to wear PPE
- attend training in the use of PPE
- raise concerns that PPE wasn't being used appropriately.

Evidence activity

5.5 Your responsibilities regarding the use of PPE

Describe your responsibilities with regard to the use of PPE.

AC 5.5 Describe employees' responsibilities regarding the use of PPE

The Health and Safety at Work etc. Act 1974 (see Table 11.4) states that it is your duty while at work to take reasonable care of yourself and anyone else who may be affected by your actions. In relation to prevention and control of infection, this means knowing:

- what PPE to use, when and how to use it, and why
- the correct procedures for putting it on and taking it off
- appropriate decontamination and disposal methods.

You also have a responsibility to co-operate with your employer in relation to health and safety issues. This means:

- following procedures and complying with requests to use PPE – in some jobs, failure to use PPE properly can be grounds for disciplinary action, even dismissal; you can refuse to wear PPE if it puts your safety at risk, however, for example if it is the wrong size or you might be at risk because of poor fit
- making sure you get proper training regarding the use of PPE
- raising concerns when you feel that PPE isn't being used appropriately
- suggesting changes in its use that you think would be beneficial.

(Source: www.direct.gov.uk; 'A short guide to the Personal Protective Equipment at Work Regulations 1992', HSE, 2005)

AC 5.7 Describe the correct practice in the application and removal of PPE

It is important that you know the correct procedure for putting on and removing a range of PPE (see Figure 11.6).

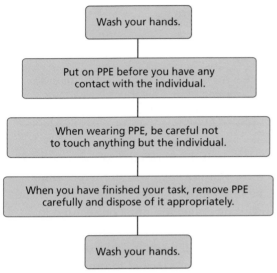

Wash your hands.

Put on PPE before you have any contact with the individual.

When wearing PPE, be careful not to touch anything but the individual.

When you have finished your task, remove PPE carefully and dispose of it appropriately.

Wash your hands.

Figure 11.6 Five key points about the use of PPE

Application of PPE

Gown or apron
● If you need to wear a gown or apron, put that on first. Choose the appropriate gown for the task and the right size for you. The opening should be at the back and it should be secured at the neck and waist.

Face and eye protection
● Face protection goes on next. Some masks are fastened with ties, others with elastic. If yours has ties, place it over your mouth, nose and chin and tie the upper set at the back of your head and the lower set at the base of your head/ top of your neck. If it has elastic head bands, separate the two bands, hold the mask over your nose, mouth and chin, then stretch the lower band round the base of your head/top of your neck and the upper band round the upper back of your head. Adjust to fit.
● Eye protection is third to go on. Position goggles or a visor over your eyes and secure them to your head using the ear pieces or head band. Adjust to fit.

Gloves
● Gloves are last to go on. Choose the type needed for the task in the size that fits you best. Insert your hands and adjust for comfort and so that you do not feel restricted. If you are wearing a gown, tuck the cuffs under each glove to provide a continuous barrier protection for your skin.

When wearing PPE, safe work practice dictates that you:

● do not touch or adjust your PPE while working
● do not touch anything with contaminated gloves
● take off your gloves if they get torn, and wash your hands before putting on a new pair
● remove shoes before you leave the setting
● take off your hat when you have finished the identified task.

Removing PPE
At the end of an activity, the outside of anything on your front and arms is considered to be contaminated. Clean areas are the inside of the gloves and gown, the back of the gown and apron, and the ties and elastic of face and eye protection.

● As gloves are the most contaminated items of PPE, they are taken off first. Using a gloved hand, grasp the outside of the opposite glove near the wrist and peel the glove away from the hand so that it is inside out. Holding the removed glove in the other, gloved hand, slide one or two fingers of the ungloved hand under the wrist of the remaining glove and peel it off from the inside, creating a bag for both gloves. Dispose of as appropriate.
● Eye protection comes off next. Grasp the 'clean' ear or head pieces and lift away from your face. Dispose of as appropriate.
● Body protection is third to come off. Untie your apron, roll up so only the 'clean' part is visible and dispose of appropriately. Remove a gown by:
  ● slipping your hands inside at the neck and shoulder, and peeling away from the shoulders
  ● slipping the fingers of one hand under the cuff of the opposite arm and, using your

hand in the sleeve, grasping the gown from inside
- pushing the sleeve off the opposite arm.
- Fold or roll into a bundle with only the 'clean' part visible and drop into the appropriate container.
- Finally, but most importantly, wash your hands. Good hand washing technique is covered in AC 6.2.

(Source: www.cdc.gov)

AC 5.8 Describe the correct procedure for disposal of used PPE

Clinical waste includes all items contaminated by body fluids and waste, which are or could be infectious.

Single-use PPE, for example white or clear plastic aprons and disposable gloves, masks and eye protection, should be used for just one procedure or **episode of care**. If the item becomes contaminated by body fluids or waste, it must be disposed of as clinical waste in a yellow bag or container for collection and incineration by trained personnel. If it is not contaminated it should be double bagged and disposed of as domestic waste.

Reusable PPE should be decontaminated according to the manufacturer's instructions.

Blue disposable plastic aprons should be used for food handling only and disposed of in domestic waste bins. Domestic household gloves should be washed with detergent and hot water and left to dry after each use to remove visible soil. If they are worn frequently, are torn or becoming stained, they should be disposed of in domestic waste bins and replaced.

Waste bins should be lidded, foot-operated and kept clean, and the bags within them should never be filled more than two-thirds full. Waste bags awaiting collection must be secured to prevent leakage and labelled to show the place of origin. They should be stored in a designated area that is kept clean and locked to prevent access by the public, animals and vermin.

LO6 Understand the importance of good personal hygiene in the prevention and control of infections

AC 6.1 Describe the key principles of good personal hygiene

Infection prevention and control is based on the use of practices and procedures that reduce the likelihood of infection being spread from one person, object, place or part of the body to another. High standards of personal hygiene are key for infection prevention and control, not least because much of health and social care requires being in very close proximity with individuals.

Ten top tips for maintaining good personal hygiene

1 Keep your hands clean. This is top of the list in controlling the spread of infections, such as those that cause diarrhoea, vomiting and respiratory disease. You will read about good hand washing technique in AC 6.2.

Evidence activity

6.1 The key principles of good personal hygiene

How do you maintain good personal hygiene? In what ways could you improve your personal hygiene? Why is it so important for a health or social care worker to maintain good personal hygiene?

2 Shower or bathe daily. Perspiration and dirt provide the perfect environment for many bacteria, fungi and viruses to live and reproduce, and stale sweat is not pleasant to smell. Use a good quality, unperfumed antiperspirant.

3 Keep your hair clean and tidy, and cover it or tie it back if it is longer than collar length, especially when handling or serving food and drink. By paying regular attention to your hair, you will look and smell fresh and also be aware of any infestations.

4 Keep your nails short and clean. Bitten nails look unpleasant, and dirt under nails harbours a range of **micro-organisms**. False nails are also a health and safety hazard and should not be worn at work.

5 Keep your feet clean and covered up. Dirty, sweaty feet look unpleasant and are a **reservoir** for micro-organisms.

6 Keep your clothes clean. Parasites such as fleas and pubic lice can live in clothing, and dirty clothing smells, particularly if you smoke. Do not wear sleeves longer than your elbows at work, to enable you to wash your hands and forearms effectively.

7 Keep your teeth clean. Nothing looks worse than dirty, stained teeth, and an unclean mouth provides ideal living conditions for the bacteria that cause bad breath.

8 Do not wear jewellery or body piercings, apart from a plain ring, metal ear studs and a fob watch. Jewellery can carry micro-organisms and piercings can be infected, especially when new.

9 Cover wounds with a coloured plaster and check what you can and cannot do while wearing a plaster, especially if you work with food.

10 Either shave regularly or keep facial hair clean and tidy. Your organisation may have requirements with regard to beards and moustaches.

You should also ensure you encourage others to maintain good hygiene.

AC 6.2 Demonstrate good hand washing technique

AC 6.3 Describe the correct sequence for hand washing

Hand hygiene involves washing with soap and water to ensure that all areas are decontaminated (see Figure 11.7). It is a standard precaution against the spread of infection and should be carried out prior to any activity with an individual, whether your hands are visibly dirty or not.

1 Wet hands and forearms, and apply soap.
2 Rub palm to palm.
3 Rub with fingers interlaced.
4 Massage between fingers, right palm over back of left hand, left palm over back of right hand.
5 Scrub with fingers locked, including fingertips.
6 Rub in a circular movement, with thumbs locked.
7 Rinse thoroughly.
8 Dry palms and backs of hands using a paper towel.
9 Work towel between fingers.
10 Dry around and under nails.

(Source: 'Good practice in infection prevention and control', Royal College of Nursing, 2005)

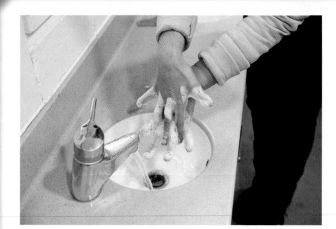

Figure 11.7 Effective hand washing

Evidence activity

6.3 The correct sequence for hand washing

Role play washing your hands to a colleague, to show that you know the correct sequence for washing your hands effectively.

When alcohol gel is used, it should be applied using this same technique. See unit HSC 037 for a diagram on the correct hand washing technique.

AC 6.4 Explain when and why hand washing should be carried out

Hands are top of the list when it comes to the spread of infection, and hand hygiene contributes significantly to reducing the risks of cross infection. In fact, it is known to be the single most important thing we can do to reduce the spread of disease.

Hand washing should be carried out **before**:

- having direct contact with a patient, such as when giving personal care or carrying out first aid or healthcare procedures such as catheter care, PEG feeding or collecting specimens
- administering medication
- using PPE
- handling food.

Hand washing should be carried out **after**:

- having direct contact with a patient, as above
- removing PPE, including gloves
- using the toilet, coughing, sneezing, touching personal clothing or hair, etc.
- domestic activities, such as handling raw and waste food, cleaning and making beds.

Time to think

6.4 Now wash your hands

When do you wash your hands at work? Do you think you wash them often enough?

If not, what prevents you from washing them? Shortage of time? The condition of your skin? The soap isn't very nice? There are never enough towels?

Evidence activity

6.4 When and why hand washing should be carried out

Think of five or six activities that you carry out in your day-to-day work. For which of these activities would you need to wash your hands? When would you wash them: before the activity, after the activity, or before *and* after? Why?

AC 6.5 Describe the types of products that should be used for hand washing

You have a duty of care to the people with whom you work, their family and friends, your colleagues and yourself to help prevent cross infection. For this reason, you should raise the alarm if hand washing facilities and products (see Figure 11.8) aren't available for everyone to use.

Evidence activity

6.5 Types of products that should be used for hand washing

This activity gives you the opportunity to demonstrate your knowledge of the types of products that should be used for hand washing.

Survey your workplace for hand washing products and facilities. Does it score well? Or are there any shortfalls in provision? To whom should you report shortfalls? Why is it important that hand washing products and facilities are in good supply?

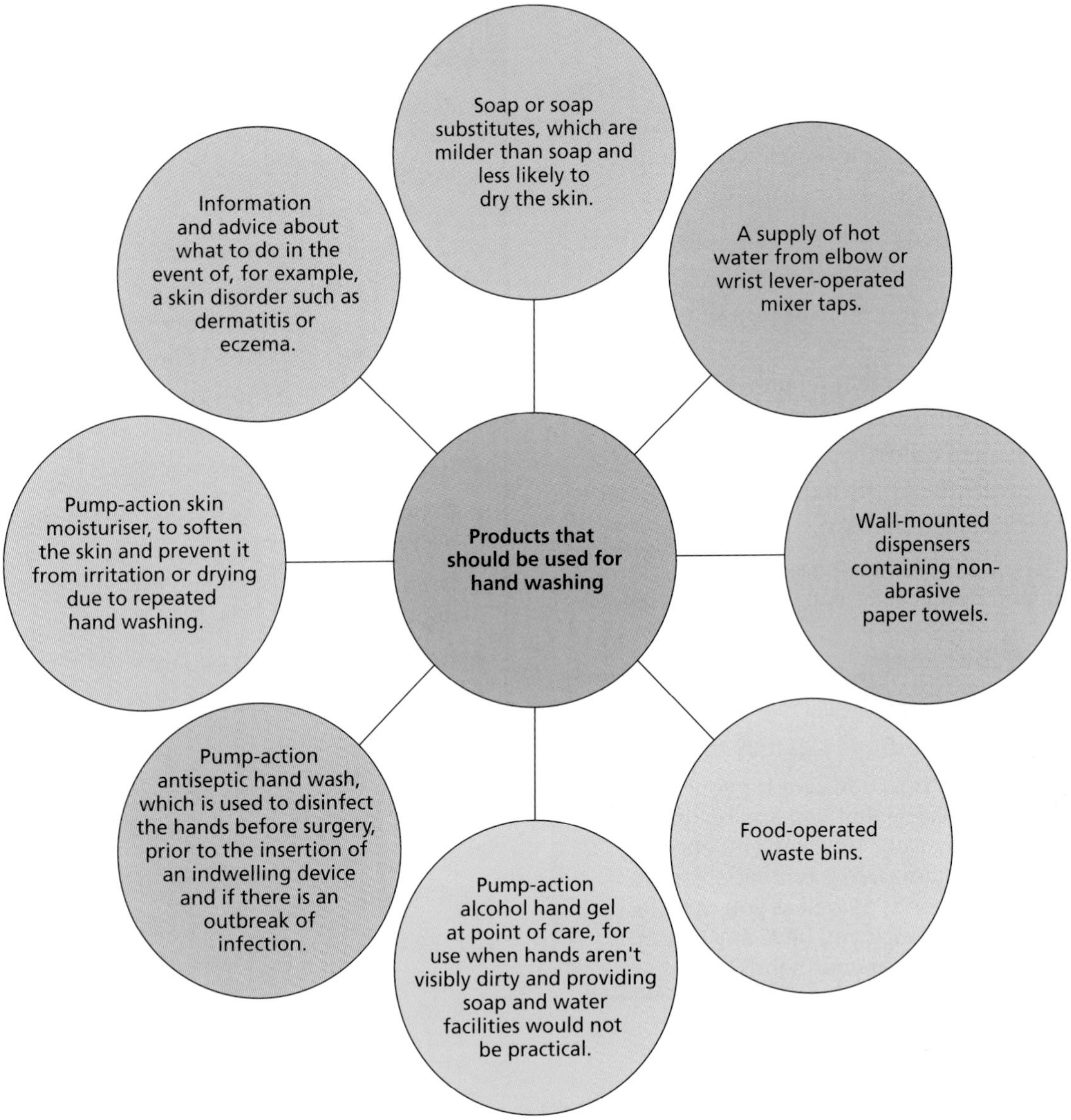
Soap or soap substitutes, which are milder than soap and less likely to dry the skin.
A supply of hot water from elbow or wrist lever-operated mixer taps.
Wall-mounted dispensers containing non-abrasive paper towels.
Food-operated waste bins.
Pump-action alcohol hand gel at point of care, for use when hands aren't visibly dirty and providing soap and water facilities would not be practical.
Pump-action antiseptic hand wash, which is used to disinfect the hands before surgery, prior to the insertion of an indwelling device and if there is an outbreak of infection.
Pump-action skin moisturiser, to soften the skin and prevent it from irritation or drying due to repeated hand washing.
Information and advice about what to do in the event of, for example, a skin disorder such as dermatitis or eczema.
Products that should be used for hand washing

Figure 11.8 Products that should be used for hand washing

AC 6.6 Describe correct procedures that relate to skincare

Healthy, intact skin provides an effective barrier against cross infection. Cover any breaks in your skin with an impermeable waterproof dressing and check the dressing regularly, replacing it when necessary. Keep your hands in good condition by using a good-quality **barrier hand cream**.

Key term

A **barrier hand cream** helps reduce the effects of skin contact with harmful substances.

Occupational skin diseases are caused by irritants and allergies. Soap, water and alcohol gel used for hand hygiene can cause irritation, such as irritant contact dermatitis; latex rubber gloves can cause allergies, such as allergic contact dermatitis. Signs of occupational skin disease include dryness, redness, itching, inflammation and vesicles. The skin may eventually become cracked, scaly and thickened. In addition, existing skin disorders such as eczema can be made worse by frequent hand washing. If, as a result of wearing gloves and washing your hands, you develop signs of an occupational skin disease or an existing condition gets worse, seek medical advice from an appropriate person, for example your GP or occupational health officer.

Gloves protect against the risk of infection, but wearing them can cause skin problems, for example when the gloves are inappropriate to the task, are too large or too small, or are damaged. Sensible precautionary measures will help to reduce skin problems:

- Never wear gloves for more than one hour at a time, particularly single-use gloves.
- Never use lubricants such as powder to help put on gloves.
- Never use barrier cream when wearing gloves.
- After taking off gloves, wash and dry your hands, using a mild soap and a non-abrasive paper towel, and apply a quality moisturiser to return lost oils to the skin.

(Source: 'Hand protection and skin care management', Medical Research Council, 2006)

Evidence activity

6.6 Correct procedures relating to skincare

Keep a record of how you care for your hands at work. Are you happy that you are looking after them sufficiently well? How can you improve your skincare regime? Why is it important to look after your hands as well as you can? To whom can you speak if you have any concerns about the condition of your hands?

Legislation

- Personal Protective Equipment at Work Regulations (PPE) 2002
- Health and Safety at Work, etc. Act (HASWA) 1974
- Management of Health and Safety at Work Regulations 1999
- Provision and Use of Work Equipment Regulations (PUWER) 1998
- Control of Substances Hazardous to Health Regulations (COSHH) 2002
- Health and Social Care Act (2012)
- Department of Health (2004) Standards for Better Health (England only)
- Food Safety Act 1990 and the Food Hygiene Regulations 2006
- Hazardous Waste Regulations 2005
- The Waste (England and Wales) Regulations 2011
- The Health Act 2006

Useful resources

Websites

Royal College of Nursing
www.rcn.org.uk

Healthcare Republic
www.healthcarerepublic.com (a website for healthcare professionals)

Health Protection Agency
www.hpa.org.uk

Chartered Institute of Environmental Health
www.cieh.org

Care Quality Commission
www.cqc.org.uk

Care Council for Wales
www.ccwales.org.uk

Scottish Care Council
www.sssc.uk.com

Northern Ireland Social Care Council
www.niscc.info

General Medical Council
www.gmc-uk.org

Nursing and Midwifery Council
www.nmc-uk.org

Health and Care Professions Council
www.hpc-uk.org

Office for Standards in Education, Children's Services and Skills
www.ofsted.gov.uk

Skills for Health
www.skillsforhealth.org.uk

Skills for Care
www.skillsforcare.org.uk

Health information for patients
www.patient.co.uk

NHS
www.nhs.uk

Children's health information
http://kidshealth.org

BUPA
www.bupa.co.uk

Centre for Disease Prevention and Control
www.cdc.gov

Unit LD 201

Understand the context of supporting individuals with learning disabilities

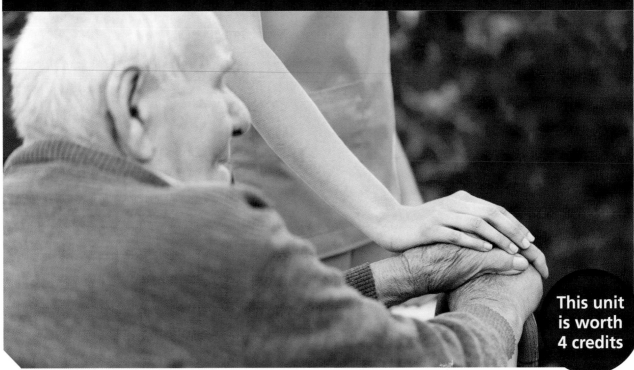

This unit is worth 4 credits

What are you finding out?

According to **Mencap**, there are around 1.5 million people who have a learning disability within the United Kingdom. Due to advances in health and social care and the fact that people are living longer, this figure is set to increase. One of the biggest problems for people who have learning disabilities is that other people generally don't understand what it means for someone to have a learning disability. It is not an illness or a disease, and it is not always possible to tell if a person has a learning disability. Having a learning disability does not mean a person has mental health problems; some people who have a learning disability may develop mental health problems as a result of inadequate care and discrimination, however.

A learning disability does not define a person. It is merely a label used to diagnose people. People with learning disabilities are all individuals with

the right to the same life chances as other people. These people are individuals just like you and me.

By the end of this unit you will:

1 Understand the legislation and policies that support the human rights and inclusion of individuals with learning disabilities.
2 Understand the nature and characteristics of learning disability.
3 Understand the historical context of learning disability.
4 Understand the basic principles and practice of advocacy, empowerment and active participation in relation to supporting individuals with learning disabilities and their families.
5 Understand how views and attitudes impact on the lives of individuals with learning disabilities and their family carers.
6 Know how to promote communication with individuals with learning disabilities.

LO1 Understand the legislation and policies that support the human rights and inclusion of individuals with learning disabilities

AC 1.1 Identify legislation and policies designed to promote the human rights, inclusion, equal life chances and citizenship of individuals with learning disabilities

Most of the laws concerning people who have a learning disability also apply to other people. The main laws that are likely to make a difference to the lives of people who have learning disabilities are concerned with promoting:

- human rights
- anti-discriminatory behaviour
- **equality**
- **inclusion**
- **citizenship**.

Legislation that is aimed at promoting the human rights, inclusion, equal life chances and citizenship of individuals with learning disabilities includes:

The Human Rights Act 1998

There are 18 articles or protocols which explain fundamental human rights, contained in the European Convention on Human Rights. The Act makes it unlawful for public bodies to breach the rights that are set out there.

The Disability Discrimination Act 1995

This Act is designed to prevent discrimination on the grounds of disability, in things like being

Key terms

Mencap is the leading UK charity for people who have a learning disability and their families.

Equality relates to being equal, especially to having the same political, social and economic rights.

Inclusion is a state of being free from exclusion.

Citizenship relates to being a citizen of a particular community with the duties, rights and privileges of this status.

offered a job, education, transport, etc. It means that it is against the law to discriminate against people with disabilities.

The Mental Capacity Act 2005

The Mental Capacity Act is designed to protect people who may lack capacity to make some decisions for themselves, and is also meant to help empower them wherever possible. Anyone who works with or cares for an adult who lacks capacity must comply with this Act when making decisions or acting on behalf of that person. The Act states that every adult has the right to make their own decisions and must be assumed to be able to do so unless it can be proved that they do not. Decisions made on behalf of someone should be done with their best interests at heart, and they should be the least restrictive options, in terms of personal freedom, available.

Mental Health Act 2007

This Act defines mental disorder in such a way that it could apply to learning disabilities as well as mental illness. However, the Mental Capacity Act is normally more appropriate legislation to refer to for people with learning disabilities.

The Equality Act 2010

This Act brings together various separate legislation that already existed, including the Disability Discrimination Act, into one Act that promotes equality for all.

The Health and Social Care Act (2012)

This Act is a huge reorganization of the NHS and is very wide-reaching. It is still being implemented but some of its consequences may affect people with learning disabilities.

Valuing People Now was a UK government's three-year strategy for making the lives of people with learning disabilities and their families better by improving services. In particular, the strategy aimed to make significant improvements in giving adults who have learning disabilities more choice and control over their lives through **person-centred planning**, advocacy and **direct payments** (see page 212 for definition). The government-led

Key terms

Capacity, in this context, means the ability to understand information that has been given to individuals to make a decision.

The **direct payments scheme** is a UK government initiative in the field of Social Services that gives users money directly to pay for their own care, rather than through the traditional route of a Local Government Authority providing care for them.

Person-centred planning is a process of life planning for individuals, based around the principles of inclusion and the social model of disability.

approach of *Valuing People Now* has changed since 2012, as there has not been a replacement or updated strategy put in place. The implication is that continuing to implement the vision set out in *Valuing People Now* lies at a local level, with Learning Disability Partnerships, Local Authorities and Health Authorities. While Valuing People Now is no longer available on an active government website, you can access it at the national archives **http://tinyurl.com/q45gmje**

Organisations that provide support for people who have learning disabilities should have policies in place which aim to reinforce this legislation. These policies set out the guidelines that all health and social care workers have to adhere to in order to ensure people who have learning disabilities are given the same opportunities as any other member of society.

AC 1.2 Explain how legislation and policies influence the day-to-day experiences of individuals with learning disabilities and their families

Policies are drawn up in line with current legislation. Policies can be drawn up nationally at governmental level and also locally by organisations. Policymakers can influence important decisions that affect people's everyday lives.

Policies should be based on the social model of disability, aimed at empowering people. People who have learning disabilities are the experts in their own lives and their views are an essential part of any evidence base. Involving these people throughout the process of policy development will help identify gaps in knowledge and give an indication of whether the policy will work in the short and long term. Understanding the perspective, needs and priorities of people who have learning disabilities will develop better policy and deliver effective services.

The different legislation and policies outlined in AC 1.1 seek to improve the lives of people with disabilities, You should refer to AC 1.1 to find out about the goals and purpose of each of the legislation and policies and how they may impact individuals and their families.

Evidence activity

1.2 How legislation and policies influence individuals and their families

- Think about the legislation and policies that are relevant to the people you support. How do legislation and associated policies influence the day-to-day experiences of these people and their families?
- Take a look at the policies within your place of work and make a note of any that promote human rights, inclusion, equal life chances and citizenship for the service users for whom you provide support.
- How do the policies support these aspects of a person's life?

LO2 Understand the nature and characteristics of learning disability

AC 2.1 Explain what is meant by 'learning disability'

Defining the term 'learning disability' is not easy, because it does not have clear-cut edges. No two people have the same level of 'ability' in the way they learn, and every person's experience of their learning disability will be individual to them.

In medical terms, learning disabilities are known as **neurological disorders**. In simple terms, a learning disability may result when a person's brain development is affected, either before they are born, during their birth or in early childhood.

Learning disabilities are lifelong conditions that cannot be cured, and they can have a significant impact on the person's life. People with learning disabilities find it harder than other people to learn, understand and communicate. Some people with a mild learning disability may be able to communicate effectively and look after themselves, but may take a bit longer to learn new skills. Others may not be able to communicate at all and may have more than one disability. You may have heard learning disabilities described as mild, moderate, severe or profound (see Figure 12.1). If you hear these terms being used, it is important to remember that these are not separate conditions, they are simply stages along the scale of ability/disability.

Key term

Neurological disorders are disorders of the brain.

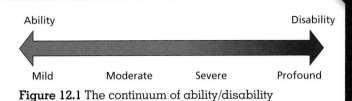

Figure 12.1 The continuum of ability/disability

- **Mild-moderate** – can talk easily and look after themselves, but take a bit longer than usual to learn new skills
- **Severe** – people often use basic words and gestures to communicate their needs. They need a high level of support
- **Profound** – severely limited understanding, often having multiple disabilities

Evidence activity

2.1 Explain what is meant by 'learning disability'
How would you explain the meaning of the term 'learning disability' to a new member of staff within your organisation?

AC 2.2 Give examples of causes of learning disabilities

Learning disabilities are caused by the way the brain develops, either before, during or after birth. There are several factors that can affect the development of the brain.

Before birth (pre-natal)

- Causes affecting the mother, for example rubella (German measles), listeria (food poisoning), or excessive intake of alcohol, tobacco or recreational drugs.
- A child can also be born with a learning disability if certain genes are passed on by a parent. This is called an **inherited** learning disability. The two most common causes of inherited learning disability are **Fragile X syndrome** and **Down's syndrome**. Neither syndrome is itself a learning disability, but people who have either condition are likely also to have a learning disability. Fragile X syndrome is the most common cause of inherited learning disability, but not all people with Fragile X

Evidence activity

2.2 Causes of learning disabilities

Think about the service users you are supporting at the moment and, while respecting confidentiality, use any information that is available to you to identify the cause of their learning disabilities. Where on the continuum of learning disabilities do your individuals sit?

syndrome have a learning disability. All people who have Down's syndrome have some kind of learning disability.

During birth (peri-natal)

The most common cause of learning disability is problems during the birth that stop enough oxygen getting to the baby's brain.

After birth (post-natal) or during childhood

Caused by illness, such as **meningitis**, or injury in early childhood. Sometimes there is no known cause for a learning disability. There is a lot of information available about particular syndromes and conditions. Check out the Useful Resources at the end of this chapter.

AC 2.3 Describe the medical and social models of disability

Models of disability provide a framework for understanding the way in which people with impairments experience their disability. It is commonly accepted that there are two contrasting models of disability within our society. These are known as the 'medical model' (see Figure 12.2) and the 'social model' (see Figure 12.3).

The Medical model of disability

- The **medical model** views the person who has a disability as the problem. This model holds the belief that the person who has a disability should adapt to fit in with society. If the person cannot fit in with society then that is their problem. The emphasis is on dependence, which is backed up by the stereotypes of disability that lend themselves to pity, fear and patronising attitudes. The main focus is on the disability rather than on the person.
- The medical model highlights that people who are disabled cannot participate in society because their disability prevents them from doing so.

The social model of disability

- The **social model** of disability was developed with the input of people who have a disability. Instead of emphasising the disability, the social model centralises the person. It emphasises dignity, independence, choice and privacy.

This model makes an important distinction between impairment and disability:

Time to think

2.3 How do you feel about disability?

It is important at this stage to examine how you feel about people who have a disability. Think about the assumptions that are commonly made about people who have a disability in general.

In a few words, what would you say are common assumptions often made about this section of the population? For example, would you say 'they need help'? Or would you say you 'feel sorry for them'? Or would you say 'people are disabled because of their environment'?

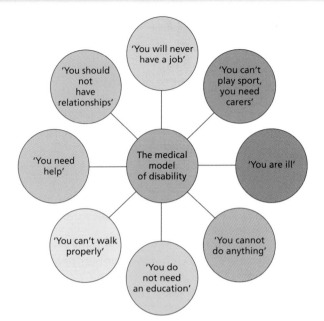

Figure 12.2 The medical model of disability

Figure 12.3 The social model of disability

- Impairment is seen as something not working properly with part of the body, mind or senses, for example a person may have a physical impairment, a sensory impairment or a learning impairment.
- Disability occurs when a person is excluded by society because of their impairment, from something that other people in society take for granted. That might be the chance to attend an event, access a service or get involved in an activity. The exclusion may affect a person's choices to live independently, to earn a living, to be kept informed, or just to make choices for themselves.

The social model of disability says that disabilities are created by barriers in society. These barriers generally fall into three categories:

- The environment – including inaccessible buildings and services.
- Attitudes – including prejudice and stereotyping.
- Organisations – including inflexible policies, practices and procedures.
- Some people wrongly assume that the impairment causes the disability. The social model, however, believes that it is the choices society makes that create the disability. If things

were organised differently, people would suddenly be enabled – even though their impairment hadn't changed.

Evidence activity

2.3 The medical and social models of disability

- Look at the assumptions you made within the Time to Think box on page 214. Would you say your beliefs support the medical model or the social model of disability?
- Take a look at the environment in which you work. Are there any aspects of the environment that could disable a person? If so, what changes could be made to make the environment more enabling?

AC 2.4 State the approximate proportion of individuals with a learning disability for whom the cause is 'not known'

Reasons for finding out the cause

There are a number of reasons for finding out the cause of a person's learning disability. First, individuals and their families want to know and have a right to know. There are also health factors to consider, as some forms of learning disability or syndrome can increase the likelihood of certain health problems occurring. Genetic counselling may also be required both for the family and for

Evidence activity

2.4 The cause of learning disability

Think about the individuals you support. Do any of them have a learning disability for which the cause has never been identified?

Evidence activity

2.5 The impact on a family of having a member with a learning disability

Choose two service users for whom you provide support and, while maintaining confidentiality, develop a case study. For the two service users, identify the impact that their learning disability has on other members of their family, taking into account:

- financial impact – perhaps some members of the family cannot work because they provide a lot of care at home?
- relationship impact – how do you think the relationship between family members might be affected?
- domestic impact – how is home life affected?
- social impact – how are interactions with friends affected?
- self-identity impact
- healthcare implications.

the person with the learning disability, especially where there is a wish to start a family.

We identified some of the causes of learning disability in AC 2.2; the British Institute of Learning Disabilities (BILD), however, identifies that for 50 per cent of people who have a mild learning disability, no cause has been identified. For people who have severe or profound learning disabilities, no cause has been found for around 25 per cent of them.

AC 2.5 Describe the possible impact on a family of having a member with a learning disability

Over 60 per cent of people with learning disabilities live with family carers, who often make a lot of sacrifices to support the person.

Family members who provide care for those with a learning disability can suffer immense emotional and physical strain, and getting respite from their role can be made difficult by the adverse effects this can have on the person for whom they are caring.

While every family has stresses and strains, these are very often exacerbated in families where a member has a learning disability. Depending on the family members and the amount of support they receive, and on the person who has the learning disability, this can impact on every aspect of the family's needs, including financial, domestic, healthcare, relationship and self-identity. This can

also impact on other aspects of family life, leading to significant extra costs and complications.

A child who does not have a learning disability will usually mature and become more independent, eventually leaving the family home. A child with a learning disability, however, may not follow this pattern, and is more likely to remain within the family home into adulthood. This person may also require prolonged periods of intensive care. This could impact upon everyday occurrences such as family outings, which could become complicated or even impossible.

LO3 Understand the historical context of learning disability

AC 3.1 Explain types of services that have been provided for individuals with learning disabilities over time

Little is written about the lives of people with learning disabilities before the eighteenth century. There are, however, references to 'village idiots', but it is thought that these people represent only a small minority of those we would describe today as having a learning disability. Literacy skills were less in demand than labouring skills, so mild learning disabilities would easily go unnoticed.

The Poor Laws 1834

The Poor Laws of 1834 led to the construction of purpose-built institutions ('asylums') to house people described as 'mad' or 'mentally weak'. They had harsh and rigid regimes, and contained many people who had learning disabilities. These people had little choice and were not valued as people. The asylums became overcrowded, and conditions worsened as attitudes changed and the people who were housed there began to be regarded as dangerous and a drain on society.

The Radner Commission

The development of institutions continued into the early twentieth century (see Figure 12.4), though the purpose of moving people to them changed. Laws were passed that encouraged the building of schools for 'mentally disabled' children, and in 1908 the Radner Commission stated that 'Feeble-mindedness is largely inherited'. It was suggested that such people were genetically inferior and so needed to be segregated from the rest of society.

The Mental Deficiency Act 1913

The 1913 Mental Deficiency Act stated that any person admitted to an institution had to be certified as a 'mentally defective'. The institutions were now renamed 'colonies', and their purpose was to separate their residents from the rest of society. In 1929, the Wood Committee suggested that such people were a threat to society.

Figure 12.4 What does institutionalisation mean to you?

During the periods between the two World Wars, the numbers of people admitted to institutions increased. Laws were passed to further segregate all people who had learning disabilities – and their families – from the rest of society. Proposals were introduced to round up and separate all families of 'feeble minded people', including the 'insane, epileptics and drunks', to name but a few.

Eugenics

It was suggested that such people would 'take over' and 'infect' others, and that a 'racial disaster' would ensue. The Eugenics Society was a group that believed that society was in decline and that there was a need to separate those with learning disabilities, keeping men and women apart so they would not procreate. History shows that the theories of eugenics have been used to justify many atrocities committed against people with a learning disability and the mentally ill, as well as many other groups, not least the millions of victims of the Holocaust.

Fortunately the UK drew back from such unthinkable measures. However, this kind of mind-set continued to affect the huge numbers of people admitted to institutions right up until the late 1980s.

The IQ test

In the 1930s, the IQ test was introduced – people scoring low on the test were categorised as 'mentally defective' and as unable to learn.

The introduction of the NHS 1946

The introduction of the National Health Service (NHS) in 1946 and the development of the medical model of disability had an impact. The term 'mentally handicapped' came into use, and the 'institutions' turned into hospitals, with the emphasis now on caring for their residents. Society moved from seeing the 'mentally handicapped' as dangerous and degenerate, to viewing them more sympathetically as people in need of treatment – although still as a drain on the public purse. People with learning disabilities remained segregated and isolated, and the standard of care in the hospitals was extremely poor. This remained the case right up until the closure of the long-stay hospitals.

The Mental Health Act 1959

In 1959, the Mental Health Act began the idea that some people might not need to be cared for in a hospital. It was also the first time that people with a 'mental illness' were distinguished from those described as having a 'mental handicap'.

'Better services for the Mentally Handicapped' 1971

In 1967, national newspapers started to draw attention to the bad conditions in 'mental handicap' hospitals. In 1971, the government published a paper, 'Better services for the mentally handicapped', in response to continued reports about appalling conditions in the hospitals. This paper laid the foundations for 'Care in the community', with the expectation that half of the people in hospitals should be living in the local community by 1990.

Normalisation, 1980s

During the 1980s, the concept of 'normalisation' began to influence the delivery of care for people who had a learning disability. Normalisation emphasises the 'value of the individual', their right to choice and opportunity, and the right to any extra support they need to fulfil their potential. At this time there was also recognition that existence of institutions for people with learning difficulties and mental health issues were a major barrier to inclusion.

The National Health Service and Community Care Act 1990

The idea that everyone in society has the right to a life with choice, opportunity and respect, and with extra support according to their needs, helped to change the way services were planned and delivered. The National Health Service and Community Care Act 1990 recognised the right of disabled people to be an equal part of society, with access to the necessary support.

Today

We might like to believe that the task of de-institutionalising the care of people with a learning disability is now complete. Nearly all the long-stay hospitals are now closed, and many

Evidence activity

3.1 Services
- Find out about the history of the individuals you work with. Were any of them 'cared for' within an institution?
- Make a note of the differences between the care that was provided within institutions and the support provided by your organisation.

rights are now law, as detailed in the Disability Discrimination Act.

The reality is, however, that many people are still denied the things most people take for granted, such as a decent income, somewhere appropriate to live, the chance to work, take part in leisure opportunities and make choices in education.

Attitudes and understanding

Today's services aim to enable people and promote equal treatment and inclusion. This brings with it new challenges and responsibilities, the greatest of which is to change public attitudes towards people with a learning disability and to increase understanding.

(Source: www.mencap.org.uk)

AC 3.2 Describe how past ways of working may affect present services

People who have worked in health and social care for some time may remember some of the institutions, and may have indeed worked in them. Some health and social care workers may therefore have adopted the medical model approach to disability. This will, without a shadow of a doubt, affect the care and support that these workers deliver.

Evidence activity

3.2 Past ways of working and present services

How do you think past ways of working may affect present ways of working?

AC 3.3 Identify some of the key changes in the lives of individuals who have learning disabilities

There have been major changes in the lives of individuals who have a learning disability. We have already discussed the institutionalised medical model approach to care and support. Person-centred planning has generally led to positive changes for people who have learning disabilities. Mencap, however, reports that people who have a learning disability are still treated differently.

Where people live

There have been major changes in the living arrangements of people who have a learning disability. With a move away from an institutionalised approach to care, more people are being empowered to maintain their independence for as long as possible. While over 60 per cent of people who have a learning disability live with their family, there are also a significant number of people who maintain their independence within their community through supported living.

Daytime activities

With the introduction of self-directed support, service users are able to make choices about where they go and what they want to do during the daytime. Self-directed support should enable service users to decide:

- how to live their lives
- where and with whom to live
- what to do during the day
- how to spend their leisure time
- what to spend money on
- with whom they are friends.

Research and investigate

3.3 Employment
Using any information that is available to you, take a look at why people who have a learning disability find it difficult to get paid work.

Employment

Mencap reports that only 1 in 10 people who have a learning disability is in employment. They are more excluded from the workplace than any other group of disabled people. Where they do work, it is often for low pay and part-time hours. Research shows that 65 per cent of people with a learning disability want to work, and that they make highly valued employees when given the right support.

Sexual relationships and parenthood

Discussions surrounding sexuality are uncomfortable for 'able bodied' people. This is a very private area of a person's life and one that we choose not to discuss openly. People who have learning disabilities also have sexual feelings and may want to engage in close personal relationships. Some organisations run courses for people who have learning disabilities where they are taught about social and personal development. Because people with learning disabilities are a vulnerable group there are many aspects that need to be considered to ensure any relationship remains safe and healthy.

All too often, support services start with the belief that people who have a learning disability will not make good parents and that, if they have

Evidence activity

3.1, 3.3 Key changes in the lives of individuals who have learning disabilities
Make a poster that identifies the key changes in the lives of people who have learning disabilities.

The poster should take into account where people live, daytime activities, employment, sexual relationships and parenthood, and the provision of healthcare.

Case study

3.4 Frank

Frank is a young man who has learning disabilities. He confides in his support worker about the difficulties he is having with his girlfriend. Frank and his girlfriend (who also has learning disabilities) want to have sexual intercourse but they are unsure about 'safe sex'. The worker advises him of the different organisations that have up-to-date information in user-friendly formats to provide them with some knowledge of safe sex. The worker also advises Frank that these organisations can provide support and help in talking over the issues.

1 What responsibility does the support worker have at this stage?
2 What responsibility does the person with learning disabilities have?
3 Who else has responsibilities, and what are they?

children, these should be taken away. Mencap also identifies that this is backed up by research that shows that 40 per cent of parents who have a learning disability do not live with their children. Not all parents with a learning disability can look after their own children and the welfare of the child is essential. If parents who have a learning disability are provided with adequate support, however, they should be allowed to keep their children.

Provision of healthcare

People who have a learning disability generally experience poorer health and poorer healthcare than other members of the public. As we are well aware, however, people who have a learning disability have just as much of a right to receive good healthcare as everyone else. They need healthcare in the same way that everyone else does, and some people with a learning disability will have additional health needs (for example, people with a learning disability are more likely to have epilepsy). Often, they need more support to understand information about their health, to communicate symptoms and concerns, and to manage their health.

LO4 Understand the basic principles and practice of advocacy, empowerment and active participation in relation to supporting individuals with learning disabilities and their families

AC 4.1 Explain the meaning of the term 'social inclusion'

The term 'social inclusion' has come to replace older terminology such as 'community development work'. In practical terms, social inclusion means working within the community to tackle and avoid circumstances and problems that lead to social exclusion, which include poverty, unemployment or low income, housing problems, and becoming housebound and isolated due to illness.

Historically, people with learning disabilities faced poor life chances, largely due to social exclusion. They were not accepted by mainstream society and faced stigmatisation, prejudice and even fear; this has led to such people being socially excluded to this day.

Promoting social inclusion is closely linked to empowering the individual. This means giving people with learning disabilities a voice and allowing them to make choices for themselves about the direction of their own life, based on their wishes and aspirations.

Evidence activity

4.1 Social inclusion

Explain the steps you take to ensure social inclusion within your place of work.

AC 4.2 Explain the meaning of the term 'advocacy'

The term 'advocacy' is concerned with speaking up for, or acting on behalf of, yourself or another person. The person you are speaking up for is often receiving a service from a statutory or voluntary organisation. Some people require an advocate to assist them because they are not clear about their rights as citizens, or have difficulty in fully understanding these rights. Other people may find it difficult to speak up for themselves. Advocacy can enable people to take more responsibility for and control over the decisions that affect their lives.

Advocacy can help service users to:

- make their views and wishes known
- express and present their views
- obtain independent advice and accurate information
- negotiate and resolve conflict.

AC 4.3 Describe different types of advocacy

All advocacy types are of equal value. Which type of advocacy is used, and when, should depend on what is best suited to the person who seeks it. People are different from each other, and their needs for support are also different. These needs for support may change at different stages throughout their life; the same person may ask for different types of advocacy support at different times in their life.

What is essential to all types of advocacy is that it is the person who has a learning disability who is always at the centre of the advocacy process. Advocacy can therefore be described as a person-centred process. It is about the person's needs and wants, and finding the best way to get that across to the people who need to know.

Advocacy can be likened to a box of tools. Like tools, different types of advocacy can be used together or they can be used separately, depending on the job that needs to be done.

Professional advocacy

Professional advocacy is frequently described as the 'case-work' model. It is used for short- to medium-term involvement, which often supports people in finding a solution to a problem. Professional advocacy may be required where an individual needs support with issues requiring specific expertise, for example child protection, education, housing, employment and financial matters.

Citizen advocacy

The advocate in this relationship is usually called a 'citizen advocate', and the person receiving the service is called an 'advocacy partner'. An advocacy partner is someone at risk of having their choices, wishes and decisions ignored, and who needs help in making them known and making sure they are responded to. A citizen advocate is a person who volunteers to speak up for and support an advocacy partner; they are not paid to do so. The citizen advocate is independent of service providers and families and is a member of the local community. The advocacy relationship is based on trust and confidentiality.

Crisis advocacy

Crisis advocacy provides support that aims to give the person a voice in a situation that requires a quick response. It is usually short term and aimed at helping the individual to solve a problem.

Peer advocacy

Peer advocacy is usually provided by a person who has experienced a similar situation, as people who have experienced the same things feel they have a better understanding and can be more supportive. In the past, peer advocacy occurred when people with learning disabilities lived in isolated hospitals. They were often separated from others in their community and had only each other for company. There was no one else to speak up for them other than their peers. As people with learning disabilities began to learn more about their rights and the obligations of citizenship, more of them began to speak up for each other. Peer advocacy is often of great support to an individual, but is not recognised as being either independent or unbiased.

Self-advocacy

Self-advocacy is what most of us do most of the time. It is about speaking up for yourself. This type of advocacy should always be encouraged wherever possible. Many people who have learning disabilities are able to speak up for themselves. They sometimes find it hard to get others to accept this, however, or even to listen to them. Self-advocacy groups are a good way to encourage this. These groups are run by people who have learning disabilities. These are often local groups of people who use services or have the same interests. They work together to make sure they have a say in how those services are run. Self-advocacy groups are a very good way for people to support each other; they can also help to build confidence so that people feel more able to speak up for themselves.

Legal advocacy

As the name suggests, legal advocacy is concerned with using the services of a lawyer or ombudsman which is an official appointed to investigate complaints against a company or organisation to support an individual with specific legal issues.

Time to think

4.3 Self-advocacy
How do you enable the individuals you work with to self-advocate?

Evidence activity

4.3 Types of advocacy
Give examples to demonstrate occasions when the different types of advocacy have been used within your organisation.

AC 4.4 Describe ways to build empowerment and active participation into everyday support with individuals with learning disabilities

Empowerment is a word we hear a lot, and it has become an important aspect of delivering health and social care services. Empowerment for people with learning disabilities is the process by which individuals develop increased skills to make decisions and take control over their lives. This helps individuals to achieve their goals and aspirations, thus maximising their quality of life.

A key feature in empowering people is giving them a voice and listening actively to what they have to say. Empowerment is, therefore, closely linked to the concept of person-centred care and various forms of advocacy.

Person-centred planning places the individual at the centre of all processes and uses techniques to ensure meaningful participation. This is key to empowering individuals.

For the person who has a learning disability, the subjective experience of empowerment is about rights, choice and control, which can lead them to a more **autonomous** lifestyle. For the health and social care worker, it is about anti-oppressive practice, balancing rights and responsibilities, and supporting choice and empowerment while maintaining safe and ethical practice.

Active participation can promote empowerment by enabling individuals to be involved at every stage of their needs being met. They choose what they want and have a say in this.

Key terms

Active participation is a way of working that recognises an individual's right to participate in the activities and relationships of everyday life as independently as possible; the individual is regarded as an active partner in their own care or support, rather than a passive recipient.

Autonomous means independent, not controlled by others.

Evidence activity

4.4 Empowerment and active participation
Explain the processes that are in place within your organisation to ensure the people you support are empowered and enabled to participate actively in decisions on a daily basis.

LO5 Understand how views and attitudes impact on the lives of individuals with learning disabilities and their family carers

AC 5.1 Explain how attitudes are changing in relation to individuals with learning disabilities

People who have a learning disability, and their families, have always been affected by the way they are viewed and treated by society. Sadly, the history of public and private attitudes to learning disability over time has been one of intolerance and lack of understanding.

This is now changing and individuals are becoming more and more involved in their communities. They study, work and socialise in their communities.

Evidence activity

5.1 Changing attitudes in relation to individuals with learning disabilities
Why do you think attitudes towards people who have a learning disability are changing?

AC 5.2 Give examples of positive and negative aspects of being labelled as having a learning disability

Negative aspects
The way people with learning disabilities have been portrayed has often been with a '**label**'. Terms like 'the mentally handicapped', 'the blind' and 'the mentally ill' place people in groups, which risks a stereotypical view. Being labelled as 'disabled' and 'inadequate' or not good enough also creates barriers to doing things that 'able-bodied' people enjoy and take for granted, for example in areas such as relationships, employment, education, housing, transport and much more. In addition, labelling continues the **prejudice** and **discrimination**. Anti-discriminatory legislation is helping to remove barriers and shake off negative attitudes and discrimination, but there is still a long way to go.

Key terms

A **label** is a 'tag' that we use to describe someone and is usually based on their appearance or behaviour.

A **prejudice** is an attitude or way of thinking based on an unfair pre-judgement of a person, rather than on a factual assessment.

Discrimination is the acting out of negative prejudices.

Evidence activity

5.2 Positive and negative aspects
Identify any labels that you have heard applied to people who have a learning disability. Are these labels negative or positive?

Positive aspects
In some respects, it is important to apply a 'label' to a certain condition as this will ensure the person who has a learning disability is given any support and care that is required to ensure they lead a good quality of life. It is the *type* of label that is applied that makes all the difference.

The most important aspect to remember with the use of any label is that, despite the label, the person is an individual with individual needs. This sometimes tends to be forgotten. If this view is not upheld, a more profound perception of the disability will result. Using the right positive language goes a long way to defining people with a learning disability as individuals first.

AC 5.3 Describe steps that can be taken to promote positive attitudes towards individuals with learning disabilities and their family carers

The media: It is now accepted that the way people are portrayed within the media can greatly influence public perception and attitudes.

The recognition of the social model of disability has gone a long way in changing the attitudes of health and social care workers towards people who have learning disabilities and towards recognising that the person comes first.

Some employers undertake disability awareness **training** as part of their general staff training programme, and this can go a long way in changing attitudes towards people who have learning disabilities.

More people who have learning disabilities are now using **mainstream community facilities**, such as colleges, hospitals, libraries and leisure centres. This sends out a clear message that segregation is no longer acceptable, but more could still be done to ensure that people are positively welcomed and included.

AC 5.4 Explain the roles of external agencies and others in changing attitudes, policy and practice

External agencies include advocacy services, parent/carer support groups and campaign groups. Others include colleagues, families or carers, and friends. They play an important role in facilitating and aiding change in attitude, policy and practice.

The Learning Disability Coalition, for example, is a group of support groups that represents 14 learning disability organisations and over 140 supporter organisations, which have come together to form one group with one voice. They believe that people with learning disabilities have the right to live independent lives, with the support that they need. Their aim is to make sure that the government provides enough money so that people with learning disabilities have the same choices and chances as everyone else. They do this by:

- providing a unified voice to government and other key decision makers
- gathering evidence on cuts to services at a local level

- raising awareness of the financial pressures on services for people with learning disabilities, and campaigning for better funding
- achieving an evidence-based assessment of the long-term resource requirements for people with learning disabilities.

(Source: www.learningdisabilitycoalition.org.uk)

The LDC is now working as part of the Voluntary Organisations Disability Group, and the Care and Support Alliance.

LO6 Know how to promote communication with individuals with learning disabilities

AC 6.1 Identify ways of adapting verbal and non-verbal communication when communicating with individuals who have learning disabilities

Communication is a two-way process in which messages are sent, received and understood between people or between groups of people. Communication is a basic human right, upon which we build relationships, make friends and control our existence. It is the way we become independent and make choices. It is the way we learn and express our thoughts, feelings and emotions. The British Institute of Learning Disabilities (BILD) estimates that between 50 and 90 per cent of people who have learning difficulties also experience difficulties with communication. People who have learning disabilities do not have one recognised tool to help them communicate and every person is different. It is, therefore, essential that an assessment is undertaken to ensure effective methods of communication are identified for each individual person.

Generally, people in societies develop common languages in order that they can live together with a shared method of communication. In fact, communication is a fundamental part of society.

People who find it difficult to communicate, or are undervalued in their societies, will automatically feel excluded unless those around them are prepared to adapt their method of communication. Effective communication is therefore essential in order to promote the principles associated with independence, choice, rights and inclusion.

Methods of communication vary and can be either verbal or non-verbal. A high percentage of communication is non-verbal.

- When communicating verbally it is important not to overestimate language skills. Equally it is important that the pace of communication is consistent with the person's level of understanding.
- **Objects of reference**, pictures, signs and symbols are all powerful ways to communicate meaning.
- **British Sign Language** (BSL) has long been established as a language used by people who have a hearing impairment.
- **Braille** enables people who have a visual impairment to read.
- People with more complex learning disabilities may not be able to use any recognised means of communication and will therefore be dependent on others to interpret their needs and choices through observation and by responding to their communicative behaviour.

See SHC 31 for more information on communication.

Key terms

Objects of reference are objects that are used to communicate by them representing actions and activities, such as an individual using a cup to indicate that they are thirsty or a key to indicate that they would like to go out.

British Sign Language is a visual form of communicating that involves hand signs and facial expressions.

Braille is a tactile form of communicating that involves touching a series of raised dots that represent letters and numbers.

Evidence activity

6.1 Adapting verbal and non-verbal communication

- Explain how the communication requirements of individuals are assessed within your organisation.
- Think about the service users you support. Identify ways in which the methods of verbal and non-verbal communication have been adapted to facilitate communication with these individuals.

AC 6.2 Explain why it is important to use language that is both 'age appropriate' and 'ability appropriate' when communicating with individuals with learning disabilities

When communicating with people who have a learning disability, it is essential that the communication takes place at a pace and in a manner that the individual can process. This means that the information should be both 'age appropriate' and 'ability appropriate'. Communication must also take into account the person as a whole and sensitive consideration should be given to the person's cultural and religious beliefs.

Evidence activity

6.2 Age- and ability-appropriate language

- Explain why it is important to use language that is both age appropriate and ability appropriate.
- How do you ensure you take these factors into account when communicating with service users?
- What could be a consequence of not taking these factors into consideration?

AC 6.3 Describe ways of checking whether an individual has understood a communication, and how to address any misunderstandings

When communicating with a person who has a learning disability it is essential that the person understands what has been communicated. It may be immediately obvious if the person has understood. They may give a sign that they have understood, such as a thumbs up, or a lack of a sign may indicate they are happy with what is being said.

Within your role as a care worker you will want to help individuals communicate to the best of their ability and to promote understanding of their needs and preferences whenever appropriate. There will be times, however, when you find that you are having difficulty communicating and are unsure whether an individual has understood what you have communicated to them. Hopefully you will know your service users well, but it is also important to seek advice from a senior member of staff. Individuals who are unable to communicate successfully with you, or understand what you are communicating to them, may become distressed.

The extent of this frustration and distress will vary from person to person but will be apparent through verbal communication, body language or facial expression.

Legislation

- Equality Act 2010
- Human Rights Act 1998
- Mental Capacity Act 2005
- The Health and Social Care Act 2012
- The Disability Discrimination Act 1995

Useful resources

Websites

About Learning Disabilities
www.aboutlearningdisabilities.co.uk

Easyhealth
www.easyhealth.org.uk

The Foundation for People with Learning Difficulties
www.learningdisabilities.org.uk

Learning Disability Coalition
www.learningdisabilitycoalition.org.uk

Mencap
www.mencap.org.uk

Office for Disability Issues
www.officefordisability.gov.uk

Understanding Individual Needs
www.understandingindividualneeds.com

Evidence activity

6.3 Checking understanding and addressing misunderstandings

- How do you check understanding when you are communicating with service users?
- How do you address any misunderstandings as they arise?

Unit SS MU 3.1

Understand sensory loss

This unit is worth 3 credits

What are you finding out?

In this unit you will learn about the different types of sensory loss, as well as the range of factors that can impact on individuals who have sensory loss and the ways services are provided.

You will also learn more about the different methods of communication that are used by individuals with different types of sensory loss, including the role of the environment in facilitating effective communication and the positive impact of effective communication on the lives of individuals.

This unit will also look at the main causes and conditions of sensory loss, the meaning of congenital and acquired sensory loss, and the factors that influence the incidence of sensory loss in the population. Finally, this chapter will end by

developing your knowledge around recognising when an individual may be experiencing sight loss, hearing loss or both, and the actions that may be taken as well as the sources of support available to individuals.

By the end of this unit you will:

1 Understand the factors that impact on individuals with sensory loss.
2 Understand the importance of effective communication for individuals with sensory loss.
3 Understand the main causes and conditions of sensory loss.
4 Know how to recognise when an individual may be experiencing sight and/or hearing loss and actions that may be taken.

LO1 Understand the factors that impact on an individual with sensory loss

AC 1.1 Analyse how a range of factors can impact on individuals with sensory loss

Sensory loss occurs when an individual's sight and/or hearing becomes impaired.

- Sight loss refers to individuals who are unable to see (are 'blind'), as well as to individuals who are able to partially see, for example can see shadows.
- Hearing loss similarly refers to individuals who are unable to hear (are 'deaf'), as well as to individuals who are able to partially hear, for example can hear low tones.
- Some individuals experience both sight and hearing loss and this is referred to as dual sensory loss or 'deaf blindness'. The Department of Health's report 'Think dual sensory' defined deaf blindness as follows:

'A person is regarded as deaf blind if their combined sight and hearing impairment cause difficulties with communication, access to information and mobility. This includes people with a progressive sight and hearing loss.'

(Source: 'Think dual sensory', Department of Health, 1995)

There is a range of factors that can impact on individuals with sensory loss. Let us consider in more detail the impact of each of the following: communication, information, familiar layouts and routines, mobility.

Communication

- As you read in Unit SHC 31, **communication** involves both verbal and non-verbal ways of

Key term

Impairment is an injury, illness or condition that causes or is likely to cause a loss in the body's functions.

expressing what we think and feel, and what we perceive that others are telling us.

- An individual who has a sight loss will not be able to understand the visual cues of how another person is feeling, i.e. their facial expressions or body language, and therefore may not realise that the person is angry or upset and may come across unintentionally as insensitive.
- An individual who has a hearing loss may find it difficult to understand what another person is trying to express, either through the words they use or the tone or pitch of their voice, and may therefore rely on what they perceive the person is expressing through their physical gestures and facial expressions; this may lead to misunderstandings.
- Individuals who have a dual sensory loss may find it difficult to make themselves understood and to understand others; this may lead to them feeling isolated and becoming withdrawn.

You can support individuals by using symbols, objects of reference, sign language and other communication systems. You must also always take into account individuals' cultural beliefs and preferences with regards to the use of touch and proximity to others when communicating. Specialist organisations such as Sense and the RNIB can provide additional support, information and guidance.

Information

- Under the Equality Act 2010 there is a legal duty to make reasonable adjustments to ensure equality of access to services for people who have disabilities. Being able to find out about and access services will very much depend on the **information** that is made available about these, including the different formats in which it is provided.
  - An individual who has a sight loss will require information in a format that they can use, e.g. some individuals may prefer information in a spoken rather than written format.
  - An individual who has a hearing loss may find it difficult to follow verbal instructions

and may prefer information to be written down clearly and concisely.

- An individual who has a dual sensory loss may require assistance from someone else to ensure they can understand and use the information available; this may create dependency on others but at the same time be a method of enabling the individual to make their own choices and decisions.

Familiar layouts and routines

- The environment, including **layouts and routines**, has a key role to play in how individuals may experience their sensory loss.

Not being able to move around in their environment may make individuals feel that they have lost their sense of freedom, independence, security and control as well as make them more dependent on others to help them make sense of their environment.

- An individual who has a sight loss will benefit from the lighting and colour contrast in rooms being taken into consideration. They will also benefit from carefully planned room layouts and routines to enable them to be as independent as possible when undertaking their daily living activities, e.g. by being able to find their own way round their home.
- An individual who has a hearing loss will benefit from the background noise in rooms being taken into consideration, as well as from familiar layouts and routines to enable them to be as independent as possible.
- An individual who has dual sensory loss may also benefit from familiar layouts and routines; sufficient time to learn these will be required.

Mobility

- **Mobility** will also impact on individuals who have a sensory loss, as our ability to move around is underpinned by use of our senses.
  - An individual who has a sight loss and poor mobility may not be able to follow visual signs to the local shops, for example. They may feel that they are not able to go out

and so become fearful of doing so; learning with the assistance of another person the routes to places they want to go can help to address this.

- An individual who has a hearing loss and poor mobility may not be aware of the sound of a fire alarm in a building, for example. This may place themselves and others in danger if they do not leave the building quickly; technology can help to address this.
- An individual who has a dual sensory loss as well as poor mobility may also develop fear and/or lose confidence in moving around both within and outside of their home.

Additional support to assist individuals with mobilising comes in the form of mobility aids. For example, white canes are used by individuals who are blind or visually impaired; red and white striped canes are used by individuals who have both vision and hearing impairments to move around their environment and to alert others of their needs. Guide dogs and hearing dogs are trained to respond to sounds both inside and outside of the home as well as guide individuals to move around their environments. Tactile signs and maps are also available in Braille, text and pictures.

See AC 2.2 for more information on how the environment facilitates effective communication for people with sensory loss.

AC 1.2 Analyse how societal attitudes and beliefs impact on individuals with sensory loss

The **attitudes** and **beliefs** of others in society will also have a significant impact on how individuals experience sensory loss.

Time to think

1.2 Societal attitudes

Read through the comments below, made about individuals who have sensory loss. Consider how you would feel if these were made about you or someone you know.

Key terms

Societal attitudes are society's positive and negative views towards, for example, the needs of individuals who have sensory loss.

Societal beliefs are society's positive and negative assumptions about, for example, the abilities of individuals who have sensory loss.

These comments show that the nature of attitudes and beliefs can be both positive and negative. Read through Table 13.1, which details some of the positive and negative effects these attitudes and beliefs can have on individuals.

Comments about individuals who have sensory loss

'She's very brave going out on her own.'

'I don't know what to say when I see him in the mornings, because he can't hear or see me.'

'His personal assistant is very good, I'd rather speak to her.'

'She's just like me or you; it just takes a little bit more careful thinking and planning to help her be independent.'

'She's always been my friend and that will never change, even now that she can't see me very well.'

Positive attitudes and beliefs	Positive impacts on individuals who have sensory loss
'She is hearing impaired and still has a right to do the activities she enjoys.'	Acknowledging an individual's right to take part in activities makes the individual feel valued and more likely to continue doing the activities they enjoy.
'I understand that you must be feeling scared about not being able to see when you go out.'	Showing an individual that you understand how they may be feeling will act as a support and enable the individual to express their fears and concerns. This is a necessary step for overcoming these.
Negative attitudes and beliefs	**Negative impacts on individuals who have sensory loss**
'He won't be able to live independently any more, as he might fall due to not being able to see.'	The individual may begin to believe that they can't manage independently and may feel depressed over losing their sight.
'I don't think she'll be able to carry on going out on her own and meeting up with her friends, as she won't be able to hear them properly.'	The individual may become socially isolated and find it embarrassing to go out, believing that they won't be able to feel included by their friends any longer.

Table 13.1 The impact of societal attitudes and beliefs on individuals

Research and investigate

1.2 Attitudes and beliefs

Find out from different individuals what their experiences have been of society's attitudes and beliefs towards their sensory loss.

AC 1.3 Explore how a range of factors, societal attitudes and beliefs impacts on service provision

The experience of accessing and using services for individuals who have sensory loss may also range from positive to negative, depending on the attitudes and beliefs of those who work in the services and others who may access the services. Services include GPs, hospitals, leisure centres, shops and restaurants; a range of other factors such as communication, information, mobility and the environment may also impact on the way services are provided and managed. New initiatives and a change in thinking have seen a shift in society's attitudes towards person-centred planning and delivery that place the individual very much at the centre of all service provision.

Time to think

1.3 Service provision

Read through Figure 13.1, which includes some examples of how service provision can be affected. Can you think of any other examples?

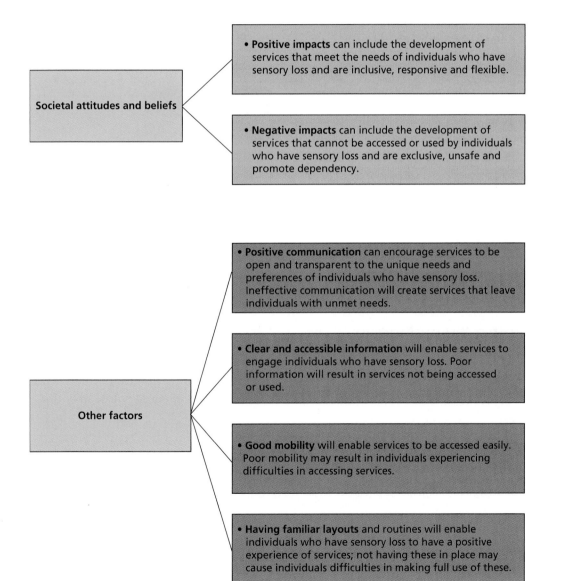

Figure 13.1 The impact of societal attitudes and beliefs and other factors on service provision

Involving individuals who have sensory loss in providing training to personnel and raising awareness within society by actively using community services and facilities is integral to this.

Case study

1.1, 1.2, 1.3 Gwen

Gwen has Down's syndrome as well as visual and hearing impairments. She is meeting with her care and support team for the first time to discuss her needs, strengths, abilities and preferences.

1 What factors may impact on Gwen?
2 How may societal attitudes and beliefs impact on Gwen?
3 How may societal attitudes, beliefs and other factors impact on the service provided by the care and support team and on other services Gwen may use?

Evidence activity

1.1, 1.2, 1.3 Factors that impact on individuals who have sensory loss

Identify three individuals you work with or know who have sight loss, hearing loss or both.

For each individual, examine in detail:

● A range of factors that can impact on them and the provision of services for them.
● Societal beliefs and attitudes that can impact on them and the provision of services. Remember to give consideration to both positive and negative impacts.

Time to think

1.3 Successful services?

Reflect on the three individuals you identified for the Evidence Activity above.

● How effective are the services available to each individual?
● What improvements can be made?

LO2 Understand the importance of effective communication for individuals with sensory loss

AC 2.1 Explain the methods of communication used by individuals with: sight loss, hearing loss and deaf blindness

Individuals who have sensory loss will communicate with others in different ways and will very often, like all of us, use more than one method to do so. Look at Figure 13.2 and box below, which identify some of the methods of communicating that individuals who have different types of sensory loss may use.

Sight loss

Individuals who have sight loss can use: Braille, large printed words, a magnifying glass or enlarge words/font on a photocopier. Other methods include using capitals and/or using a marker to make words easier to read, or using a ruler or paper to underline so there is no glare

Hearing loss

Individuals who have hearing loss can use: objects of reference, gestures and facial expressions, photographs, pictures and symbols, British Sign Language, Makaton, lip reading, interpreters, telephone relay services, hearing aids, speech-to-text reporters, loop systems

Dual sensory loss

Individuals who have dual sensory loss can use: manual alphabets, haptic communication, intervenors, communication guides, touch with objects or tactile communication, Braille, the moon alphabet and objects of reference

Figure 13.2 Communication methods used by individuals who have different types of sensory loss

Different methods of communicating

- **Braille** is a tactile form of communicating that involves touching a series of raised dots that represent letters and numbers. It is a system of writing and printing for blind or visually impaired people.
- **British Sign Language** is a visual form of communicating that involves hand signs and facial expressions.
- **Communication guides** are trained professionals who support deaf blind individuals to participate in day-to-day activities.
- **Haptic communication** is a tactile form of communicating that involves making signs on a part of the body, such as on the individual's back or shoulder, which describe what is happening visually.
- **Intervenors** are trained professionals who support deaf blind individuals to experience the world around them.
- **Lip reading** is a visual form of communication that involves observing a person's lip shapes, gestures and facial movements.

- **Makaton** is a visual form of communication for individuals who have learning disabilities and communication difficulties, in which gestures are used in combination with pictures, signs and symbols to communicate messages.
- **Manual alphabets** are a tactile form of communicating that involve spelling out words on individuals' hands.
- **Objects of reference** are objects that are used to communicate. They represent actions and activities, such as an individual using a cup to indicate that they are thirsty or a key to indicate that they would like to go out.
- **Speech-to-text reporters** are a communication aid that listens to what is said and then converts this into a format that can be used.
- **Moon alphabet** is a tactile form of communication that involves embossed shapes that can be read by touch.
- **Tactile communication** is a type of communication that involves touch.

It is important that the communication methods used with individuals are suitable for their type of sensory loss as well as for their unique needs and preferences, which will vary not only from one individual to another but also may vary throughout an individual's life.

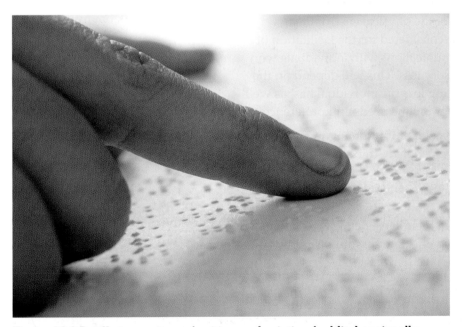

Figure 13.3 Braille is a system of writing and printing for blind or visually impaired people

AC 2.2 Describe how the environment facilitates effective communication for people with sensory loss

As we read in AC 1.1, the **physical environment** has a key role to play in facilitating effective communication for individuals who have sensory loss.

- For an individual who has sight loss, for example, contrasting colours on a person's identity badge can determine who the person is, and the careful positioning of lighting can indicate the positioning of a person with whom they are communicating.

- For an individual who has hearing loss, smaller spaces where background noises and sounds are minimised, seating arrangements that enable individuals to sit close to one another, and good lighting that enables individuals to read each other's lips, observe each other's facial expressions and gestures, can all make communications more effective.

- These aspects of the physical environment should also be considered for the facilitation of effective communications with individuals who have dual sensory loss. This will depend on the sight and hearing loss the individual has, as well as on their other unique needs and preferences.

An individual's **social environment** must also be considered, as the people within the individual's social network and their personal attitudes and beliefs (see AC 1.2) are integral to facilitating effective communications between individuals and others involved in their lives. Below is a list of ten tips for facilitating effective communications with individuals who have sensory loss.

1 Find out the individual's preferred methods of communication; do not make assumptions about what methods are best to use.

2 Be patient and be prepared to try different methods of communication with individuals to find out which best meet their needs.

3 Ensure you make yourself known to the individual at the start of all communications.

4 Prepare the environment where the communication will take place before it begins.

5 Be aware of your body language and facial expression when communicating with an individual as this will affect the tone of the conversation, e.g. smiling as opposed to frowning when greeting an individual will convey a positive tone when you speak.

6 Ensure you provide sufficient time for all communications, as these may take longer with an individual who has a sensory loss.

7 Clarify an individual's understanding as well as yours during all communications and not just at the end.

8 Observe an individual during communications, including what they are trying to express.

9 Remain positive throughout all communications.

10 Obtain feedback from the individual and any others involved in communications regarding how effective they found it. Be prepared to work with them to make improvements. For example, the RNIB suggests making things 'bigger, bolder and brighter'; Figure 13.4 provides some suggestions of how to do so, can you think of any others?

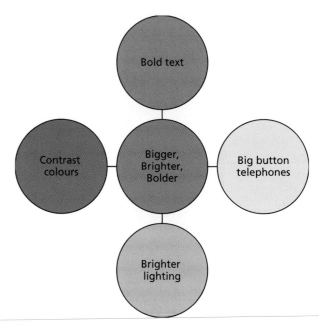

Figure 13.4 Examples of how to incorporate 'bigger, brighter, bolder'

AC 2.3 Explain how effective communication may have a positive impact on the lives of individuals with sensory loss

Using the most suitable methods of communication for an individual who has sensory loss will ensure that effective communications take place and that these in turn have a positive impact on individuals' lives. As you read in AC 2.1, communication methods used by individuals who have sensory loss vary. Often methods used are a combination of several different types of communication, involving **intensive interactions** and **total communication approaches**.

Intensive interactions can have a positive impact on individuals who are deaf blind and who may have become disinterested, withdrawn and/or isolated from the world around them and the people within it. Enabling an individual to lead the pace of interactions can have a positive impact on their self-esteem. Repeating back sounds and movements can lead to the development of a way of communicating for the individual that can be understood by others; this in turn can lead to the individual forming relationships with others and expressing their choices and decisions about day-to-day activities.

Total communication approaches can also have a positive impact on individuals' lives by providing them with a means to express what they think, feel and want. This in turn will enable individuals who have sensory loss to maintain control of their lives, while at the same time reducing any frustration and anxiety they may experience at not being able to express themselves. Total communication

approaches therefore can provide individuals who have sensory loss with the ability to live their lives to their full potential, as well as to challenge the attitudes and beliefs that others may have about their abilities and needs.

Case study

2.1, 2.2, 2.3 Aurek

Aurek leads a team of carers in supporting individuals who have sensory loss to live independently. As part of his job role Aurek provides information, guidance and training to the team. He is putting together a training update on the importance of effective communication for individuals who have sensory loss.

1   What communication methods used by individuals who have sight loss, hearing loss and deaf blindness can Aurek explain to the team?
2   What information can Aurek provide to the team about how the environment facilitates effective communication for people who have a sensory loss?
3   What information and examples can Aurek provide to the team about how effective communication may have a positive impact on the lives of people who have a sensory loss?

Evidence activity

2.1, 2.2, 2.3 Effective communication

Reflect on the three individuals you identified for the evidence activity on page 232.

● For each individual explain, with examples, the communication methods they use. Detail how the environment facilitates effective communication for each individual and the positive impact of this on their lives.

Key terms

Intensive interactions are practical communication approaches used to engage and involve individuals who are congenitally deaf blind.

Total communication approaches are practical communication approaches used with individuals who have a sensory loss. They involve the use of a mixture of different communication methods suitable for the individual.

Time to think

2.3 Are you an effective communicator?

Reflect on the communications you have with individuals who have sensory loss.

● How do your communications impact positively on their lives?
● What could you do differently and why?

LO3 Understand the main causes and conditions of sensory loss

AC 3.1 Identify the main causes of sensory loss

In this unit you have learned about the factors that impact on the different types of sensory loss and the importance of effective communications with individuals. We are now going to find out more about the main causes of sensory loss.

There is a variety of reasons why individuals are born with or acquire sight loss, hearing loss or both. These reasons include:

- infections, such as **toxoplasmosis**, acquired during pregnancy
- being born prematurely
- rare **syndromes** such as **Usher syndrome**
- illnesses such as **Meniere's disease**
- accidents that involve a head injury
- ageing such as **macular degeneration**, **glaucoma**
- eye diseases such as **diabetic retinopathy**, **cataracts**
- ear conditions such as **conductive hearing loss**, **sensorineural hearing loss**

AC 3.2 Define congenital sensory loss and acquired sensory loss

The causes of sensory loss can range from those that occur at birth (congenital sensory loss) to those that are acquired later on in an individual's life (acquired sensory loss). Figure 13.5 provides some more information about these.

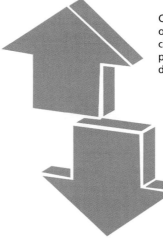

Congenital sensory loss can occur at birth or before a child develops language as part of their early years development

Acquired sensory loss can occur after a child develops language as part of their early years development and at any time during their life

Figure 13.5 Congenital and acquired sensory loss

AC 3.3 Identify the demographic factors that influence the incidence of sensory loss in the population

Research commissioned by the charity Sense shows that there is likely to be nearly 250,000 people aged over 70 with dual sensory loss in the UK by 2015, a figure that is expected to rise to almost 500,000 by 2030.

Sixty-two per cent of the deaf blind population is aged over 70 and the numbers will increase dramatically over the next 20 years as a result of the ageing population. There are 356,000 deaf blind people in the UK, of whom 220,000 are over the age of 70 with significant combined visual impairment and hearing loss.

(Source: Sense, 2010)

This increase in incidence is in line with an ageing population as well as an increase in other underlying conditions that cause sight loss in the UK, such as obesity and Type II diabetes. Other factors that may influence the incidence of sensory loss in a population include the following:

- Poverty – this can lead to individuals who experience sensory or hearing loss seeking medical attention too late. A poor diet and little exercise can also impact on individuals' well-being and can lead to conditions such as diabetes and obesity, which can cause sensory loss.
- Lifestyle – smoking can increase an individual's chances of sight loss.

Case study

3.1, 3.2, 3.3 Amelita

Amelita is working with a newly recruited support worker who has not previously worked with individuals who have sensory loss. As part of this support worker's induction Amelita plans to discuss with her the main causes and conditions of sensory loss.

1. What causes of sensory loss should form part of Amelita's discussion?
2. How can Amelita explain to the support worker the difference between congenital and acquired sensory loss?
3. What demographic factors that influence the incidence of sensory loss in the population should Amelita discuss?

Evidence activity

3.1, 3.2, 3.3 Understanding sensory loss

Develop a presentation for your team that includes information about the following:

- the main causes of sight loss, hearing loss and dual sensory loss
- the meanings of congenital and acquired sensory loss
- the demographic factors that influence the incidence of sensory loss in the population.

Time to think

3.3 Do you understand the demographics?

Reflect on research undertaken into the demographic factors that influence the incidence of sensory loss in the population.

Do you agree with it? Why?

LO4 Know how to recognise when an individual may be experiencing sight and/or hearing loss and actions that may be taken

AC 4.1 Identify the indicators and signs of sight loss, hearing loss and deaf blindness

Some individuals may be reluctant or afraid to acknowledge that they are experiencing loss of their sight, hearing or both, and so it is important that you and others involved in the individual's life are vigilant and are able to support them to identify when they are having difficulties and to seek help as soon as possible.

Table 13.2 outlines some of the common indicators and signs of each of these types of sensory loss; have you and/or individuals with whom you work come across any others?

Type of sensory loss	Indicators and signs
Sight loss	**Physical** – falling over, bumping into things, spilling drinks, reaching out tentatively for items, holding items up close to their eyes.
	Individual – experiencing visual disturbances such as distorted images, bright lights, double vision.
Hearing loss	**Physical** – ringing or hissing in the ears, feeling dizzy, difficulty hearing others clearly particularly where there is background noise, leaning forwards when listening to others speak, turning up the volume of the television and/or radio higher than usual.
	Individual – asking others to repeat what they said, feeling tired due to having to concentrate when others are talking, avoiding situations that involve interacting with others.
Deaf blindness	**Physical** – the combined indicators and signs of sight and hearing loss detailed above.
	Individual – the combined indicators and signs of sight and hearing loss detailed above.

Table 13.2 Indicators and signs of sensory loss

Evidence activity

4.1 Indicators and signs of sensory loss

Draw a spidergram of the indicators and signs of each of the following types of sensory loss:
- sight loss
- hearing loss
- deaf blindness.

AC 4.2 Explain actions that should be taken if there are concerns about onset of sensory loss or changes in sensory status

As you read in AC 4.1, sometimes individuals may be reluctant to acknowledge the onset of sensory loss or changes in sensory status, or may not be fully aware of it. The actions to take in these situations will depend on your work setting's agreed ways of working as well as on the scope of your job role and responsibilities. Below are a number of good practice actions to take if there are concerns:

- Do not ignore any concerns.
- Identify the concerns and monitor them.
- Discuss your concerns with the individual and/or the individual's family and/or others involved in their life.

- Maintain a safe environment for the individual, e.g. by removing potential hazards and improving lighting.
- Encourage the individual to use sensory aids prescribed for them, e.g. glasses, hearing aids, and check the suitability of these by seeking advice from an occupational therapist.
- Carry out checks that the individual's sensory aids are in good working order, e.g. that they are clean and still suitable for their needs, that the batteries are working.
- Make a referral to the individual's GP, or an **optometrist** or **audiologist**, to assess the individual's sensory loss.
- Record and report all concerns, findings and actions to all team members through the individual's plan of care so that there is a consistent approach.

Key terms

An **optometrist** is a healthcare professional who specialises in the eyes and vision. Optometry is the branch of medicine concerned with vision.

An **audiologist** is a healthcare professional who specialises in the ears and hearing. Audiology is the branch of medicine concerned with the sense of hearing.

Research and investigate

4.2 Supporting a person with sensory needs
Find out from your work setting the actions that may be taken when individuals experience sensory loss or changes in sensory status.

Time to think

4.2 Do you know the actions to take?
Read through your work setting's agreed ways of working for actions to take if there are concerns about the onset of sensory loss or changes in the sensory status of individuals.

- Have you or others with whom you work had to take these actions? What happened?
- Are there any improvements that could have been made to the reporting and recording process?

Evidence activity

4.2 Actions to take
Discuss with your manager the actions that should be taken in your work setting if you or others have concerns about the onset of sensory loss or changes in individuals' sensory status.

Provide examples of when and how to do this.

AC 4.3 Identify sources of support for those who may be experiencing onset of sensory loss

Experiencing a gradual or sudden onset of sensory loss can be a worrying and stressful time for individuals. Being able to direct individuals to people and organisations that may be able to offer additional support will be very important in their experience of sensory loss.

There are many different organisations and services that can provide support to individuals experiencing sensory loss.

- National charities, such as:
  - Sense, for deaf blind people, provides advice, information and specialist services for individuals who have dual sensory loss.
  - Action on Hearing Loss provides services, information and support for individuals who have hearing loss.
  - The Royal National Institute of Blind People (RNIB) provides practical and emotional support for individuals who have sight loss.
- Local voluntary organisations can provide a range of information and advice services.
- Social services can be contacted for information on practical support and financial assistance available.
- Support groups for individuals who are experiencing sensory loss can be particularly valuable for sharing experiences, fears and concerns.

Information is also available from helplines and online resources, as well as through professionals such as those working in **ophthalmology** and **audiology** (see page 240 for definition) clinics, occupational therapists and health professionals such as the individual's GP and consultant.

Key terms

Ophthalmology is the branch of medicine concerned with the anatomy, physiology and diseases of the eye.

Audiology is the branch of medicine concerned with the sense of hearing.

Legislation

- **Equality Act 2010**
- **Health and Social Care Act 2012**
- **Human Rights Act 1998**

Case study

4.1, 4.2, 4.3 Max

Max is a senior residential care worker providing support to a team of residential carers as well as key working six older individuals with varying degrees of sensory loss. As part of the team's on-going training Max has put together a set of guidelines on how to recognise when an individual may be experiencing sight and/or hearing loss and the actions that should be taken.

1 What indicators and signs of sight loss, hearing loss and deaf blindness should Max include?
2 What actions could Max explain should be taken if there are concerns about individuals in relation to the onset of sensory loss or changes in sensory status?
3 What sources of support could Max make the team aware of that are available for individuals who are experiencing the onset of sensory loss?

Evidence activity

4.3 Sources of support

Identify the sources of support available from your work setting, your local area and nationally for individuals who may be experiencing the onset of sensory loss.

Useful resources

Websites

Action on Hearing Loss
www.actiononhearingloss.org.uk

Deafblind UK
http://deafblind.org.uk

Royal National Institute of Blind People
www.rnib.org.uk

Sense
www.sense.org.uk

Vision Aware
www.visionaware.org

Publications

Butler, S.J. (2004) *Hearing and Sight Loss – A handbook for professional carers*. London: Age Concern England.

Robertson, J. and Emerson, E. (2010) *Estimating the Number of People with Co-occurring Vision and Hearing Impairments in the UK*. Lancaster: CeDR.

Reports

Department of Health (1995) 'Think dual sensory – Good practice guidelines for older people with dual sensory loss'

Snow, A. and Telling, A. (2011) 'Developing good practice with people who have sensory impairment and limited communication skills: a framework for reflective practice'. London: Sense.

Optional
Group C Units

Unit DEM 312

Understand and enable interaction and communication with individuals who have dementia

This unit is worth 4 credits

What are you finding out?

Being able to communicate positively by valuing individuals' identity and uniqueness is central to developing positive and effective relationships and enabling trust and empathy with individuals who have dementia.

In this unit you will learn about how to enable positive interactions and communications with individuals who have dementia, including the different factors that may affect how an individual communicates with others. You will also learn more about the range of verbal and non-verbal techniques that is available and that can be effective when interacting with individuals who have dementia.

This unit will also help you to explore in more detail positive interaction approaches that are

effective with individuals who have dementia, including how to use aspects of the physical and social environment and reminiscence techniques.

By the end of this unit you will:

1 Understand the factors that can affect the interactions and communication of individuals with dementia.
2 Be able to communicate with an individual who has dementia using a range of verbal and non-verbal techniques.
3 Be able to communicate positively with an individual who has dementia by valuing their individuality.
4 Be able to use positive interaction approaches with individuals who have dementia.

LO1 Understand the factors that can affect the interactions and communication of individuals with dementia

AC 1.1 Explain how different forms of dementia may affect the way an individual communicates

Communicating with others involves sharing and receiving information as well as expressing what we think and feel. Depending on the type of dementia individuals have and how far it has progressed they may experience difficulties communicating with others, being understood, saying what they mean and showing how they feel. Let us take a closer look at how the four most common forms of dementia may affect the way individuals communicate.

Alzheimer's disease

As you read in DEM 301, 62 per cent* of people living with dementia have Alzheimer's disease. This form of dementia causes brain cells to die and nerve cells to stop working. The resulting memory loss may mean that an individual has difficulties remembering what was said to them 5 minutes ago, but may be able to recall people and places from 10 years ago. This may result in the individual forgetting people's names or that a relative has passed away, not being able to hold a conversation with others, repeating what they just said, or using muddled language or incorrect words that you and others cannot understand.

Vascular dementia

Seventeen per cent* of people living with dementia have vascular dementia. Vascular dementia is caused when the brain is damaged due to lack of oxygen, resulting in deterioration in individuals' thinking skills and difficulties with orientation. It is common for individuals to lose items frequently and not to be able to think logically where the items could be; this may result in losing items being the focus of their conversations, and may also lead to individuals blaming others for stealing their items, which can create difficulties in building trust within relationships with you and others. Communications with individuals who have this form of dementia may feel awkward as they will take a lot longer to respond to you and others because of difficulties in expressing what they want to say.

Individuals who have vascular dementia may also become disorientated and confused; as a result they may spend long amounts of time sleeping during the day and wandering, feeling restless, at night. When individuals are confused about the time of day or about their surroundings they may feel tired and frightened, they may not understand what you are saying to them or may respond inappropriately.

Dementia with Lewy bodies

Four per cent* of people living with dementia have dementia with Lewy bodies. Deposits known as Lewy bodies in nerve cells cause difficulties in how the brain works. Auditory and visual hallucinations can occur in individuals who have dementia with Lewy bodies. During auditory hallucinations individuals may for example hear people talking to them or hear other noises such as banging or tapping; although these are not real they seem very real to the individual experiencing them. An individual who experiences visual hallucinations may see a family member who has passed away or see other people standing in their room. Both types of hallucination may cause individuals to feel embarrassed and/or frightened and they may become the focus of their conversations with others.

Individuals who have this form of dementia may also display varying levels of communication skills, i.e. they may use quite complex language one moment and then become non-verbal the next. This means the methods they use to communicate with others will vary greatly, which can often lead to misunderstandings and to the individual becoming distressed and/or frustrated if they are not understood.

Fronto-temporal dementia

Two per cent* of people living with dementia have fronto-temporal dementia, which presents itself in people under the age of 65. Nerve cells in the frontal and temporal lobes of the brain die and the connections between the nerve cells deteriorate.

1.1 Dementia and communication
Develop a presentation for your team on how Alzheimer's disease, vascular dementia, dementia with Lewy bodies and fronto-temporal dementia may each affect the way an individual communicates.

A common experience of individuals who have this form of dementia is forgetting their inhibitions and showing changes in their personality. This may lead to the use of inappropriate language towards others and to other inappropriate behaviours, such as undressing in public, which may cause distress and embarrassment and lead individuals to become increasingly isolated as others may feel unsure or frightened about communicating with them.

* Source: Dementia 2014 infographic, Alzheimer's Society

AC 1.2 Explain how physical and mental health factors may need to be considered when communicating with an individual who has dementia

It is not only different forms of dementia that may affect the way an individual communicates. It is important to take into account other physical and mental health factors that can also have an impact.

- **Physical factors** – as an individual's dementia progresses and they continue to lose their **language skills**, non-verbal forms of communication become even more important. This will need to be taken into account when communicating with individuals. It is important that your body language and facial expressions convey the same meaning as what you are saying and that you are able to spend time with the individual to ensure that you have time to interpret what they are trying to express through their body language too, such as that they are feeling unwell, happy, insecure, angry or frightened.

  An individual who has dementia may also experience a deterioration in the **ability to hear**. This too will need to be taken into account by ensuring that the location in which you are

communicating is quiet and well lit, and by making sure you stand opposite the individual so they can see you and your face if they lip read and also see your facial expressions. A deterioration in **vision** may also occur for some individuals who have dementia and so it is important that this is taken into account when communicating with them. They may no longer be able to use signs and **objects of reference** to communicate and may need you to use other ways of communicating. It is also important to take into account your physical closeness to individuals when communicating with them so that they feel you are respecting their personal space and not being intimidating. You must be prepared to make physical contact when appropriate, for example placing your hand on an individual's shoulder if they are feeling upset.

- **Mental health** – mental well-being involves feeling good about yourself, enjoying how you live your life, being able to manage the different stresses in life and being an active part of your family and friends. Individuals who have dementia may experience mental ill health as they may feel depressed knowing that they have dementia and being aware that their memory and skills are deteriorating.

  Having a dementia diagnosis will mean a change in lifestyle. How individuals have lived their lives may need to change drastically, i.e. where they live and the tasks they are able to complete independently may change. This can in turn cause changes in how individuals think about themselves and others, as well as how they respond to others.

  Some forms of dementia, as we read in AC1.1, can cause changes in individuals' personalities. This may impact on whether individuals can continue working or supporting themselves and

Key term

Objects of reference are objects that are used to communicate by them representing actions and activities, such as an individual using a cup to indicate that they are thirsty or a key to indicate that they would like to go out.

1.2 Factors impacting on communication

Research the impact of physical and mental health factors on communications with an individual who has dementia.

Think about how you and others need to adapt the communication methods you use with individuals in line with their physical skills, abilities and mental well-being.

their family, both emotionally and financially. This may also make it difficult for family members and friends to spend time with them, as they may find the dementia too upsetting; the individual may consequently experience feelings of loss and isolation.

AC 1.3 Describe how to support different communication abilities and needs of an individual with dementia who has a sensory impairment

Sensory impairments must also be taken into account when communicating with individuals who have dementia, as most of the information we share with and communicate to others comes from sight and hearing. An individual who has dementia may also experience a loss of their sight, hearing, smell, touch, taste and/ or spatial awareness. Read through the tips in Table 14.1 on useful ways to support the different

communication abilities and needs of individuals who have dementia and sight or hearing loss – do you have any other useful tips?

Some individuals who have dementia may experience a dual sensory impairment in which they may have a loss in both their vision and hearing. Read through the tips below for additional support with individuals' different communication needs and abilities.

- Get to know the individual, i.e. find out their preferred method of communicating with you; remember each individual is unique.
- Respect the individual, i.e. do not make assumptions about what an individual's communication abilities or needs are; doing so is disrespectful and can affect individuals' self-esteem.
- Use touch, e.g. place your hand gently on the individual's to let them know that you are there, identify who you are, for example by spelling out your name on their hand.
- Respect the individual's privacy by letting them know when you leave.
- Use objects of reference, e.g. provide individuals with opportunities to hold items and feel them if they are unable to see them, so that they can understand what you are talking about.
- Respect the individual's environment, i.e. respect the location of items in the individual's home; failing to return them to the same locations can create confusion and disorientation.

Sensory impairment	Tips for supporting different communication abilities and needs of individuals who have dementia
Sight loss	<ul><li>Use the individual's name so that they know you are talking to them.</li><li>Always identify yourself so the individual knows with whom they are communicating.</li><li>Don't stop using body language, as doing so will affect your tone of voice and therefore affect how what you are trying to communicate is interpreted.</li><li>Speak naturally so the individual does not feel patronised.</li><li>Speak clearly so the individual can understand what you are saying.</li></ul>
Hearing loss	<ul><li>Be patient when communicating with individuals so they feel respected.</li><li>Don't shout, as this can be interpreted as aggressive by the individual.</li><li>Find a suitable place to communicate, i.e. one that is well lit and quiet.</li><li>If an individual doesn't understand you, re-phrase what you are saying.</li><li>Be aware of your and the individual's body language and facial expressions when communicating.</li></ul>

Table 14.1 Tips for supporting different communication abilities and needs of individuals who have dementia

AC 1.4 Describe the impact the behaviours of carers and others may have on an individual with dementia

Being an active part of a family and group of friends contributes to your mental well-being. Similarly, for individuals who have dementia, the interactions they have with their family, friends, partner, neighbours and other professionals, such as care workers, advocates, nurses and speech and language therapists, will also have an impact on their well-being.

Let us consider the role of Dementia Care Mapping (DCM) in understanding the impact that the behaviours of carers and others may have on an individual who has dementia. Dementia Care Mapping is a person-centred approach to dementia care that involves observing individuals who have dementia and those who work with them over a period of time to gain a better understanding of what they react positively and negatively to. This is done by recording all the interactions the individual has; **personal enhancers** reflect those interactions that have a positive effect on the individual's well-being, and **personal detractors** reflect those interactions that have a negative effect. This approach was developed by the Bradford Dementia Group led by Professor Tom Kitwood and is used to get a better insight into and understanding of the individual who has dementia. It also provides an opportunity for carers and others involved in the individual's life to improve the quality of care they provide, as well as improving the interactions and well-being of the individual.

How an individual experiences dementia will be affected by both the positive and negative behaviours of carers and others. Examples of some of these have been provided in Table 14.2:

Carers	Examples of impact that carers' behaviour may have on individuals who have dementia
Partner	• Positive – living with the individual will make the individual feel safe and secure • Negative – having arguments with the individual will create a sense of mistrust and may make the individual aggressive
Family	• Positive – sharing important events with the individual will create a sense of belonging • Negative – doing what's best for the individual without taking their views into account can be frustrating for the individual
Friends	• Positive – spending time with the individual and doing activities they enjoy will promote empathy and a sense of fun • Negative – reducing contact with an individual can make them feel rejected and less worthy
Neighbours	• Positive – taking an interest in the individual can make the individual feel valued • Negative – asking too many questions about the individual's life can be upsetting for the individual and may make them anxious
Others	• Positive – sharing news about what's going on in the community can make individuals feel like they belong • Negative – not maintaining regular contact can be distressing and confusing for the individual
Care worker	• Positive – supporting the individual with daily living activities will enable the individual to retain their independence • Negative – doing activities for rather than with an individual will create dependency and a sense of despair

Table 14.2 The impact of carers' behaviour on people with dementia

Colleagues	• Positive – enabling an individual to be involved in their support plan will promote their sense of being in control
	• Negative – restricting an individual's choices and risks they take can create a sense of unworthiness
Managers	• Positive – involving the individual in evaluating the service will make the individual feel involved
	• Negative – not upholding an individual's rights and responsibilities will make an individual frustrated
Social worker	• Positive – enabling an individual's needs to be met will make the individual feel reassured
	• Negative – not informing an individual of the services and options available will make them feel isolated
Occupational therapist	• Positive – enabling individuals to remain living at home will make them feel safe
	• Negative – not providing suitable equipment and aids for individuals' homes may put them at risk and increase their sense of hopelessness
GP	• Positive – referrals to specialist health or social care professionals can make an individual feel that others are taking a genuine interest in them
	• Negative – not understanding the individual's personal experience of dementia can make an individual not ask for help again
Speech and language therapist	• Positive – enabling an individual to communicate with others can improve their self-esteem and feelings of well-being
	• Negative – not taking into account an individual's background and beliefs can make the individual withdraw and not communicate
Physiotherapist	• Positive – enabling an individual to mobilise can improve their physical health
	• Negative – not providing individuals with sufficient information about the benefits of exercises can make an individual's physical health deteriorate
Pharmacist	• Positive – providing information, advice and guidance on the use of medication prescribed can assist an individual who is thinking about refusing their medication
	• Negative – not providing information, advice and guidance on other medications or remedies available may prevent the individual from considering these
Nurse	• Positive – meeting an individual's care and treatment needs can improve an individual's relationships with others
	• Negative – not carrying out an assessment can mean that the individual does not access the support they require
Psychologist	• Positive – assessing an individual's memory can provide relief and bring comfort to an individual
	• Negative – not explaining aspects of an individual's emotional health clearly to them may result in their anxiety levels increasing
Admiral nurses	• Positive – providing emotional support to an individual will make them feel valued
	• Negative – not being honest with an individual may make the individual feel angry →

Table 14.2 (Continued)

Independent mental capacity advocate	• Positive – representing an individual who lacks capacity to make their own decisions will make the individual feel important
	• Negative – not getting to know an individual may mean that they will continue to lose the sense of who they are
Community psychiatric nurse	• Positive – providing care, treatment and support to individuals will enhance an individual's self-esteem
	• Negative – not being honest with an individual may make the individual feel anxious
Dementia care advisors	• Positive – diagnosing early an individual's dementia can bring comfort
	• Negative – not providing information about future care needs may increase an individual's anxiety
Advocate	• Positive – representing an individual's views and preferences will make the individual feel valued
	• Negative – not involving individuals fully in decisions may result in individuals not making their own decisions
Support groups	• Positive – sharing experiences with other individuals who have dementia can promote empathy
	• Negative – participating in activities with other individuals who are in latter stages of dementia may make the individual fearful of the future

Table 14.2 (Continued)

The Bradford Dementia Group has researched this and developed a number of personal enhancers and personal detractors. Look through Table 14.3, which includes details of the positive and negative effects that these detractors can have on an individual who has dementia.

Effects of personal enhancers on individuals who have dementia	Effects of personal detractors on individuals who have dementia
Warmth – showing a genuine interest in an individual will make them feel valued and important and promote **empathy**.	**Intimidation** – threatening an individual will make them feel afraid and unable to trust you. The individual may express how they are feeling by not communicating or being aggressive.
Respect – treating a person who has dementia as an adult and as an individual will encourage them to build on their strengths and abilities.	**Infantilisation** – treating an individual like a child may make the individual feel less worthy and unable to be themselves.
Inclusion – ensuring an individual is an active part of what is happening in their life will encourage them to express what they think and feel.	**Ignoring** – not acknowledging that an individual is able to participate as an active partner may result in them not being able to make their own choices and decisions.
Validation, Holding – an individual will feel reassured and safe if they know that you are taking seriously their fears and feelings.	**Invalidation, Withholding** – an individual may feel that they cannot trust you and that you do not care, and so their fears and anxieties may become worse.
Acceptance, Acknowledgement – an individual will gain comfort from feeling that you are encouraging them to be themselves.	**Labelling** – an individual will lose their sense of who they are if you treat them like everyone else rather than as a unique person. ➡

Table 14.3 Personal enhancers and personal detractors

Genuineness – an individual's relationship with you will develop if you are honest and transparent.	**Betrayal** – an individual will feel angry and anxious if you are not honest and do not support them in what you have agreed with them.
Empowerment, Enabling, Facilitation – ensuring an individual remains an active participant in their lives will make them feel in control and help them to work towards their wishes and goals in life.	**Disempowerment, Imposition** – an individual may stop using their abilities and strengths, or come to believe they do not have them, if you do not support them.
Collaboration – working together with an individual will enable them to retain a sense of dignity and pride.	**Objectification** – an individual may feel depressed or frightened if they sense they are losing control of their life.
Celebration – recognising what an individual has achieved will enhance their self-esteem.	**Disparagement** – saying to an individual that they are not capable or useless may make them think that this is true, and they may become even more frustrated and depressed.
Relaxed pace, Belonging, Fun – ensuring an individual feels comfortable and that they are an active part of their life will enhance their feelings of well-being.	**Outpacing** – not enabling the individual to live their life according to how they want to and at their own pace will affect their decisions and abilities to be an active part of their life.

Table 14.3 (Continued)

(Source: Kitwood, 1997, Dementia Reconsidered)

Key terms

Empathy is the ability to understand and share how someone else may be feeling.

Dementia care mapping is an observational tool used to evaluate the quality of dementia care from the perspective of the individual.

Personal enhancers are interactions that have a positive effect on the individual's well-being.

Personal detractors are interactions that have a negative effect on the individual's well-being.

Time to think

1.4 Are you aware of the impact of your behaviour and that of others?

Reflect on the behaviours that you and others with whom you work use in your work setting when working with individuals who have dementia.

- Are they positive or negative?
- How can you improve the behaviours that you and others use in your work setting?

Case study

1.2, 1.3, 1.4 Sabrina

Sabrina is a senior support worker who provides support to individuals who have dementia. Sabrina and her colleague are today observing a small group of individuals who have dementia. They are documenting their observations of both the individuals and the carers working with them as part of the Dementia Care Mapping process used in the service. Sabrina and her colleague plan to meet later with the manager and then the rest of the team to share and discuss their findings.

1 What physical and mental health factors may need to be considered by the team when communicating with individuals who have dementia?
2 How can the team support the communication abilities and needs of different individuals who have dementia as well as sensory impairments?
3 What impact may the different behaviours of carers and others have on individuals who have dementia?

Evidence activity

1.2, 1.3, 1.4 Factors that affect interactions

Reflect on an individual with whom you work who has dementia.

- Explain with examples the physical and mental health factors that may need to be considered when communicating with this individual.

- Provide details about the impact that the positive and negative behaviours of carers and others may have on the individual.

Reflect on an individual with whom you work who has dementia and a sensory impairment.

- Detail how to support the individual's different communication abilities and needs.

LO2 Be able to communicate with an individual who has dementia using a range of verbal and non-verbal techniques

AC 2.1 Demonstrate how to use different communication techniques with an individual who has dementia

As you read in AC 1.1, different forms of dementia can affect individuals in different ways. Ninety-five per cent of all our communication is non-verbal. Using a mixture of verbal and non-verbal communication techniques with individuals who have dementia is important if we are to treat each individual as a unique person and enhance their self-identity and dignity. Look at Figure 14.1, which indicates the range of verbal and non-verbal communication techniques that can be used.

Verbal communication techniques
Closed questions
The words you use when you communicate with an individual who has dementia can provide much needed reassurance and promote a sense of well-being. For example, if an individual who has dementia has forgotten what they want to do next, warm words will reassure them; asking **closed questions**, such as 'Do you want to make some lunch?' or 'Do you need to use the bathroom?', will help the individual to remember what it was they wanted to do.

Tone
The **tone** of your voice will also influence whether the individual who has dementia feels they can trust you and whether they feel reassured when they communicate with you. For example, if an individual repeatedly asks you the same question, your tone of voice will reflect whether you're becoming irritated by this or whether you are taking a genuine interest in talking with them. Acknowledging their question and gently

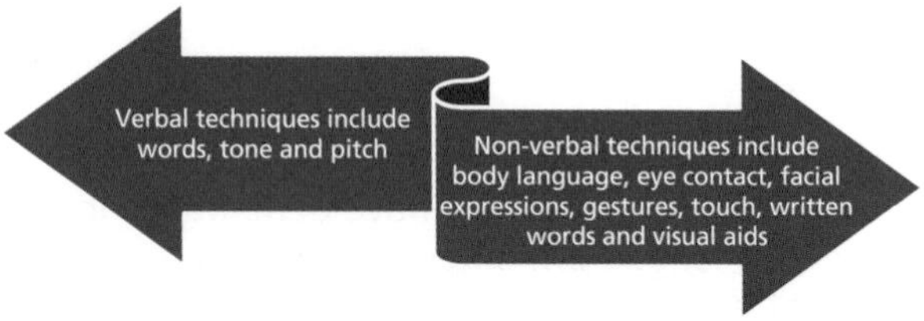

Key terms

Verbal communication methods are ways of communicating using speech, tone and **pitch**.

Closed questions are questions that encourage a 'yes'/'no' or 'true'/'false' response.

Verbal techniques include words, tone and pitch

Non-verbal techniques include body language, eye contact, facial expressions, gestures, touch, written words and visual aids

Figure 14.1 Verbal and non-verbal communication techniques

suggesting they try another activity will promote a sense of well-being.

Similarly, how low or high the tone of your voice is also conveys to an individual who has dementia whether you are being positive and supportive or negative and frustrated. For example, if an individual accuses you of stealing their handbag it is important not to take this too personally or to dismiss what the individual is saying. Acknowledging their concerns, reassuring them with some warm words and gently persuading them to let you help them to look for their lost item will promote feelings of well-being, reassurance and security.

Non-verbal communication techniques

There are also a number of **non-verbal communication** techniques that can be used to promote positive interactions and communications with individuals who have dementia. Visual aids such as photographs and pictures can enable an individual to **reminisce** about the people and places you are talking about with them, especially if they cannot remember these, and can also be helpful for signposting an individual to find their way round the building.

Body language

Your body language and facial expressions can reflect how you are feeling so it is important that you are aware of these when you are communicating with an individual who has dementia. For example, if an individual who has dementia exposes themselves in front of others, do not look shocked; ensure your body language reflects that you are calm as you support them to go to a private area. In this way you will not make the individual feel humiliated or embarrassed by what they have done.

Touch

Touch can be used when an individual who has dementia feels upset or frightened. Placing your hand on theirs or putting your hand on

> ### Key terms
>
> **Non-verbal communication** is ways of communicating using body language, facial expression, eye contact, touch, behaviour, gestures and visual aids.
>
> **Reminiscence** is an approach used to recall memories from the past, e.g. through talking about past events or looking at old family photographs. See AC 4.5 For more information.
>
> **Tone** is the quality of a person's voice, i.e. irritable, calm, anxious.
>
> **Pitch** is the height or depth of a person's voice, i.e. low tone and high tone.

their shoulder will show the individual that you genuinely care about them and how they are feeling. Similarly, touch can also be used to prompt an individual to complete a task they may have forgotten to do, for example placing a fork in their hand can encourage an individual to eat.

Eye contact

Eye contact can be used in a variety of different ways too, depending on the individual and the situation. For example, when assisting an individual with intimate personal care tasks, avoiding eye contact with them will reduce the embarrassment or humiliation that they may feel about being helped by others. When an individual is worried about not recognising their surroundings or others who have come to visit them, maintaining eye contact with them can promote feelings of safety and calmness.

Reminiscence, reality orientation therapy and validation

It is important to find out as much as you can about an individual's preferred communication methods so as to promote a sense of well-being and to avoid any misunderstandings or negative reactions that may cause the individual to feel distressed and anxious.

For example, life history and reminiscence work is a good way of communicating with the individual and finding out more about who they are, including their past work life, places they have travelled to, important events in their life. Methods can include developing life history books with photographs or using life story boxes with personal items. Reality orientation therapy can enable an individual to communicate with others by reminding them of what is real through for example the use of photographs. See AC 4.1 for more information on the reality orientation approach. Validation approaches can make the individual feel supported and understood by acknowledging their feelings and enabling them to distract their thoughts. See unit SHC 31 for more information on communication, and the different methods of communicating.

AC 2.2 Show how observation of behaviour is an effective tool in interpreting the needs of an individual with dementia

Being able to communicate effectively with an individual who has dementia involves finding out not only how the individual prefers to communicate but also how an individual expresses what they are thinking and feeling. As you read in AC 1.4, Dementia Care Mapping is a person-centred approach to dementia care that involves observing individuals who have dementia and those who work with them over a period of time. This allows you to gain a better understanding of what they react positively and negatively to by recording all the interactions the individual has, including those that have a positive effect on the individual's well-being (personal enhancers) and those that have a negative effect (personal detractors).

Observations can therefore be an important source of information in relation to quickly identifying any behaviours that are a cause of concern. An **ABC chart** can be used to record information about what is occurring in the individual's environment:

'**A**' refers to the antecedent, the activity or event that immediately precedes a behaviour that is a cause for concern.

'**B**' refers to the behaviour being observed.

'**C**' refers to the consequence or the event that immediately follows the response to the individual. For example, an individual who has dementia may refuse to eat and throw their plate on the floor when informed that it is lunch time. The senior carer may find that providing the individual with verbal information is an antecedent to this behaviour. The consequence may be that the individual is provided with lunch later on in their room. It may become clear at a later stage that the individual is engaging in this behaviour to express their frustration at not understanding what is being said and having lunch on their own.

Read through the top five benefits of observing the behaviour of an individual who has dementia:

1 Observing their behaviour can help you to **empathise** with the individual, including how they are feeling and experiencing the type of dementia/s they have.
2 This can help you to identify what elements of **relationships** are important to the individual, i.e. by finding out the interactions that enhance their well-being.
3 This is a way of **respecting** the individual by spending time finding out their unique needs.
4 This can help to **improve the quality of care and support** an individual receives, by enabling their carers and others who work with them to gain an insight into how the individual communicates.
5 This can help to **improve the quality of life** for an individual, by enabling their carers and others who work with them to increase the number of positive interactions and communications they use, thereby decreasing the individual's sense of ill-being.

AC 2.3 Analyse ways of responding to the behaviour of an individual with dementia, taking account of the abilities and needs of the individual, carers and others

Responding to the behaviour of an individual who has dementia will involve finding out first and foremost what the individual's behaviour means, as the same behaviours can have different meanings for different individuals. Using positive and person-centred approaches will ensure that the abilities and needs of the individual, their carers and others involved in their lives are taken into account. Including and involving individuals' carers and others in these approaches is vital to ensure consistency and to enable the individual to feel safe and secure in their living environment.

See AC 1.4 for the different responses to behaviour and the positive and negative impacts these can have on the individual. Read through the list of behaviours below that some individuals who have dementia may show, including what they may mean and how you can respond to these. Do you know of any others?

- **Restlessness** – this may involve an individual getting up and sitting down repeatedly, getting in and out of bed repeatedly, walking up and down for long periods of time. These behaviours may indicate that the individual feels insecure, is in pain, feels anxious or wants to do an activity. Once you have found out what the behaviour indicates you can then respond to it. An individual who is insecure may need reassurance about where they are. An individual who is in pain or feeling anxious may need medical help, but also may need your help to calm down: a touch on their hand and shoulder may help. An individual who wants to do an activity may need support from you in engaging in an activity that they enjoy.
- **Not recognising people and places** – this may involve individuals mistaking who their family and friends are, or not recognising who and where they themselves are. This may mean that the form of dementia that the individual has has damaged the part of the brain that interprets the meanings of what their eyes see. This may mean the individual may have difficulties recognising people and places, or may mistake them for something else. Empathising with individuals, showing them items that are familiar to them, like a favourite item of clothing or a painting, can help them to feel secure and reassured again.
- **Repetitive actions** – this may involve individuals repeating the same information, question or action again and again. This may indicate that the individual has forgotten what they have said and what the response was or what they want to do. It may also be an individual's way of expressing that they are feeling anxious about something else. With these behaviours it is important to remain calm, not to ignore their question or action, and to observe their non-verbal communication as their facial expressions and body language may help you to find out what the individual is trying to express.
- **Losing items** – this may involve individuals not remembering where they have placed items, with some individuals fearing that others may have stolen or hidden their items deliberately. This may be as a result of memory loss and a deterioration of an individual's ability to think rationally and logically. It is important not to dismiss an individual's concerns and instead to work together with the individual to help them find the items they have lost so as to avoid causing them more distress.
- **Aggression** – this may involve individuals being violent towards others or shouting out inappropriately. This could result from a number of reasons, including the individual feeling depressed at losing their abilities, frustrated with losing their independence, or seeing and hearing things that are not real. As well as seeking medical help it is important that you remain calm, do not become angry yourself or shout back at the individual. Distracting the individual can be a useful technique for responding to these behaviours, as this removes the negative focus.

Case study

2.1, 2.2, 2.3 Jakob

Jakob is a senior care assistant in a residential care service and is working closely with an individual who has dementia who has recently moved in. Jakob has been informed that the individual finds it difficult at times to express verbally what he wants and feels, and gets very angry and upset at these times.

1 What different communication techniques could Jakob use with the individual?
2 How could observation of this individual's behaviour be an effective tool in interpreting his needs?
3 How could Jakob respond to this individual's behaviour?

Time to think

2.3 Do you know what an individual's behaviours mean?

Reflect on the behaviours that an individual with whom you work shows.

- What do these mean?
- How do you respond to these? Why do you respond in this way?

Research and investigate

2.2 Dementia Care Mapping

Find out more about the Dementia Care Mapping process.

Evidence activity

2.1, 2.2, 2.3 Communication techniques

- Reflect on an individual who has dementia with whom you work. Detail the different communication techniques you use with this individual and how observation of their behaviours can be useful for interpreting their needs. Provide details and examples of the different ways that you respond to their behaviours, taking account of the abilities and needs of the individual, you, carers and others.
- You will also need to be observed by your assessor demonstrating how to use different communication techniques with an individual who has dementia and showing how observation of behaviour is an effective tool in interpreting the needs of an individual with dementia.

LO3 Be able to communicate positively with an individual who has dementia by valuing their individuality

AC 3.1 Show how the communication style, abilities and needs of an individual who has dementia can be used to develop their care plan

Professor Tom Kitwood, the founder of person-centred dementia care, once said: 'Once you've met one person with dementia… you've met one person with dementia.'

This citation captures well how each individual who has dementia is a unique person, with unique abilities and needs and their own individual way of **communicating**. Getting to know an individual who has dementia is an on-going process and the information that is gathered about the individual can be used to develop a plan of care; this must be done only with the agreement of all those involved. Having a plan of care in place for individuals who have dementia will enable their holistic needs and preferences to be met. This will also involve taking into account their preferred communication style, abilities and needs as this will not only enable them to express themselves but will also enable them to engage in positive interactions with others.

Figure 14.2 shows different ways of developing a **care plan** for an individual who has dementia.

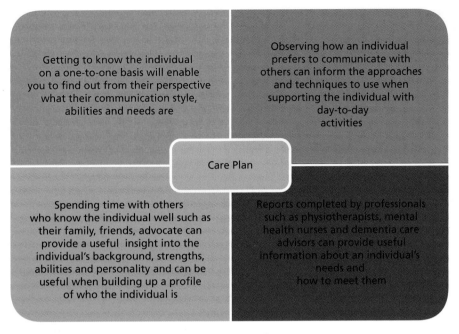

Figure 14.2 Developing an individual's care plan

Communication style is an individual's preferred way of communicating with others, e.g. by using big gestures, a calm manner.

An individual's **plan of care** is the document where day-to-day requirements and preferences for care and support are detailed. It may be known by other names, e.g. support plan, individual plan or care delivery plan.

Time to think

3.1 **Do you know how to develop individuals' care plans?**

Reflect on how you develop a care plan for an individual.

Do you take into account the individual's communication style, abilities and needs?

AC 3.2 Demonstrate how the individual's preferred method/s of interacting can be used to reinforce their identity and uniqueness

Once you have found out and documented an individual's preferred method/s of interacting with others you must then use this information to adapt your communication and approaches to reinforce the individual's identity and uniqueness.

Table 14.4 details some different ways of using individuals' preferred methods of interacting with others.

Adapting how you communicate with each individual who has dementia will mean not only that you are ensuring that they are able to interact with others, but also that you are respecting who they are. In doing this you are also reinforcing back to the individual their identity and uniqueness, two aspects that are crucial for living and enjoying life fully.

Preferred method of interacting	Examples of how to reinforce an individual's identity and uniqueness
Verbal communication	<ul><li>Use key words and phrases that are familiar to an individual</li><li>Speak clearly</li><li>Use short sentences</li><li>Use closed questions</li><li>Give the individual time to respond</li><li>Do not interrupt an individual</li><li>Listen attentively</li></ul>
Non-verbal communication	<ul><li>Use body language and gestures</li><li>Use facial expressions</li><li>Use visual aids, such as photographs, pictures, signs and **flash cards**</li><li>Use touch when appropriate</li><li>Observe carefully what an individual is expressing</li><li>Be aware of what your body language is saying</li></ul>

Table 14.4 Reinforcing an individual's identity and uniqueness

Key terms

Identity is the individual characteristics by which a person is recognised or known.

Flash cards are cards that contain key information and that aid communication and learning.

Evidence activity

3.1, 3.2 Valuing individuality

- Reflect on an individual who has dementia who you know and work with and with whom you have developed a care plan. Detail how you used the individual's communication style, abilities and needs to develop their care plan. Include how the individual's preferred method/s of interacting can be used to reinforce their identity and uniqueness.
- You will also need to be observed by your assessor showing how you use an individual's communication style, abilities and needs to develop their care plan, and demonstrating how you use the individual's preferred method/s of interacting to reinforce their identity and uniqueness.

Case study

3.1, 3.2 Catarina

Catarina is a senior support worker providing support to individuals who have dementia to enable them to continue to live in their own homes. Catarina is meeting today with Marta, who has dementia, her sister, dementia nurse and advocate to put in place a plan of care and support. Marta is a very quiet and private person; she is also very independent and enjoys being active.

1 How can Marta's style of communicating, abilities and needs be used to develop her care plan?
2 How can Marta's preferred methods of interacting be used to reinforce her identity and uniqueness?

Research and investigate

3.2 Effective communication

Research different approaches used for communicating with an individual who has dementia.

LO4 Be able to use positive interaction approaches with individuals who have dementia

AC 4.1 Explain the difference between a reality orientation approach to interactions and a validation approach

There are a number of different techniques and ways of working with individuals who have dementia. Three of the most common are detailed below; take note of what each involves and the differences between how each can be used.

Reality orientation approach
What is it?

- The reality orientation approach is a way of presenting information to an individual who has dementia about the time, their surroundings and others with whom they interact. The aim is to try to place the individual in the here and now, reminding them of the day, place, time and situation in which they are.

How can it be used with individuals who have dementia?

- It helps individuals who have memory loss to understand their surroundings by using everyday cues, such as clocks and calendars, to understand what time it is or where they are.
- It helps individuals to distinguish between what is real and what is not. For example, if an individual asks to speak to his sister who passed away 10 years ago, then he may be shown a photograph of his sister's grave and reminded that she has passed away.
- This approach does not take into consideration an individual's feelings or background. Showing an individual a photograph of their sister's grave may make the individual grieve all over again for their relative every time they look at it, as it may be as though they are just now learning of her death. This approach is not widely used now for this reason.

Interactions
What are they?

- Interactions involve providing an individual who has dementia with different opportunities to gain enjoyment and stimulation.

How can interactions be used with individuals who have dementia?

- They can help individuals to remain an active part of their local community, e.g. by maintaining relationships with family members, visiting friends, going out shopping.
- They can help individuals to engage in activities that they find enjoyable and stimulating. Taking part in activities with others can reduce an individual's feelings of loneliness and can increase their sense of well-being.
- They can help individuals retain a sense of who they are and a valued role in life. For example, supporting an individual to do the gardening can remind the individual and others involved in their life that they still have the skills to do so; reminiscing about the past can remind the individual about their different achievements in life.
- This approach uses interactions as a means of enabling individuals to retain a sense of who they are in an enjoyable, calm and dignified way.

Validation approach
What is it?

- The validation approach is a person-centred approach that involves seeing an individual's experience of dementia from their perspective. It uses non-judgemental acceptance and empathy to show the individual that their expressed feelings are valid, and focuses on the feelings being expressed rather than the actual content of speech.

How can it be used with individuals who have dementia?

- It helps individuals to express how they are feeling without confrontation. For example, if an individual is upset that he can no longer go to work like he used to, the individual is not reminded that he is unable to work. Instead, his feelings are acknowledged and he may then be distracted with an activity or a different topic of conversation.

- It helps individuals to feel less stressed and anxious. By expressing both verbally and non-verbally what they are thinking and feeling, individuals will be more likely to continue to engage with others and less likely to withdraw into themselves and become isolated.
- This approach is holistic and takes into account an individual's feelings and background. It is a means of enabling individuals to retain a sense of who they are in an enjoyable, calm and dignified way.

AC 4.2 Demonstrate a positive interaction with an individual who has dementia

The availability of approaches for interacting with individuals who have dementia can provide useful ways of communicating with individuals and enabling them to remain in control of their lives. Positive interactions with individuals who have dementia involve promoting **person-centred values** such as dignity, respect, individuality and independence. Read through these top five tips for achieving positive interactions with an individual who has dementia.

1 **Be positive** – ensure your body language, gestures, facial expressions, tone of voice and the words that you use are positive, as the individual will be able to sense this and it will contribute to their mental health and well-being. Using different forms of communication and understanding the individual's body language can be useful for informing your own when interacting with the individual.

2 **Be supportive** – ensure that you spend time with the individual, getting to know who they are, their strengths, abilities, skills and needs, as this means the individual will feel valued and respected. It is important to be supportive so that the individual knows you are taking a genuine interest in them

3 **Be engaging** – ensure that you have the individual's full attention; ensure you empathise with them and their experience of dementia; do not confront them (see Figure 14.3). Keep the focus on the individual and what's important to them. It is important to be an active listener so that you are able to respond to individuals' emotions positively.

4 **Be flexible** – ensure you use distractions when an approach or an interaction isn't effective and then try again, adapting the way you do this to meet the individual's needs. It is also important to look for triggers to manage challenging situations.

5 **Be fun** – ensure interactions are enjoyable and relaxing as this will lessen an individual's anxiety, fear and/or stress.

Key term

Person-centred values are principles on which care and support are based, such as respecting individuality, rights, choice, privacy, independence, dignity, respect, partnership.

Research and investigate

4.2 Positive interactions
Research positive interaction approaches with individuals who have dementia. Think about the approaches you use, and the approaches others you work with use. What are the differences between these and what approaches are most effective?

Time to think

4.2 Do you know how to use positive interactions?
Reflect on a positive interaction with an individual who has dementia.

- How could this have been improved?
- What could you have done differently?

Figure 14.3 Show empathy in your interactions

AC 4.3 Demonstrate how to use aspects of the physical environment to enable positive interactions with individuals with dementia

Enabling positive interactions with individuals who have dementia is achieved not only by the approaches and techniques you and others use, but also by giving consideration to an individual's surroundings.

Adapting an individual's physical environment can be an effective way of responding to their behaviours. Let us consider the role of the physical environment in responding to three of the behaviours that individuals who have dementia may experience, i.e. restlessness, aggression and not recognising their surroundings, which you read about in AC 2.3.

- An individual who has dementia and who is restless may repeatedly feel the need to walk up and down, and may be at risk of falling or walking out of the house on to a busy road.

Moving items that could be obstacles can reduce the risk of the individual falling and/or tripping. Similarly, adapting the exit doors and routes of an individual's house, e.g. by covering door handles or placing a curtain over a door, can make it less obvious to the individual that this is an exit door and route out of their house. An individual will be more likely to remain in an environment that is warm and inviting than one that is not. Similarly, putting on an individual's favourite piece of music in the background can prove stimulating for the individual and engage them.

- An individual who has dementia and who is verbally or physically aggressive towards others will need some quiet time to calm down. Adapting the environment by having a small private area or room where the individual can go and relax quietly, or rooms that are themed or that have colour coded doors – such as for eating, watching films or interacting with others – can provide visual prompts as well as be sources of stimulation and distraction for individuals who have dementia and display aggression. Sensory gardens are other sources of relaxation that can involve individuals who have dementia in participating in outdoor activities, engaging with others and as a basis for reminiscence work.

- An individual who has dementia and who does not recognise their surroundings may feel lost, helpless and very anxious. Signposting the way to and from an individual's room – for example with colour coded doors or by using a series of photographs, pictures or symbols on the walls that the individual recognises and can understand – can be very comforting and reassuring for the individual, as well as being an effective way to maintain their independence.

AC 4.4 Demonstrate how to use aspects of the social environment to enable positive interactions with individuals with dementia

Aspects of the social environment must also be considered when enabling positive interactions with individuals who have dementia, in terms of the relationships and interactions they have with others involved in their lives. The social environment can provide an individual with interactions that create stimulation and enjoyment, for example:

- meeting with family and friends
- talking about their early life, past career and good memories
- engaging in their familiar activities, such as attending church and clubs, playing golf, going on favourite walks
- other activities, such as reminiscing or listening to their favourite music
- continuing their social routines, such as going to the hairdressers or out for coffee.

A positive social environment will have a positive impact on an individual's well-being. Professor Tom Kitwood believes that people have five psychological needs, with love as a central need (Kitwood, 1997). Let us consider each of Kitwood's five needs, which underpin person-centred care, and the role of the social environment in each of these:

1 **Comfort** – as you read in AC 2.1, individuals who have dementia may feel distressed, anxious and lost. It is important therefore that those involved in their lives can provide them with reassurance, comfort and the confidence to use their strengths and abilities.

2 **Attachment** – feeling close to others and an active part of our communities is essential to well-being. Individuals who have dementia will also have this need and may feel it even more strongly when they cannot recognise the people in their immediate environment or do not know where they are. Ensuring individuals feel at home and are **active partners** in their care and support is very important.

3 **Inclusion** – feeling part of a group can be difficult for individuals who have dementia if they do not have a sense of who they are and do not feel confident about their strengths and abilities. Individualised support will enable individuals to feel included in conversations and activities with others, for example.

4 **Occupation** – all of us need to feel involved and have a purpose in life. Ensuring individuals who have dementia participate in meaningful activities and in aspects of their lives that are important to them will have a positive impact.

5 **Identity** – as you read in AC 3.1, Professor Tom Kitwood once said: 'Once you've met one person with dementia… you've met one person with dementia.' He was reinforcing that an individual who has dementia is still a unique human being and that therefore their experience of dementia will also be unique. It is important for this reason that all interactions are based on an individual's personality, background, culture, strengths, needs and abilities so that they can maintain a sense and feeling of who they are.

The social environment can therefore be the source of interactions which create stimulation and enjoyment through for example opportunities to meet with family and friends, being able to talk about an individual's childhood and early life including their past career and other memories

Key term

Active partners is a way of working that recognises an individual's right to participate in the activities and relationships of everyday life as independently as possible.

they may have, engaging with familiar activities i.e. attendance at church, clubs, playing golf, favourite walks, engaging with activities, i.e. reminiscence, listening to favourite music and continuing social routines such as going to the hairdressers, out for coffee, etc. Family and friends have an important role to play as they know the individual well and will know about their favourite memories, important family events and where they like going and with whom they like socialising as well as being able to share in positive relationships and enjoy social activities with them.

AC 4.5 Demonstrate how reminiscence techniques can be used to facilitate a positive interaction with an individual who has dementia

We all reminisce from time to time about memories from our past, e.g. about our childhood, past events and situations that we have been in. Reminiscence techniques can be used to facilitate positive interactions with individuals who have

> **Key term**
>
> **Reminiscence** is an approach used to recall memories from the past, e.g. through talking about past events or looking at old family photographs.

dementia by being structured around each of the five senses. These techniques can be beneficial not only to individuals who have dementia but also to all those others who use them.

Read through Table 14.5, which provides some of the different ways that reminiscence techniques can be used to facilitate positive interactions with individuals who have dementia.

Being able to use **reminiscence** and other positive interaction approaches with individuals who have dementia is reliant on the individual as well as on the skills, abilities and understanding of others using these. Remember always to respect whether an individual, or those involved in their lives, wants to be involved and if so which approaches they want to use.

Reminiscence technique	Methods of facilitating a positive interaction
Visual	Looking through photographs and pictures that symbolise important events and people in an individual's life can remind the individual of who they are. It can also provide a valuable way to gain greater insight into an individual's background and life, which can in turn be used to communicate and interact with them in everyday conversations.
Auditory	Listening to music and making sounds using different items and instruments can enable individuals to relax and enjoy time spent together with others. It can also be a useful way to distract individuals from feelings of frustration, loss and anxiety they may experience from time to time.
Smell	Providing individuals with an opportunity to smell their favourite food can be stimulating for individuals and remind them of different places and/or people they visited and knew. It can also enable individuals to want to spend some time having a meal with a relative.
Taste	Providing individuals with an opportunity to taste different foods and drinks can be stimulating for individuals. It can also be the basis for topics of conversation that individuals find interesting.
Touch	Providing individuals with an opportunity to touch different items and textures may mean that they feel a connection to these and are able to use these to express how they are feeling. It can also be an outlet for an individual who is finding it difficult or confusing to communicate and interact with others.

Table 14.5 Reminiscence techniques

Case study

4.1, 4.2, 4.3, 4.4, 4.5 Silvia

Silvia is a senior care assistant and provides support and supervision to a small team of carers working with individuals who have dementia. Silvia has been asked by her manager to develop an information pack for the team on using positive interaction approaches with individuals who have dementia.

1 What details about the differences between reality orientation, interactions and validation approaches must Silvia include in the information pack?
2 What examples can Silvia use of positive interactions with individuals who have dementia?

3 What aspects of the physical environment that can be used to enable positive interactions with individuals who have dementia can Silvia include in the information pack?
4 What aspects of the social environment that can be used to enable positive interactions with individuals who have dementia can Silvia include in the information pack?
5 What reminiscence techniques that can be used to facilitate positive interactions with individuals who have dementia can Silvia include in the information pack?

Evidence activity

4.1, 4.2, 4.3, 4.4, 4.5 Positive interaction approaches

- Reflect on an individual who has dementia whom you know and with whom you work. Explain how to use the following three approaches with the individual: reality orientation, interactions and validation. Explain the differences between each approach and include examples of positive interactions.
- Explain how to use aspects of both the physical and social environment, as well as reminiscence techniques, to enable positive interactions with the individual.
- You will also need to be observed by your assessor having a positive interaction with an individual who has dementia, using aspects of the physical and social environment as well as reminiscence techniques to facilitate a positive interaction.

Legislation

- Equality Act 2010
- Health and Social Care Act 2012
- Human Rights Act 1998
- Mental Capacity Act 2005

Useful resources

Websites

Alzheimer's Research UK
www.alzheimersresearchuk.org

Alzheimer's Society
http://alzheimers.org.uk

Carers Trust
www.carers.org

Dementia UK
www.dementiauk.org

Publications

Alzheimer's Society (2001) *Quality Dementia Care in Care Homes: Person-centred standards*. London: Alzheimer's Society.

Brooker, D. (2006) *Person-centred Dementia Care: Making services better* (Bradford Dementia Group Good Practice Guides). London: Jessica Kingsley Publishers.

Kitwood, T. (1997) *Dementia Reconsidered: The person comes first*. Buckingham: Open University Press.

Stokes, G. (2003) *Challenging Behaviour in Dementia: A person-centred approach*. London: Speechmarks Publishing.

This unit
is worth
4 credits

What are you finding out?

In this unit you will learn about the key requirements for moving and positioning individuals as part of their plan of care according to their specific needs. To be able to do this you will need to understand more about the anatomy and physiology of the human body. You will also need to know about the key pieces of legislation and the key aspects of your work setting's policies and procedures in relation to moving and positioning individuals safely and correctly.

Being able to minimise risk and to prepare individuals before moving and positioning involves accessing risk assessment documentation, carrying out preparatory checks and communicating effectively with individuals. In this unit, you will also learn more about how to follow an individual's care plan, use equipment and involve

the individual, as well as how to report and record moving and positioning an individual, and when to seek advice and/or involve others.

By the end of this unit you will:

1 Understand anatomy and physiology in relation to moving and positioning individuals.
2 Understand legislation and agreed ways of working in relation to moving and positioning individuals.
3 Be able to minimise risk before moving and positioning individuals.
4 Be able to prepare individuals before moving and positioning.
5 Be able to move and position an individual.
6 Know when to seek advice from and/or involve others when moving and positioning an individual.

LO1 Understand anatomy and physiology in relation to moving and positioning individuals

AC 1.1 Outline the anatomy and physiology of the human body in relation to the importance of correct moving and positioning of individuals

To be able to move and position individuals safely and correctly you first need to have an understanding of the human body. You need to know how its various different parts are structured and how they relate to one another when the body moves from one position to another. Bones can become more brittle and can not only cause pain but also break more easily with the ageing process; this may result in reduced mobility.

The Human skeleton

The human skeleton is made up of 206 bones. Its functions include protecting the body and its organs, as well as moving the body and maintaining its shape. The main bones are in the: skull, spine, shoulder, arm, hand, chest, pelvis, leg, ankle and foot.

The Spine

The spine consists of five sections, each made up of individual bones or vertebrae (see Figure 15.1):

- the cervical spine (includes the neck and seven vertebrae)
- the thoracic spine (includes 12 vertebrae)
- the lumbar spine (the lower back, includes five vertebrae)
- the sacrum (includes five vertebrae)
- the coccyx (the base of the spine, includes four vertebrae).

Intervertebral discs are situated in between each vertebra. These act like cushions that are stretched or squeezed as the vertebrae move; they act as the

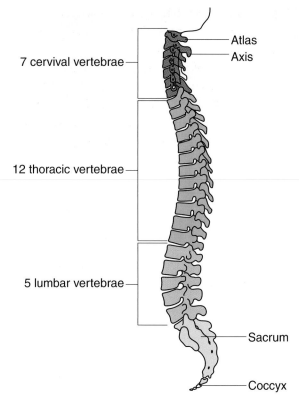

7 cervival vertebrae

Atlas

Axis

12 thoracic vertebrae

5 lumbar vertebrae

Sacrum

Coccyx

Figure 15.1 The spinal column

spine's shock absorbing system and help you to move.

Bones

Our bones are designed to be strong, but when too much pressure is exerted on them they can break or fracture. While moving and positioning individuals, for example, fractures can be caused by individuals being knocked by equipment and aids. Individuals being twisted when moving from one position to another or exerting pressure on individuals' limbs when moving them can also result in breaks or fractures. Joints such as the knee and shoulder may become stiffer and less flexible with the ageing process; this again may result in reduced mobility.

Joints

Joints are located where two or more bones connect; we use these to move our bodies. There are three different main types of joints in our bodies:

- Fibrous – immoveable joints that are held together by only a ligament, such as the bones in the skull.

> **Key terms**
>
> **Anatomy** means the structure of the human body.
>
> **Physiology** means the functions of different parts of the human body.

- Cartilaginous – partially moveable joints that are connected to bones with cartilage, such as the vertebrae in the spine.
- Synovial – moveable joints that are held in place by muscles and ligaments, such as the elbow and knee (see Figure 15.2). Ligaments connect bones and support joints to remain in place. There are six types of synovial joints that enable the body to move:
  - Pivot – allow one bone to rotate around another, such as at the top of the neck between the atlas and axis bones, which allows us to move our head from one side to another.
  - Ball and socket – allow bones to flex, extend and rotate, such as the shoulder and hip.
  - Condyloid – allow bones to flex and extend, such as the wrist.
  - Saddle – allow bones to flex, extend and rotate, such as the thumb.
  - Gliding – allow bones to glide, such as the wrist and ankle.
  - Hinge – allow bones to flex and extend, such as the elbow and knee.

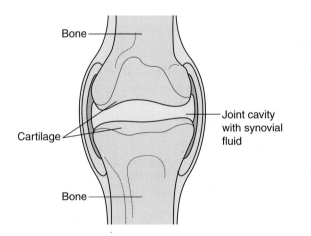

Figure 15.2 A synovial joint

Labels: Bone, Cartilage, Bone, Joint cavity with synovial fluid

Research and investigate

1.1 Anatomy and physiology

Research the anatomy and physiology of the human body in relation to moving and positioning. How is the human skeleton made up? What are the main bones? What are the main types of joints and muscles that can be found in the human body? Look into the functions of the cervical spine, thoracic spine, lumber spine, sacrum and coccyx

Like bones, joints can be damaged and ligaments sprained if a joint is forced into an unnatural movement, such as by a care worker not ensuring their body and spine are naturally aligned or when an individual is suddenly moved from a sitting to a standing position without prior warning.

Muscles

Muscles may become stiffer and lose their mass with the ageing process and when not used, thus making mobility more difficult. There are also three types of muscles found in the human body:

- Skeletal muscles are attached to the vertebrae. They enable a part of the body to move by changing length as they contract or shorten, such as bending the elbow from straight to fully flexed, caused by a contraction of the biceps muscle.
- Smooth or involuntary muscles use involuntary contractions and are attached to internal organs.
- Cardiac muscles are found only in the heart and also work by contracting.

Like bones and joints, muscles can be forced into an unnatural movement when individuals are being moved and positioned incorrectly, such as supporting an individual to stand by pulling on their arms or pushing on an individual's body to sit them up in their chair.

Our bodies are designed to enable us to move in different ways. There are certain positions that bring our bodies into natural alignment, where nothing is being forced or pulled. For example, a natural position for the body when starting to move and position an individual is referred to as the neutral position: standing upright, legs together, knees straight, toes pointing forwards, arms down by the sides and palms facing forwards. Moving in a way that is natural for the structure of our body prevents us, and those who we are supporting, from sustaining injuries or experiencing pain and distress.

AC 1.2 Describe the impact of specific conditions on the correct movement and positioning of an individual

Moving and positioning individuals safely and correctly must be done as part of their **plan of care**. This must also be done in line with the individual guidelines, policies and procedures in place in your work setting that you and your colleagues are required to read, understand and put into practice. Individuals' plans of care will include details about any specific conditions that they may have that affect how their bodies move. This information is used to risk assess and put into place moving and positioning practices that meet individuals' specific needs and that are safe to use. Read through Table 15.1, which details the impact of two specific conditions on the correct movement and positioning of individuals. Can you think of any others?

Specific condition	Impact on the correct movement and positioning of individuals
Brittle bone disease	Individuals who have brittle bone disease have significantly reduced bone strength, which makes their bones more susceptible to fractures. They also have very relaxed joints, which increases the likelihood of injuries. Ways of moving individuals safely, as well as seating and resting arrangements, need to be tailored to each individual.
Muscular dystrophy	Individuals who have muscular dystrophy have increased weakening and wasting of the muscles, which makes muscles more susceptible to damage. Some individuals who have this condition may be able to walk; others may need to use a wheelchair to mobilise. Common difficulties experienced by individuals who have this condition include increased fatigue as muscles deteriorate and poor balance due to muscles being weak. Safe techniques to use may include the use of specialist moving and positioning equipment, such as a **standing frame**.
Rheumatoid Arthritis	Individuals who have rheumatoid arthritis will have pain, swelling and stiffness of, for example, the joints in the shoulders, wrists, knees and ankles. Safe techniques to use may include avoiding placing too much pressure on these joints and supporting the affected joint when moving and positioning.
Parkinson's	Individuals who have Parkinson's will have stiff muscles and experience tremors as well as difficulties with their balance which makes their ability to move slower and more difficult. Safe techniques to use may include the use of specialist moving and positioning equipment such as a transfer board as well as providing individuals with sufficient time to move.
Amputation	Individuals who have had a limb amputated will have pain and reduced mobility if their muscles are not used and tighten up which can limit an individual's ability to move around. Safe techniques to use include supporting the limbs affected and maintaining their alignment during moving and positioning.
Cerebral Palsy	Individuals who have cerebral palsy will have stiff and rigid muscles in several limbs which will make moving around and co-ordination to do so difficult. Some individuals may find it difficult to stay in one position for long or to complete small movements. Safe techniques to use include the use of mobility aids such as a walking frame.
Stroke	Individuals who have had a stroke may experience difficulties with being able to move around as well as pain and stiffness in their muscles. Safe techniques to use may include supporting and aligning the body during and after moves such as by ensuring the weaker limb is supported during the move and after when being re-positioned with, for example, pillows.

Table 15.1 The impact of conditions on the correct movement and positioning of individuals

Case study

1.1, 1.2 Ismet

Ismet is a senior residential care worker. As part of his job role he provides support with personal care tasks, including moving and positioning, to individuals who have Parkinson's disease.

1 What impact can Parkinson's disease have on the correct moving and positioning of different individuals? Why?
2 How can Ismet support individuals with correct moving and positioning?
3 How are safe practices for moving and positioning related to the anatomy and physiology of the human body?

Evidence activity

1.1, 1.2 Anatomy and physiology

- Produce a presentation for a group of carers to explain the importance of correct moving and positioning of individuals in relation to the anatomy and physiology of the human body.
- Provide details of the impact of three specific conditions on the correct movement and positioning of individuals.

Time to think

1.1, 1.2 Do you understand the anatomy and physiology of the human body?

Read through again the details included in ACs 1.1 and 1.2 of the anatomy and physiology of the human body.

How is this related to the correct moving and positioning of individuals?

LO2 Understand legislation and agreed ways of working when moving and positioning individuals

AC 2.1 Describe how legislation and agreed ways of working affect working practices related to moving and positioning individuals

Safe practices and correct techniques for moving and positioning individuals are underpinned by legislation, your work setting's policies and procedures, and guidelines for individuals that may also be in place. Complying with legislation such as that shown in Table 15.2 will ensure that you and your employer protect individuals, yourself and others from injuries and accidents, fulfil your legal requirements, and follow best practice.

The agreed ways of working that you have in your work setting will also enable you to follow current, safe and correct techniques that are suitable for the needs of each individual you and others assist with moving and positioning. Agreed ways of working will include important details about the individual and the factors that must be taken into account when moving and positioning, such as:

- how the moving or positioning activity is to be carried out, e.g. where, by whom, how
- whether the individual has a specific condition that will affect this, e.g. one that may restrict their movement or make the move difficult
- whether there is any specific equipment or aid that needs to be used, such as a hoist
- whether there are any constraints in the environment where the moving and positioning activity is to be carried out, such as a small space or a slippery floor
- it is important that you and your employer are fully aware of the maximum weights that can be lifted safely; it is important that you both refer to the guidance provided by the HSE.

Being aware of the legislation that exists and understanding your own work setting's agreed ways of working, including how these affect working practices related to moving and positioning individuals, will promote the safety, health and well-being of individuals, yourself and

Legislation	It relates to moving and positioning individuals by stating that:
Health & Safety at Work etc. Act (HASAWA) 1974	• Risks must be identified, controlled and reduced. • Information and training must be provided and complied with. • Equipment must be provided and maintained.
Management of Health & Safety at Work Regulations (MHSWR) 1999	• **Risk assessments** must be undertaken. • Potential **hazards** and risks must be identified. • Risks must be evaluated.
Workplace (Health, Safety and Welfare) Regulations 1992	• Employers must ensure the health and safety and welfare of employees. • Employers must provide a safe environment. • Equipment must be maintained.
Manual Handling Operations Regulations (MHOR) 1992 (as amended 2002)	• Employers must avoid where possible any hazardous manual handling activities • Risks must be assessed (i.e. what the task involves, and the load, the environment as well as the needs and skills of the handler). • The risks of injury must be reduced.
Lifting Operations and Lifting Equipment Regulations (LOLER) 1998	• Equipment used must be fit for purpose and maintained. • Problems with equipment must be reported and recorded.

Table 15.2 Moving and handling legislation

others with whom you work. This will not only prevent accidents from occurring but may also reduce the risks of injury to you and others.

Key terms

Risk assessment is the framework for identifying, avoiding, minimising and controlling potential dangers.

A hazard is a danger that exists and has the potential to cause harm.

Research and investigate

2.1 Agreed ways of working

Find out from your manager how legislation and agreed ways of working affect practices for moving and positioning individuals in your work setting.

Time to think

2.1 Do you know the legislation and your agreed ways of working?

Read through your work setting's policies and procedures for moving and positioning individuals.

What do these say about moving and positioning individuals and the relevant legislation that underpins them?

AC 2.2 Describe what health and safety factors need to be taken into account when moving and positioning individuals, and any equipment used to do this

This section looks at the key health and safety factors to consider when moving and positioning individuals and using equipment. It includes important points in relation to the moving and positioning activity, the load you are moving or positioning, and the environment in which you are working.

Think about the key health and safety factors that you would need to consider if you were required to assist an individual to move from a chair to their bed:

● **The moving and positioning activity:** Why are you carrying out this activity? Is this achievable? Are you familiar with your work setting's policies and procedures for moving and positioning individuals? If so, have you read and understood them? Are you wearing suitable clothing and footwear? Will assisting the individual to move from a chair to a bed involve you bending down, stooping down low or adjusting the height of the bed? How will you do this safely? How long will it take? Will it require two of you to support the individual to move safely; if so how will you co-ordinate your movements? Will it require the use of equipment and aids? If so, how will you make sure these are clean, in good working order and safe to use?

- **The load or people you are moving or positioning:** Have you read through the individual's care plan and risk assessment? Are there any moving guidelines specific to this individual? If so, have you read and understood them? Does the individual have any specific conditions that may affect how you move and position them? Have you discussed the move with the individual? Has the individual taken part in this activity before or is it their first time? Have you assessed the individual prior to the move for any changes to their health and well-being that may be present? Have you assessed the individual in terms of their weight and height and the type and size of equipment to use? Can the individual weight-bear? Is the individual unsteady? What is the individual's general mobility? Do you know how to promote the individual's independence and encourage them to do as much as they can for themselves? Do you know how to take into account any medical equipment that the individual may have attached such as a catheter?

- **Yourself and others:** Have you been trained in moving this individual and using the equipment and aids that this individual may require? Do you feel confident and competent to do so? Have your colleagues been trained? Are the right people, and the number, available to carry out the procedure? Do they feel confident and competent to do so? If you have any questions or require any assistance do you know who you can go to in your work setting? What is the state of your health and well-being? Do you have the correct clothing and footwear for the procedure, and are you wearing this correctly?

- **The environment in which you are working:** Have you assessed the environment where the move will take place for any likely dangers? Will there be sufficient space to carry out the move? Do any small items of furniture require moving prior to the move to enable it to happen safely? Are there any hazards such as uneven surface levels, or any other obstructions that may cause you to trip over? How will you protect the individual's privacy and dignity during the move, e.g. will you close a door or a curtain? Is the temperature in the room comfortable, i.e. not too hot or too cold?

  Ensuring that you plan how you move and position individuals, including how you take into account relevant health and safety factors, is integral to understanding and following your agreed ways of working in your work setting and the legislation requirements that underpin these.

- **The equipment you will need:** Have you checked whether the equipment is safe to use? Has it been maintained properly? Is it available when you need it? Is it safe to use? Is it in good working order? Has the individual used the equipment before? Did the individual experience any difficulties with using it?

Case study

2.1, 2.2 Sharon

Sharon is a senior residential carer, and today will be inducting a new carer in relation to moving and positioning two individuals who have physical disabilities.

1 What details will Sharon provide to the new carer about how legislation and agreed ways of working affect working practices related to moving and positioning individuals?
2 What details will Sharon provide to the new carer about the health and safety factors to be taken into account when moving and positioning individuals and any equipment used to do this?

LO3 Be able to minimise risk before moving and positioning individuals

AC 3.1 Access up-to-date copies of risk assessment documentation

Now that you have learned more about the legislation and agreed ways of working that are relevant to moving and positioning individuals, including the health and safety factors that must be taken into account, let us think about the different ways you can minimise **risk** before moving and positioning individuals.

Records of risk assessments undertaken for moving and positioning individuals are very important as they can be used to pass on information to others and are evidence that risks prior to a move have not only been identified but are also being monitored and reviewed on an on-going basis.

Risk assessments must be kept secure as they contain **personal** and in some cases **sensitive information**, but their contents must still be accessible to all those who need to read and understand them before moving and positioning individuals.

It is important that risk assessment documentation is revised every time there is a change – such as in relation to an additional risk, a change in the individual's health and well-being, or a change in working practices – so that the details recorded on the documentation are up to date and can be complied with when moving and positioning individuals. Risk assessments must be completed every time you move and position individuals; it is also important to check these before every move in case of any changes that have arisen.

AC 3.2 Carry out preparatory checks using the individual's care plan and the moving and handling risk assessment

Accessing up-to-date copies of risk assessments before moving and positioning individuals is part of the numerous preparatory checks that must be carried out before moving and positioning individuals to ensure that the move can be carried out safely and competently. You will need to think about the individual's moving and positioning needs, including whether they can be involved in the procedure as well as how their general health and well-being may affect their moving and positioning.

The individual's **care plan** is an important document. It includes specific information about the individual that you will need to know before moving them, such as their weight and height, as well as details of any specific conditions they have that may affect how they are moved and positioned. This will also include what the individual is able to do themselves, the level of support they require, whether they have any medical conditions or other limitations, if they have previously experienced any difficulties with the equipment used to move them, how they mobilise, and how often they will require moving to another position.

The **moving and handling risk assessment** is another important document that is crucial to carrying out preparatory checks. This relates to the practices and techniques that have been agreed for carrying out the actual moving and positioning activity. It includes the individual's specific requirements, including their level of participation in the activity and how to remove potential dangers and minimise potential risks that may exist in the immediate environment before moving and positioning the individual.

AC 3.3 Identify any immediate risks to the individual

Being able to minimise risk before moving and positioning individuals involves being vigilant and using your knowledge of the individuals with whom you work, in order to identify whether there are any IMMEDIATE risks to the individuals. Do this by:

I **I**dentifying any unusual changes in the individual, such as in their mood or health.

M **M**onitoring the unusual changes you notice.

M **M**onitoring how you and others are feeling, such as your levels of fatigue.

E **E**xamining carefully the safety and cleanliness of the equipment to be used.

D **D**eciding how the environment may place the individual at risk, such as if there is a slippery floor or a gloomy corridor.

I **I**dentifying whether the working conditions are suitable, such as that there is sufficient light, space.

A **A**cting within the remit of your job role and responsibilities, i.e. only doing what you have been trained to do.

T **T**rusting your instincts – if you feel something is wrong, you're probably right.

E **E**stablishing whether you and others are trained and feel competent to carry out the activity.

AC 3.4 Describe actions to take in relation to identified risks

It is very important to ensure that risks are reduced as much as possible to avoid causing any danger, illness or harm to individuals, or to you or others once they have been identified in relation to moving and positioning individuals. The actions to take in relation to identified risks will depend on what the risks are, the severity of those risks, and your job role and responsibilities, as well as on the agreed ways of working in your work setting.

The key actions to take when risks have been identified include not only the preparatory checks you learned about in AC 3.2, but also the following measures, which are aimed at reducing them, and relate to:

- **Your competence:** Only carry out moving and positioning activities within the remit of your job role, after having the required training, and provided that you feel confident and well to be able to do so. If you do not feel confident or physically fit then seek additional support from a senior colleague.

- **Assistance from others:** Always report any measures for reducing risks about which you feel concerned; be prepared to explain why you are concerned. Report any unsafe practices that you observe or any difficulties you have in following the manufacturer's instructions for the use of equipment and aids.

In situations when it is difficult to remove a risk, such as when supporting an individual who is unsteady from falling when going outside for a walk, a risk assessment must be done to determine the level of risk; the higher the level of risk, the more severe the likelihood of harm will be. Risk control measures must then be put in place to minimise the risks if these cannot be eliminated and may consist of one or several controls. For example, providing two health or social care workers to support the individual to go for a walk outside as well as the use of a mobility aid. Similarly, any new risks identified must also be documented in an individual's plan of care, including when an individual refuses to co-operate in a move.

AC 3.5 Describe what action should be taken if the individual's wishes conflict with their plan of care in relation to health and safety and their risk assessment

As discussed in AC 3.1, minimising risk before moving and positioning individuals involves accessing up-to-date copies of risk assessment documentation, including individuals' plans of care and moving and positioning guidelines. What would you do if an individual's wishes were in conflict with these?

Before deciding on the actions to take, you must try and find out why an individual disagrees with their care plan and risk assessment. There could be a number of reasons for this, some examples of which are given below. Once you have established what the reason is, you can then begin to try and work with the individual to address this, as shown below.

- For an individual who has recently moved into a new care setting and doesn't wish to depend on others in being assisted to move and position, it may help if you or someone they know well spends some time ensuring the individual feels settled and understands the role of others in the team. You must also report this incident to a person in a more senior position to you.
- An individual who feels afraid of being moved in a hoist may benefit from seeing you or others in a hoist first. They may also like to try the hoist first without it being moved. You may also be able to suggest to a person in a more senior position alternative equipment or aids that the individual could use, with which they may feel more comfortable.
- When it becomes evident that an individual does not fully understand how their wishes are in conflict with their plan of care, listen to their views and respect them. You can then spend some time explaining why it is important to follow their plan of care and risk assessment. If the individual takes the decision to disagree with you, as is their right, you should respect this decision and explain politely that although you respect their right to make their own choices and decisions, you are unable to comply with their wishes as that may put you, them or

others at risk. Let them know that you will seek additional assistance from someone in a more senior position to you to help them.

It is important that the needs of the individual remain the focus and that a balance between their needs and wishes and the health or social care worker's rights is maintained. If an individual changes their mind on how much support they require when being moved:

- take their views seriously
- document this in their plan of care and inform your manager.
- Remember, it is important to encourage individuals to be independent and take control of their moving and handling activities as long as this is within their abilities and limitations.

AC 3.6 Prepare the immediate environment, ensuring that there is adequate space for the move in agreement with all concerned and that potential hazards are removed

Prior to moving and positioning individuals you must also be able to minimise risk in your working environment. Some of the preparatory checks we considered in AC 2.2 included ensuring there is sufficient space, removing potential hazards such as small items of furniture, protecting the individual's privacy and dignity, and ensuring the conditions are comfortable in the environment in which you are working.

Figure 15.3 details the important questions to ask yourself when ensuring that there is adequate space for the move in agreement with all concerned and that potential hazards are removed.

> Is there sufficient space to move with ease? Is there sufficient space to use equipment and aids? Is there sufficient space to carry out the move safely? What do I need to do if there isn't adequate space? How will I gain the agreement of all those involved?

- Adequate Space

> What are the potential hazards? Who do these hazards place at risk? Why? What do I need to do? Why? How will I gain the agreement of all those involved?

- Potential Hazards

Figure 15.3 Questions to ask when preparing the immediate environment

Ensuring that there is adequate space for the move to be carried out and that potential hazards are removed before moving and positioning individuals will reduce the risk of you, your colleagues or individuals getting injured. For example, we learned in AC 1.1 how carrying out unsafe manoeuvres, e.g. in places where there is very little space, could cause an individual's bone to fracture, or a care worker's joints to be damaged and ligaments sprained if their body and spine are not naturally aligned before carrying out a move. Muscles in both care workers and individuals can also be forced into an unnatural movement when individuals are moved and positioned incorrectly, such as supporting an individual to stand by pulling on their arms.

Ensuring you have the agreement of all concerned must also be part of your preparatory checks so as to promote the individual's rights, encourage their co-operation in the move, and comply with the remit of your job role and responsibilities in relation to moving furniture or items such as a small table or television.

Other things to consider include ensuring there are no risks or trip hazards, and that any equipment that is attached to the individual can move while the person is moved and handled otherwise it may obstruct the move, cause an accident to the health or social care worker or even injure the individual. Remember the importance of returning all equipment afterwards to its correct location so that it can be located easily afterwards when needed.

Time to think

3.6 LO3 Can you minimise risks before moving and positioning individuals?

Next time you move and position an individual reflect on how you prepared the immediate environment.

- How did you ensure there was adequate space for the move?
- How did you ensure you removed potential hazards?
- How did you obtain agreement from all those involved?

AC 3.7 Apply standard precautions for infection prevention and control

Minimising risk before moving and positioning individuals not only relates to reducing the occurrence of potential accidents and injuries but also to the prevention of illnesses and fatalities that may occur as a result of **infections**. Before moving and positioning individuals it is very important that you apply standard **precautions** for infection prevention and control.

Hands

One of the main ways that infections can spread from person to person in health and social care settings is via our hands. Before moving and positioning individuals it is therefore important that you wash your hands (see Unit IC 01 AC 6.2), as prior to the move you may have been carrying out other tasks that may have brought you into contact with different individuals, with body fluids or other **hazardous materials** such as used laundry or waste products. Ensure you wash your hands after coming into contact with a patient and before working with another.

General health and hygiene

As well as washing your hands effectively it is also important you look after your health and hygiene so that you do not spread infections to individuals and others at work. Ensuring that you are not unwell when you are working, have had all necessary vaccinations and boosters, cover any breaks in the skin with a dressing, and follow medical advice, for example in relation to health or skin conditions, is essential for infection prevention and control.

Key terms

Infection is the process of contamination.

Precautions are measures taken in advance to prevent infections from occurring.

Hazardous materials are materials that have the potential to cause harm and illness.

Clean uniforms

Maintaining a good overall level of personal hygiene is key to preventing infections spreading. Before moving and positioning individuals it is important that you are wearing clean clothes and shoes, and that jewellery and other accessories are removed as these can be routes for infection and can also cause tears in aprons and gloves. You must also put on disposable gloves prior to moving and positioning an individual as doing so will act as an additional barrier to infection. Ensure you do not wear your uniform outside as this could spread infection and bacteria.

Equipment

As well as via our hands, infections can also be spread via objects that are contaminated. This includes moving and positioning equipment and aids such as hoists, slings and walking frames. Making preparatory checks that these are clean both before and after use will reduce the risk of infections spreading.

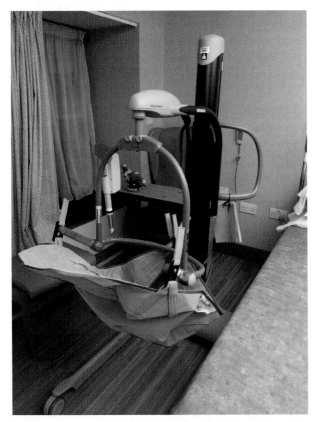

Figure 15.4 Infections can be spread via equipment such as hoists and slings if they are not cleaned properly.

3.6, 3.7 **Time to think**

Can you minimise risks before moving and positioning individuals?

Reflect on the three individuals you chose for the Evidence Activity on minimising risk and the different precautions you applied for infection prevention and control.

Were there any differences between the precautions you applied for each individual? Why?

LO4 Be able to prepare individuals before moving and positioning

AC 4.1 Demonstrate effective communication with the individual to ensure they understand the details and reasons for the action/activity being undertaken and agree the level of support required

Effective communication will involve you knowing how each individual prefers to communicate, i.e. using words, pictures, sounds or signs, and then ensuring you use their preferred **communication system** to explain why the moving and positioning activity is being undertaken and what it will involve. In this way you involve the individual in the moving and positioning and can begin to build up trust and a sense of working in partnership with individuals, where you are providing them with opportunities to actively ask questions about the activity. You are also allowing them to share with you any concerns they may have about the activity or any suggestions they may have for carrying out the activity in a different way. Effective communication is a two-way process where you too must listen and observe the individual to ascertain how they feel about the activity or action and whether they understand the details and agree to it being undertaken.

Key term

Communication system means the unique methods used by an individual to communicate; can include words, sounds, pictures, signs.

Ensuring that you agree with individuals the level of support they require is also very important. Sometimes it can be difficult for an individual to express or know what level of support they require if they have never undertaken the activity or action before. Breaking down the activity or action into smaller parts and using objects as discussion points (e.g. the equipment, aids, seating) can mean the individual feels less inhibited to say what they think and feel. This will enable them to be more likely to retain a sense of ownership, as well as to maintain their independence and dignity. Agreeing the level of support with individuals in this way again means that you will be able to find out more specific information about individuals' likes, dislikes, needs, choices and preferences. Remember too that the level of support individuals require will vary even with the same individual, for example due to an individual feeling unwell or deciding that they would like to participate in a different way. So as well as their care plan it is very important that you agree with individuals the level of support required every time you provide assistance with moving and positioning.

You can do this by speaking clearly and avoiding using any difficult to understand words, making eye contact and ensuring you reassure the individual if they become upset or distressed. Remember too that this also applies to individuals who are unconscious or semi-conscious as they may still be able to hear what you say.

AC 4.2 Obtain valid consent for the planned activity

Preparing individuals before moving and positioning must also involve obtaining their agreement or permission for the planned activity. Obtaining valid consent is not only an important part of effective care and support but is also underpinned by legislation such as the Human Rights Act 1998 and the Mental Capacity Act 2005. For consent to be valid it must be in line with the UK's definition of valid consent, given **voluntarily**, be **informed** and the individual giving the consent must have the **capacity** to do so.

● For consent to be given **voluntarily** for a moving and positioning activity, permission for the activity must be solely the individual's decision and must not be influenced by you or a colleague or by someone else they know well. In other words the individual must be free to decide whether or not they agree to the planned activity.

- For consent to be **informed** the individual must be provided with all the information they require and it must be in a format that they can understand in order to make the decision themselves. This will involve providing the individual with details about the reasons for the planned activity, what it will involve and why the activity is required, as well as the consequences of the planned activity not going ahead.
- **Capacity** requires an individual to be able to understand the information provided to them and be able to use it to make a decision regarding whether or not they want to give their consent for the planned activity.

When individuals demonstrate that they are able to consent to the planned activity then it is your and other professionals' **duty of care** to respect their decision. When individuals demonstrate that the consent they have given is not valid – either due to it not being voluntary, or information not being provided in a format that they could understand, or the individual not having the capacity to make an informed decision – then you must seek advice from a more senior colleague immediately and not proceed with the activity. The process that you must follow to obtain consent must also be in accordance with your work setting's policy and procedure and within the remit of your job role and responsibilities.

It is important to obtain consent every time you carry out the activity as an individual may change their mind. It is also important to be aware that some individuals may lack the capacity to make decisions i.e. as per the Mental Capacity Act 2005, such as an individual who has dementia or an individual with mental health needs or a learning disability who is unable to give informed consent for their care. It is important to ensure that their best interests are safeguarded and that their rights are upheld.

See unit HSC 036 for more information on consent.

See unit HSC 036 for more information on consent.

Case study

4.1, 4.2 Michelle

Michelle is supporting Lianne to use a ceiling hoist for the first time today to transfer from her bed to her wheelchair. Lianne communicates using a mixture of sounds, objects of reference and eye contact.

1 How can Michelle ensure that Lianne understands the details and reason for the activity?
2 How can Michelle agree the level of support required with Lianne?
3 How can Michelle obtain Lianne's valid consent for this activity?

Evidence activity

4.1, 4.2 Effective communication and consent

- Reflect on two individuals you support with moving and positioning activities who use different communication systems. For each, detail how you support them to understand the details and reasons for the activities, and also with understanding the level of support required and obtaining valid consent. What are the differences in the support you provide to each individual? Why is this?
- You will also need to be observed by your assessor demonstrating effective communication with an individual to ensure that they understand the details and reasons for the action/activity being undertaken and agree the level of support required, and that you obtain valid consent for the planned activity.

Time to think

4.2 To consent or not consent?

Reflect on the different methods you use to obtain valid consent for the moving and positioning activities with which you support different individuals. Why do you use different methods?

Key term

Duty of care is a professional's ethical and legal responsibility to safeguard and protect the well-being of others.

Research and investigate

4.2 Consent

Research the UK's definition of valid consent.

LO5 Be able to move and position an individual

AC 5.1 Follow the care plan to ensure that the individual is positioned using the agreed technique and in a way that avoids causing undue pain or discomfort

As we learned in AC 3.2, reading and understanding the information included in individuals' care plans must form part of the preparatory checks for moving and positioning individuals safely. Following individuals' care plans will ensure that you are using only techniques that have been agreed and that avoid causing undue pain or discomfort. Working in this way will also mean that you are not only complying with your work setting's agreed ways of working but also fulfilling your legal and professional duties and responsibilities.

Following an individual's CARE PLAN involves:

C   Checking the care plan every time.

A   Agreeing to use only techniques that have been detailed in the care plan, that are safe to use, and that you and others have been trained in and are competent to use.

R   Risk assessing the individual, activity and environment before and during the activity.

E   Explaining to the individual what you and all those others involved in the activity are doing.

P   Planning every moving and positioning activity with the individual and all those others involved in the activity.

L   Listening, observing and monitoring individuals' reactions before and during the activity.

A   Alerting others immediately to any concerns or difficulties that arise during the activity, and knowing when to stop the activity.

N   Never forgetting to record afterwards the activity you completed, what was involved, how effective it was and your suggestions for any changes needed, as well as when the next moving and positioning activity is due.

AC 5.2 Demonstrate effective communication with any others involved in the manoeuvre

Moving and positioning individuals safely also involves effective communication with your colleagues and others such as individuals' families, advocates and physiotherapists. Effective communication must take place before, during and after all manoeuvres.

- **Before** moving and positioning individuals it is important to find out that all others involved have read and understood the individual's care plan, risk assessment and any other moving and handling guidelines in place so that you are all in possession of the same knowledge and therefore can be consistent in your working approaches. It is also important to agree how you will work together to achieve the manoeuvre smoothly and who will be the person responsible for leading the manoeuvre.
- **During** moving and positioning individuals you must ensure that everyone complies with the person leading the manoeuvre; this will involve listening to them and following their commands and ensuring that everyone is ready.
- **After** moving and positioning individuals it is important that you are able to communicate how the activity went with all those others involved, included what worked, what didn't and how could this be improved; documenting the findings is also essential.

AC 5.3 Describe the aids and equipment that may be used for moving and positioning

Moving and positioning may involve using specific aids and equipment that have been agreed as part of individuals' care plans and that will enable them to move and position safely, comfortably and, for some, more independently.

Remember that equipment can be split into three different types: equipment that carries the full weight of the person, i.e. a hoist; equipment that carries some of an individual's weight, i.e. a transfer board; equipment that assists the individual to move from one position to another, i.e. a glide sheet.

Read through Table 15.3, which includes some examples of aids and equipment used for moving and positioning individuals. Do you use any others?

All equipment used under the Lifting Operations and Lifting Equipment Regulations (LOLER) 1998

must be checked to ensure it is safe every time it is used. If it is faulty or unsafe then it must not be used, others must be informed and it must be removed from use. You must only use lifting equipment if you have been trained to do so and you have read and understood the manufacturer's instructions.

Research and investigate

5.3 Aids and equipment
Find out the range of aids and equipment that are available for the individuals with whom you work.

Aids for moving and positioning individuals	**Bed hoist poles** to enable an individual to sit up in bed.
	Immoturn aids to assist an individual to turn on to their side while in bed.
	Leg lifters to enable individuals to independently move an immobile leg, for example when placing it on a footstool.
	Seat assists to enable individuals to independently lift themselves safely up out of a chair.
	Walking frames to enable an individual to walk independently.
	Wedges to enable an individual to sit up in bed comfortably, for example.
	Wheelchairs to enable individuals to mobilise.
Equipment for moving and positioning individuals	**Electric ceiling hoists** to enable an individual to transfer from their bed to their chair, for example.
	Fixed bath hoists to enable an individual to get in and out of the bath.
	Mobile hoist to enable an individual to get out of a chair, for example
	Slings that are colour coded to enable individuals of different weights and heights to be safely lifted in a hoist.
	Glide sheets to enable an individual to re-position while sitting and lying.
	Handling belts to enable an individual to maintain a comfortable and steady position while moving.
	Manual hoists to enable an individual to transfer from a wheelchair to an armchair, for example.
	Slings to support individuals in a comfortable position in a hoist.
	Transfer boards to enable individuals to transfer from their wheelchair to a car seat, for example.
	Turntables to enable individuals to turn round safely and easily.

Table 15.3 Types of aids and equipment

AC 5.4 Use equipment to maintain the individual in the appropriate position

Now that you have learned more about the different types of aids and equipment for moving and positioning individuals, it is important that you are also aware of equipment that is available to maintain individuals in the appropriate position. This will mean not only that individuals will feel safe and retain their dignity and independence, but will also reduce the strain on you and others of supporting them to do so. For example:

- Foot boards are used to enable individuals to stay sitting upright in bed and prevent them from slipping downwards.
- Standing frames are used to support individuals to stand, for example after spending a whole day sitting down in their wheelchairs.
- Wedges are used to support individuals to sit up, for example on a floor mat. Pillows can act as a support to enable an individual with a weakness to a limb to remain in an upright posture when sitting in a chair, for example.

All these pieces of equipment are designed to ensure individuals remain safe, comfortable and as independent as possible.

AC 5.5 Encourage the individual's active participation in the manoeuvre

Working in partnership with individuals involves respecting their rights to take an active part in moving and positioning manoeuvres; this includes involving individuals before, during and after all manoeuvres. When planning each manoeuvre, an individual's choices, views and requirements must underpin all activities agreed. During each manoeuvre it is important to involve the individual as much as they want to be involved and always to obtain their agreement when doing so. After each manoeuvre it is crucial to remember to ask the individual what the experience was like for them and whether they have any suggestions

for improvements that could be made. The most effective manoeuvres are those where individuals are actively involved in the whole process from start to finish.

AC 5.6 Monitor the individual throughout the activity so that the procedure can be stopped if there is any adverse reaction

Alerting others immediately to any concerns or difficulties that arise during the activity and knowing when to stop the activity forms part of your responsibilities to support individuals by using agreed techniques that avoid causing pain or discomfort. Individuals may react adversely if they are in pain, feel unsafe or become suddenly unwell. Individuals who are unconscious or

> ### Key term
>
> **Active participation** is a way of working that recognises an individual's right to participate in the activities and relationships of everyday life as independently as possible; the individual is regarded as an active partner in their own care or support, rather than a passive recipient.

> ### Case study
>
> **5.2, 5.3, 5.5** Chris
>
> Chris is working with two less experienced colleagues this morning. He has been asked to work together with them to support an individual who has dementia and poor mobility to get dressed; the individual uses a ceiling hoist.
>
> 1 How can Chris communicate effectively with both his colleagues when using the hoist?
> 2 What other aids and equipment may be useful for this individual?
> 3 How can Chris and his colleagues encourage the individual to be actively involved in the manoeuvre?

confused they may not be able to express this and so it is important that you seek advice from someone who knows them well and may be able to advise you such as the individual's GP or advocate or family.

Below are examples of ways to MONITOR the individual throughout the activity.

M **M**easure the individual's blood pressure.

O **O**bserve the individual's facial expressions and body language.

N **N**ote any changes to the individual's ability to take part in the move.

I **I**nsight into possible adverse reactions the individual may show.

T **T**raining on monitoring different individuals.

O **O**bservations at regular intervals throughout the activity.

R **R**ecording adverse effects so these can be referenced when required.

AC 5.7 Demonstrate how to report and record the activity, noting when the next positioning manoeuvre is due

Reporting the activity, including when the next positioning manoeuvre is due, provides verbal information quickly to the nominated person and may relate to how the activity was undertaken, how the individual was actively involved, the effectiveness of the equipment used, and any accidents, incidents or adverse reactions that arose involving the individual, you or others.

Recording the activity in an individual's care plan, including when the next positioning manoeuvre is due, provides up-to-date written information and a permanent record that can be referred to when making any necessary changes to future manoeuvres planned with the individual. Similarly, any accidents, incidents and near misses must also be recorded to comply with agreed ways of working and with legislative requirements.

Evidence activity

5.1, 5.2, 5.3, 5.4, 5.5, 5.6, 5.7 Moving and positioning an individual

- Reflect on an individual you support to move and position. Produce a case study of this individual that details the techniques that have been agreed and are used, the aids and equipment that are used for moving and positioning, as well as how the individual is encouraged to participate actively in the manoeuvres.
- You will also need to be observed by your assessor demonstrating how to:
  - follow an individual's care plan
  - communicate effectively with others involved in the manoeuvre
  - maintain the individual in the appropriate position
  - encourage the individual's active participation
  - monitor the individual throughout the activity
  - report and record the activity and when the next manoeuvre is due.

Time to think

5.7 Do you know your work setting's reporting and recording procedures?

Reflect on an occasion when you had to report and record a moving and positioning activity.

- Did you follow your work setting's procedures?

LO6 Know when to seek advice from and/or involve others when moving and positioning an individual

AC 6.1 Describe when advice and/ or assistance should be sought to move or handle an individual safely

Being able to move and position individuals safely involves being aware of the situations that require you to seek advice and/or involve others. This acronym will HELP you to remember when these situations may arise:

H **H**aving concerns over your or others' competence – ensure you and/or others request training as soon as possible and never attempt to move or position an individual without training.

E **E**xperiencing illness or tiredness – do not attempt the move, seek advice from your manager.

L **L**acking in confidence over whether the move is still appropriate for the individual – seek advice from your manager and do not attempt the move.

P **P**ressure from others to carry out an unsafe move or one that has not been agreed as part of an individual's care plan – do not attempt the move, speak to your manager about the situation.

You may also need advice for unplanned situations that may arise during moving and handling procedures such as when your or an individual's condition suddenly deteriorates during the move or a piece of equipment stops working.

AC 6.2 Describe what sources of information are available relating to moving and positioning individuals

You have just read in AC 6.1 how your manager can be a valuable source of information when seeking advice or assistance with moving and positioning individuals safely. Depending on your work setting there may also be other people you could approach, such as the health and safety representative or senior colleagues, as well as the individuals themselves and other professionals such as physiotherapists and back care advisors. Records and documents – such as individuals' care plans, **moving and handling guidelines** and risk assessments – are other unique sources of information. Externally there are a number of useful organisations that you could approach, such as the Health and Safety Executive and the Back Care Organisation, both of which have websites, training and publications that you and others can access. You can find out more about the causes of back pain, how to prevent this as well as how to

manage any back injuries you may have sustained either recently or in the past.

Key term

Moving and handling guidelines are specific techniques to use to move and position an individual.

Case study

6.1, 6.2 Marcelle

Marcelle has recently been appointed as a senior carer and would like to improve her knowledge of moving and positioning individuals.

1 When should Marcelle seek advice/assistance in relation to moving and positioning individuals?
2 What sources of information are available to Marcelle?

Time to think

6.2 Do you know the sources of information available?

Make a list of all the sources of information that are available to you relating to moving and positioning individuals safely.

How many of these do you use?

Research and investigate

6.2 Training

Research types of training that are available on moving and positioning individuals.

Evidence activity

6.1, 6.2 Seeking advice

Reflect on two occasions when you or someone you know sought advice and/or assistance to move and handle an individual. What actions were taken and why? What sources of information were accessed and why?

Legislation

- Human Rights Act 1998
- Manual Handling Operations Regulations (MHOR) 1992 (as amended 2002)
- Mental Capacity Act 2005
- Workplace (Health, Safety and Welfare) Regulations 1992

Useful resources

Websites

Back Care Organisation

www.backcare.org.uk

Health and Safety Executive

www.hse.gov.uk

Infection Control Services

http://infectioncontrolservices.co.uk

Public Health England

www.gov.uk/government/organisations/public-health-england

Publications

Health and Safety Executive (1997) *Successful Health and Safety Management* (guidance booklet). Sudbury: HSE Books.

Bateman, M. (2006) *Tolley's Practical Risk Assessment Handbook*. Abingdon: Taylor & Francis.

Unit HSC 3003

Provide support to maintain and develop skills for everyday life

This unit is worth 4 credits

What are you finding out?

In this unit you will learn about the knowledge and skills required to work with individuals to retain, regain and develop skills for everyday life. You will learn more about the different methods for developing and maintaining individuals' skills for everyday life and the benefits of doing so, and the reasons why individuals may need support.

Being able to support individuals to plan for maintaining and developing skills for everyday life will be explored in this unit, including how to work in partnership with individuals and others. You will also learn more about how to provide effective support to individuals who wish to retain, regain or develop skills for everyday life and how to evaluate this with individuals and others.

By the end of this unit you will:

1 Understand the context of supporting skills for everyday life.
2 Be able to support individuals to plan for maintaining and developing skills for everyday life.
3 Be able to support individuals to retain, regain or develop skills for everyday life.
4 Be able to evaluate support for developing or maintaining skills for everyday life.

LO1 Understand the context of supporting skills for everyday life

AC 1.1 Compare methods for developing and maintaining skills for everyday life

As you learned from previous units, individuals who require care or support have unique needs, beliefs, values, preferences, strengths, abilities and wishes. As such, the methods that are used with individuals for developing and maintaining skills for everyday life will also vary depending on their unique characteristics.

It is important that you and others who are involved in individuals' lives and important to their well-being – such as family, advocates, colleagues, your line manager, and specialists such as **occupational therapists** and **physiotherapists** – support individuals to do as much for themselves as possible so that they continue to maintain the skills they currently have and are able to develop new skills. This method of working with individuals is referred to as **active participation** and can include many different approaches to supporting the individual to adapt their living environment, make use of **assistive technology** and improve their social well-being, as well as manage their mental and physical health.

Factors

Individuals can be supported to develop a range of different types of skills, such as those required for independent living, i.e. shopping or cleaning or for personal care, i.e. washing or grooming, or for developing relationships, i.e. communication. It is important that individuals' capacity and abilities are taken into account, including their awareness and understanding of safety aspects and the consequences of not complying with these.

Approaches can involve training, practice of skills as well as train and fade approaches that enable the individual to become more independent as they acquire more skills and understanding. Similarly, **reablement** approaches are aimed at empowering individuals to regain the skills and

Key terms

Skills are abilities required for completing tasks.

Occupational therapists are professionals who support individuals to engage in daily activities.

Physiotherapists are professionals who support individuals affected by injury, illness or disability through using movement and exercises.

Active participation is a way of working that recognises an individual's right to participate in the activities and relationships of everyday life as independently as possible; the individual is regarded as an active partner in their own care or support, rather than a passive recipient.

Assistive technologies are electronic and physical items, devices or systems that enable individuals to maintain and develop their independence and skills for everyday life.

Reablement is an approach used to support individuals to relearn or regain some of the skills they may have lost following illness or injury.

A **pill box** is a box for holding tablets that is divided into the days of the week.

confidence they lost for carrying out their activities themselves, i.e. due to illness or injury.

- **Adapting the individual's living environment** – the extent to which an individual's home is adapted will depend on their needs and the level of support they require to develop and maintain skills for everyday life.
  - An individual who requires low-level support may benefit from having a series of reminders or visual prompts for what household activities to complete each day, or the use of a **pill box** for their medication.
  - An individual who requires medium-level support may require the installation of hand rails in the bathroom or hallways so that they can continue to walk around their home safely and independently, or the use of a food trolley so that they can transport their meals and drinks safely from one room to another.
  - An individual who requires high-level support may require support from a live-in carer to remain living in their own home; the layout of their living environment may

need to be changed, for example to include a sleeping area downstairs, a walk-in shower, the installation of ramps or the widening of doors.

- **Assistive technology** – the use of assistive technology to support individuals to develop and maintain skills for everyday life will also depend on the level of support an individual requires.
  - Physical items such as tin and jar openers, **kettle tippers** and **sock and stocking aids** can enable individuals to retain their independence when preparing meals and getting dressed and undressed.
  - Electronic items such as bath and stair lifts, panic pendants, **sensor mats** and applications available for following directions and locating transport routes can enable individuals to remain living at home. These can also help them to travel to different places to do their shopping, see their friends or visit places of interest.
- **Improving an individual's social well-being** – developing and maintaining skills for everyday life involves individuals feeling independent and in control of their lives. Supporting individuals to go out to socialise and meet with others can be one method of doing this as this can be a good way for individuals to share and listen to others' aspirations and experiences. This in turn can be a motivating factor for an individual who is, for example, learning how to improve their budgeting skills or making arrangements to go on a holiday.
- **Managing mental and physical health** – mental and physical well-being is crucial to enabling individuals to develop and maintain their skills for everyday life. Supporting individuals to get to know themselves can enable them to be more confident in their own abilities and therefore more likely to want to develop new skills and maintain existing skills. Similarly, supporting individuals to eat healthily, exercise and have sufficient sleep and rest is crucial to an individual's physical well-being and therefore closely linked to maintaining their everyday skills to live their lives as they wish.

Key terms

Kettle tippers are devices that hold a kettle to provide support when tilting and pouring so as to avoid an individual having to lift it.

Sock and stocking aids are items that enable individuals with limited flexibility to put on their socks and stockings.

Sensor mats are items that are used to make others aware of when an individual who may be unsteady on their feet gets out of bed in the middle of the night, stands up or leaves a room.

Research and investigate

AC 1.1 Methods

Research different approaches for supporting individuals with different conditions to retain, regain and develop their skills for everyday life.

AC 1.2 Analyse reasons why individuals may need support to maintain, regain or develop skills for everyday life

Individuals may require support to maintain, regain or develop skills for household tasks such as washing up, emptying the bins and doing the laundry, personal tasks such as getting washed, dressed, undressed and preparing meals, and social tasks such as going out to visit friends, doing the shopping and travelling to different places. The reasons why support may be needed will vary for different individuals.

- **An individual may need support to maintain their existing skills** for everyday life if they experience depression after being bereaved, for example; losing someone who is close to them and knows them well is likely to have a significant impact on an individual's life and can lead to them withdrawing and feeling that they are no longer able to manage on their own.

Another individual may need support to maintain their skills for everyday life if they have been diagnosed with dementia, for example; a loss of memory may make it difficult for the individual to remember how to cook a meal or write a shopping list.

- **An individual may need support to regain their former skills** for everyday life if they have sustained a hip fracture as a result of a fall while out walking, for example; the individual may be in pain and may have lost some of their confidence in going outdoors.

Another individual may need support to regain their skills for everyday life if they have had a stroke; for example the individual may require support with strengthening their body's muscles and co-ordination when learning how to walk again or may require therapy to regain lost speech and understanding.

- **An individual may need support to develop new skills** for everyday life if they want to go to work or complete a college course, for example. The individual may require support with developing skills for attending a job interview or with filling out an enrolment form. This may be due to individuals not having had the opportunity to develop skills in these areas or they may have lost their confidence, motivation or their ability to use these skills due to illness or injury.

An individual who moves into their own flat for the first time may need support to develop new living skills, such as paying bills, cooking and shopping, and maintaining a clean and secure home.

AC 1.3 Explain how maintaining, regaining or developing skills can benefit individuals

Supporting individuals to maintain existing skills, regain former skills or develop new skills can benefit individuals in different ways physically, emotionally and socially.

Overall benefits for individuals can include:

- becoming more independent
- promoting higher self-esteem and sense of achievement
- increasing confidence and motivation levels
- improving physical well-being, i.e. through mobility exercises
- eating well and healthily, i.e. through learning how to cook
- socialising and maintaining communications with others such as family and friends, e.g. through learning how to use email and Skype.

Read through Table 16.1, which includes examples of some of these benefits. Can you think of any others?

Key terms

Reading aids are items that enable individuals who have a visual impairment to see small print, e.g. a hands-free magnifier.

Talking books are audio recordings of books.

Ophthalmologists are professionals who support individuals affected by eye diseases.

Self-esteem is the value an individual puts on him/herself.

These relate to key terms in Table 16.1.

Time to think

1.3 Is your support effective?

Reflect on an individual with whom you work to retain, regain and develop their skills for everyday life.

- Does your support benefit them? If yes, how? If not, why not?
- What improvements could be made?

The individual's needs		Physical benefits	Emotional benefits	Social benefits
Mavis's eyesight is deteriorating	She is worried that she will no longer be able to read. Access to a **reading aid** and to **talking books** is enabling Mavis to continue to read by herself. Mavis has also been supported to visit her GP, who has referred her to an **ophthalmologist**.	Close monitoring of Mavis's eyesight.	Mavis will feel less anxious about not being able to read. She will also be better informed about why and how quickly her eyesight is deteriorating, including the options that are available to help address this. Mavis will also retain her sense of dignity and independence at being able to continue to engage in an activity she enjoys.	Maintaining Mavis's ability to read and developing her listening skills will enable her to continue to engage with others, feel confident in her abilities and retain a sense of control over her deteriorating eyesight.
Alan has had numerous epileptic seizures	These have left Alan feeling anxious about going out on his own at night. Alan's support worker is shadowing him when he wants to go out at night until he becomes confident to go out on his own.	Alan's active participation in an activity outside of his immediate living environment.	Alan's confidence will increase when going out, and his anxiety will subside.	Going out at night means that Alan can continue to meet up with his friends, relax and enjoy his life.
Cynthia has had a head injury	This has left her with difficulties speaking and writing. Cynthia has been referred to a counsellor as she is feeling very low, and also to a speech therapist.	Improved speech. Improved writing abilities.	Cynthia's **self-esteem** will increase, and her frustrations at not being able to express herself will decrease.	Improvements to Cynthia's speech and writing will enable better communications and interactions with others.

Table 16.1 The benefits of maintaining, regaining or developing skills

Case study

`1.1, 1.2, 1.3` Stanislaw

Stanislaw is a senior residential carer who works in a residential setting with individuals who have physical disabilities. He supports a team of carers to provide care and rehabilitation to the individuals who live in the setting and also to those who live in their own homes and visit the service during the day. Stanislaw works closely with a team of therapists, including an occupational therapist, a physiotherapist, a speech and language therapist and several rehabilitation assistants. He supports individuals with a range of daily living activities, such as personal care, household tasks, communication and mobilising.

1 What different methods may Stanislaw use for developing and maintaining individuals' skills for everyday life?
2 Why may individuals need support to maintain, regain or develop skills for everyday life?
3 How can maintaining, regaining or developing skills benefit individuals?

Evidence activity

1.1, 1.2, 1.3 Supporting skills for everyday life

Identify three individuals with whom you work to retain, regain and develop their skills for everyday life.

- Provide details of the methods you use for each individual. What are the similarities and differences between each of these?
- Examine in detail for each individual the reasons why they may need support from you and others involved in their lives.
- Provide details with examples of the benefits to individuals of maintaining, regaining or developing their skills for everyday life.

LO2 Be able to support individuals to plan for maintaining and developing skills for everyday life

AC 2.1 Work with an individual and others to identify skills for everyday life that need to be supported

Identifying skills for everyday life that need to be supported can be a difficult and anxious time for some individuals as this will involve making changes to the way they live their lives. You and others with whom you work – such as the individual's family and advocates, your colleagues and line manager, specialists, and others who are important to the individual's well-being – will therefore have an important role to play in supporting individuals to identify skills for everyday life that require support; this will involve getting to know individuals and building up good working relationships that involve trust and honesty. Look at Figure 16.1, which indicates some of the other people who can work with an individual to identify skills for everyday life.

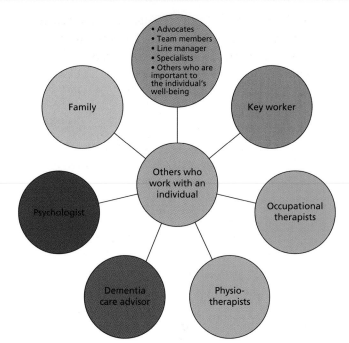

Figure 16.1 Others who can work with an individual to identify skills for everyday life

Being aware of others' roles and how to work effectively with them is integral to providing the support an individual requires. Let us think about how each of the people identified in Figure 16.1 can work with you and an individual to identify the skills for everyday life that need to be supported.

- **Family** can be instrumental in providing you with practical examples of the difficulties an individual is experiencing with everyday activities and in supporting an individual to identify and talk about these areas and the support they would like such as in maintaining their personal hygiene, doing the laundry, ironing, cooking or using the telephone.
- **Advocates** can support individuals to think about what skills they may like to develop and why. Advocates are independent and can represent an individual's views and/or feelings if the individual is unable to express these for example about whether they want to try a new sports activity or would like to go out more.
- Team members such as an individual's **key worker** or **a colleague** can provide a useful insight into the individual, as they are the worker in the setting where the person lives

or the service the person uses who is allocated specifically to support them and maintain day-to-day interactions. Being allocated specifically to an individual means that the key worker will get to know them well. This insight into the individual's feelings, thoughts and preferences can be used to support the individual emotionally when identifying skills.

- **The line manager** plays a vital role in ensuring that the support provided is being managed, reviewed and evaluated on an on going basis so as to ensure it is effective and of a good quality.
- **Occupational therapists** can support individuals to identify the skills with which they require support by talking through with them the activities in their daily lives that they are finding difficult, such as mobilising or going out. Occupational therapists can also work with you in enabling individuals to identify the skills with which they require support. They can then make suggestions for how to adapt the individual's living environment and make use of aids and equipment available.
- **Physiotherapists** can support individuals to identify the skills with which they require support when their body's functions have been affected by injury, illness or disability. They are a valuable source of information for both you and the individual and can enable individuals' recovery and promote their independence.
- A **dementia care advisor** is a named contact for individuals who have dementia as well as those who support them. Dementia care advisors can provide useful information about services available in the local area and nationally. They can also promote individuals' well-being by working closely with them and others involved in their lives to identify the skills for everyday life that need to be supported.
- **Psychologists** can provide a useful insight into how an individual thinks, feels and behaves and can equip individuals with a range of techniques to manage their lives based on their values and circumstances, e.g. when an individual needs to think about how their physical health is affecting their life and the skills that need to be supported for them to live their lives as they wish.

- Others who are important to the individual's well-being such as their friends can be a good source of informal support and information about an individual's preferences and hopes, all of which are crucial to know about when identifying skills for everyday life.

AC 2.2 Agree with the individual a plan for developing or maintaining the skills identified

Once you have identified with an individual and others involved in their lives the skills for everyday life that need to be supported, a **plan of care or support** must then be put in place for the process to follow for developing or maintaining these skills. As the example plan below shows, this will usually include detailing the goals to be achieved in the short, medium and long term, the type and level of support needed to achieve the goals identified, the roles and responsibilities of all those involved, any associated risks, including how to address these, and details about how the plan will be monitored.

When agreeing a plan with an individual it is important to remember to use the widely accepted framework of being SMART:

S **Specific** – identify clearly the goal to be achieved.

M **Measurable** – ensure you can track the progress being made on a regular basis.

A **Achievable** – be realistic about the goal to be achieved.

R **Relevant** – identify goals that are important to the individual and their well-being.

T **Time-based** – identify the timescales by which goals are to be achieved.

Key term

An individual's **plan of care** is the document where day-to-day requirements and preferences for care and support are detailed. It may be known by other names, e.g. support plan, individual plan or care delivery plan.

Jean's plan

My long-term goal is:
- To be able to prepare my own lunch (3 months from today).

My medium-term goal is:
- To feel confident using my walking frame so that I can walk to the kitchen and back again (2 months from today).

My short-term goals are:
- To begin mobilising (1 month from today).
- To begin managing my pain (1 month from today).

Difficulties I may have with achieving my goals:
- My lack of motivation to mobilise, especially when I am in pain.
- My fear of falling over again in the kitchen.

My steps for overcoming these difficulties and achieving my goals:
- Speaking to those supporting me about how I am feeling.

- Using the breathing techniques that I have been taught by the pain clinic.
- Using the walking frame provided to me.
- Using the food trolley provided to me to move my meal and drink.

Those supporting me are:
- My team of support workers.
- The physiotherapist who visits me.
- My son.

I will keep track of my progress by:
- Discussing with the support worker every day the progress I have made.
- Recording with the support worker every day the progress I have made.
- Discussing with my son every day the progress I have made.
- Discussing with the physiotherapist every Friday the progress I have made.

I will celebrate my achievements by:
- Getting my hair done.

Research and investigate

2.2 Agreeing plans
Research the different techniques and methods used for agreeing plans with individuals.

AC 2.3 Analyse possible sources of conflict that may arise when planning and ways to resolve them

The process of agreeing a plan with an individual and others involved in their lives is not easy and can bring about a number of different conflicts. Figure 16.2 identifies some of these conflicts.

Working in partnership

In AC 1.1 you read about the role that active participation plays in supporting individuals to retain, regain and develop skills for everyday life. If an **individual** has not been involved in developing their plan for how to retain, regain and develop skills for everyday life, they may not want to work towards the goals agreed in the plan. This is because they will not fully understand the

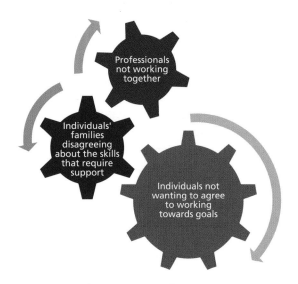

Figure 16.2 Sources of conflict

relevance or importance of doing so. Ensuring that you and others work in partnership with individuals and provide them with information in a format that they can understand, so as to **empower** (see definition on p. 291) them to make their own choices and decisions, can help to resolve such conflicts. Remember that planning is only effective when done *with* the individual not *for* them.

When individuals' **families** are involved in the planning, they may not agree with the skills identified as requiring support or with the goals to be achieved. This may be due to the family believing that they know their relative best, or believing that the skills or goals identified will not work or are not what their relative wants, or because they think the skills or goals identified will impact on the way they live their lives and they are not prepared to make these changes. Again, as with individuals, it is important that you and others are able also to work in partnership with individuals' families when planning. Acknowledging their views, beliefs and concerns, as well as providing them with practical solutions, is all part of this process.

When **professionals** from different services and agencies work together in planning with an individual, conflicts may arise over what areas need to be prioritised and who will provide the required support. It is important for all those involved to make clear their individual roles and responsibilities, including the areas of support they can and cannot provide, and for these to be respected. Having a member of the **multi-disciplinary team** with overall responsibility for communications and agreements reached can be a useful way to ensure that those involved are working towards the same agreed and shared goals.

Key terms

Empower means enabling an individual to feel in control.

A **multi-disciplinary team** is a team made up of professionals from a range of different organisations and services, each of which has its own individual roles and responsibilities.

Time to think

2.3 Do you know how to resolve conflicts?

Discuss with your manager an occasion when conflicts arose when you were planning with an individual.

- Was your manager's reflection of what happened different to yours? Why?
- Were the conflicts resolved? If yes, how?
- What could have been done differently?

AC 2.4 Support the individual to understand the plan and any processes, procedures or equipment needed to implement or monitor it

As you read in AC 1.1, active participation involves agreeing individuals' plans with them. For this to take place the individual must be aware of their plan and understand what it involves, including how they will be supported to achieve their goals and the support or equipment needed to implement or monitor it. Read through the top ten tips below for supporting an individual to understand, implement and monitor their plan.

1 Develop a plan in a **format that the individual understands**, e.g. using words, pictures, symbols or digital recordings.
2 Ensure the plan includes **goals that are important to the individual**.
3 Check with the individual their **understanding of their goals**.
4 Ask the individual to tell you about **their preferences and desires** and how their plan links to these.
5 **Provide individuals with time** to ask questions.
6 **Provide individuals with information** about the steps required to implement and monitor their plan; ensure that this information is in a format that they can understand.
7 **Provide the individual with opportunities** to tell you about their plan.
8 **Ask the individual for their ideas** about how they would like their plan implemented and monitored.
9 **Show the individual any equipment required** and provide them with the necessary information or training required before they need to use it.
10 **Seek advice and support from others** involved in the individual's life to reinforce with the individual the plan and what is required to implement or monitor it.

It is important that the plan is accessible to the individual so that it is understood and that training is provided for any tasks that require the use of equipment or specific procedures. Monitoring the plan will involve re-visiting it regularly and ensuring all progress made is documented so that it can be referenced when required.

Case study

2.1, 2.2, 2.3, 2.4 Claire

Claire works as a community-based senior carer and leads a team of community-based carers. The team provides support to individuals who have learning and physical disabilities to maintain and develop their skills for everyday life, including daily household activities such as laundry, cleaning and cooking, budgeting and travelling on public transport. Claire is also responsible for developing individual person-centred plans, and she works in partnership with individuals, their carers and other professionals to do so.

1 What methods can Claire use for working with individuals and others to identify skills for everyday life that need to be supported?
2 What methods can Claire use for agreeing with each individual a plan for developing or maintaining the skills identified?
3 What conflicts may arise when planning with individuals, their carers and other professionals?
4 How can Claire support each individual to understand their plan and any processes, procedures or equipment needed to implement or monitor it?

Evidence activity

2.1, 2.2, 2.3, 2.4 Planning for maintaining and developing skills for everyday life

Reflect on an individual with whom you work and how you agree with this individual and others involved in their lives the skills for everyday life that need to be supported. Reflect on how you support the individual to understand their person-centred plan and any processes, procedures or equipment needed to implement or monitor it.

● Read through the plan that you have agreed with this individual. Discuss with your manager

the conflicts that arose when planning, including how and why they arose and the methods that were used to resolve them.
● You will also need to be observed by your assessor working with an individual and others to identify skills for everyday life that need to be supported and agreeing with the individual a plan for developing or maintaining the skills identified, as well as supporting the individual to understand the plan and any processes, procedures or equipment needed to implement or monitor it.

LO3 Be able to support individuals to retain, regain or develop skills for everyday life

AC 3.1 Provide agreed support to develop or maintain skills, in a way that promotes active participation

Every individual has the right to participate in activities in everyday life as independently as possible. This means being able to make their own informed choices and decisions, have control over the way they live their lives and be able to experience any support they require in a positive and enjoyable way.

Active participation

Active participation as a working approach ensures that the individual is not only involved but actively leads their own support; it involves encouraging and supporting individuals to learn and develop skills for themselves. The extent to which an individual participates in developing or maintaining their skills will impact directly on the quality of life they lead. For example, when individuals show others what they are able to do it not only makes them feel positive about their abilities and strengths, it also provides them with a valuable role in their family and community that others can respect. Individuals who are not active partners in their own support will not have the opportunity to express who they are and what they like and what they don't like; they may consequently withdraw from others and feel very despondent about their lives.

Providing agreed support

Providing agreed support in a way that promotes active participation involves:

- assisting an individual with the correct type and level of support to empower them to do as much as possible for themselves
- putting in place a realistic plan that will enable the individual to achieve the new skills that they would like to develop or the former skills that they would like to maintain
- monitoring the support that is provided to ensure that it is meeting the individual's needs and promoting their active participation.

Read through below what ACTIVE PARTICIPATION involves. Is this what it means to you?

A   **A**ctive support
C   **C**ontrol over one's life
T   **T**reated as an individual
I   **I**nformed choices
V   **V**alued roles
E   **E**xpression of oneself
P   **P**erson-centred
A   **A**ctivities
R   **R**espect
T   **T**rust
I   **I**nvolved
C   **C**ollaboration with others

Figure 16.3 How would someone with physical disabilities be supported to develop and maintain their skills?

I   **I**nformed decisions
P   **P**lanning
A   **A**greeing goals
T   **T**racking progress
I   **I**dentifying what's important
O   **O**pportunities
N   **N**ew skills

AC 3.2 Give positive and constructive feedback to the individual during activities to develop or maintain their skills

Supporting individuals to develop or maintain their skills also involves giving them positive and constructive feedback during activities so that:

- they know what they are doing well
- they know the areas they need to improve or on which they need to continue working
- they feel good about themselves
- they feel motivated to continue
- they can celebrate their achievements.

When feedback is given in a positive and constructive manner it can enable individuals to work effectively with you to develop or maintain their skills. Positive and constructive feedback involves helping individuals to understand what they did well along with the areas where improvements need to be made.

- **Positive feedback** involves using positive verbal and non-verbal communication methods to communicate clearly to the individual what they have done well, such as smiling and/or using a thumbs up sign when expressing to an individual that they have completed a specific task or activity well. Positive feedback also involves recognising the progress an individual has made and what the individual has achieved. It is important that you recognise achievements no matter how small they may be so that the individual feels that they are making progress with developing or maintaining their skills, and that it is worth them continuing with the efforts they are making, no matter how difficult this may be at times. Praising an individual and providing them with encouragement to continue with the progress made are two ways of doing this.

- **Constructive feedback**, like positive feedback, is reflected not only in what you say but also how you say it and the actions you use to express this. Its purpose is to make an individual aware of the areas that require improvement and how these can be addressed. When feedback is constructive it is focused on the task or activity rather than on the person, meaning any personal comments are avoided. For example, if an individual while getting dressed puts on clothes that have got marks or stains on, negative feedback would be 'You look dirty' but constructive feedback would be 'Your clothes have got stains on them, do you want to change them?' In other words, constructive feedback involves stating the facts about an area of concern, not making personal judgements about the individual. In order for constructive feedback to be received well and to have maximum impact during activities to develop or maintain an individual's skills it needs to be balanced with positive feedback, i.e. with examples of what the individual has done well, given at the correct moment and provided in a positive manner.

Time to think

3.2 Do you know how to give feedback?

Ask an individual with whom you work in your setting about what they think of the feedback you provide to them during activities to develop or maintain their skills. Discuss with them the improvements that can be made.

- Do you agree with their feedback?
- Does any part of their feedback surprise you? Why?

Research and investigate

3.2 Giving feedback

Find out the different techniques to use for providing positive and constructive feedback.

Evidence activity

3.1, 3.2 Being able to support individuals

Arrange for your manager or a senior practitioner in your work setting to observe you supporting three individuals to retain, regain or develop skills for everyday life.

Ensure the observation is documented and records the following details for each individual:

- How you provided the agreed support to develop or maintain their skills in a way that promoted active participation.
- Examples of positive and constructive feedback you gave to each individual during activities to develop or maintain their skills.

You will also need to be observed by your assessor demonstrating both these skills.

AC 3.3 Describe actions to take if an individual becomes distressed or unable to continue

Supporting individuals to develop or maintain their skills may also require you at times to respond to individuals who become distressed or unable to continue with an activity or task. This may be due to them feeling unable to manage, being unwell or making an **informed choice** that they do not want to continue. The actions to take will depend on the scope of your job role and responsibilities as well as on the **agreed ways of working** in your work setting, which will include policies and procedures where these exist.

Key terms

Distress describes when an individual is upset, anxious or angry.

Informed choices and decisions are the processes of choosing from options and making decisions based on accurate information and knowledge that is understood by an individual.

Agreed ways of working are your work setting's policies and procedures, as well as the specific guidelines that are in place for the individuals to whom you provide care and support. They may be less formally documented with smaller employers.

If an individual becomes distressed during an activity or unable to continue, it is important that you try to find out the trigger or triggers for this. The actions you take will depend on the reasons for an individual's distress. Potential triggers and actions to take include:

- **Are they in pain?** If an individual is in pain then you may need to access medical help straight away or seek advice from someone in a more senior position to you.
- **Are they communicating to you that they are not enjoying the activity or task?** If the individual is not enjoying the activity or task then you can try providing them with a higher level of support so that they can achieve the part of the activity with which they are having difficulties, or focus on a part of the activity that they are doing well and provide them with positive and constructive feedback; then begin the activity or task again once they are no longer distressed and have calmed down.
- **Do they want to stop the activity or task?** If an individual indicates to you that they want to stop the activity or task, spend some time with them to try to understand how they are feeling and what they are thinking. This will help you to understand the difficulties or concerns they are having with the activity or task and help them to feel that you are listening to and valuing their experience of the activity. If after talking this through with the individual they still feel that they are unable to continue with the activity then you must respect their decision. Collate as much information as you can about their reasons for this and ensure you report and record this in full in line with your work setting's agreed ways of working. This may involve you and the team seeking additional advice from other professionals or specialists involved in developing or maintaining the individual's skills.

Evidence activity

3.3 Taking action

Reflect on an occasion when an individual with whom you work became distressed or unable to continue with an activity or task.

Provide details about the situation as well as the actions taken.

Case study

3.1, 3.2, 3.3 Michael

Michael works as a senior mental health support worker in a mental health project. He supports and supervises a team of support workers, who provide support to individuals who have mental health and other complex needs. Michael takes a lead role in developing the recovery model in the project and modelling the skills required by support workers to work positively with individuals and engage them in retaining, regaining or developing skills for everyday life.

1 What methods can Michael use to ensure that agreed support to develop or maintain individuals' skills promotes active participation?
2 How can Michael model the skills required by support workers to give positive and constructive feedback to individuals during activities to develop or maintain their skills?
3 What actions should Michael or a member of his team take if an individual becomes distressed or unable to continue with the activity to develop or maintain their skills?

LO4 Be able to evaluate support for developing or maintaining skills for everyday life

AC 4.1 Work with an individual and others to agree criteria and processes for evaluating support

Agreeing the criteria and processes for evaluating the support provided to individuals for developing or maintaining skills for everyday life will depend on the agreed ways of working used within your work setting. Evaluating support is an essential component of the individual receiving the most suitable and best quality support available for developing or maintaining their skills for everyday life. It can also be a method of recognising the quality of the work and approaches used by those who support individuals. An effective evaluation usually involves the following six key steps:

1 **Identifying all those involved in the support**, including those who actively participate, i.e. the individuals, and those who need and will use the findings from the **evaluation** of support provided, i.e. you and your team, your manager, the individual's family and the other professionals involved.

2 **Developing a shared understanding** with the individual and others of the purpose and importance of the support being provided, the agreed short-, medium- and long-term objectives in the agreed plan of support, the methods you have agreed to use and the reasons why.

3 **The evaluation criteria to be used** with an individual and others will involve:

- agreeing when evaluation should take place, e.g. at the end of an agreed period of time and/or at regular intervals while the support is being provided
- deciding how the findings will be reported and documented, e.g. meetings or written reports to enable a shared understanding by all those involved
- deciding what you are measuring, why and how you will measure it, including how you will know if the support being provided has been achieved.

4 **Collating both quantitative and qualitative information** to evidence how effective the support has been and also to indicate the areas that require further improvement, e.g. through observations of the individual and the support provided, team meetings with the staff involved, one-to-one interviews with all those others involved in the individual's life. It is important that the information collated is specific, relevant and reliable.

5 **Making sense of the quantitative and qualitative information** collated will involve ensuring that information is documented accurately and its **confidentiality** protected. It is also important that you agree with those who are going to receive the information the format in which they would like it presented so that they can understand it.

6 **Sharing the findings of the evaluation** of support with the individual and others will involve reporting on the areas that have worked well and what has been learned, the areas that require improvement and the changes that need to be made to improve future support.

AC 4.2 Carry out agreed role to evaluate progress towards goals and the effectiveness of methods used

In order for you to evaluate the progress being made towards agreed goals for developing or maintaining an individual's skills for everyday life and the effectiveness of the methods being used, you must work closely with the individual and all those others providing the support. Look at Figure 16.4, which identifies different evaluation methods that you could use with both individuals and your team members.

Working closely with the individual and others involved in providing the support is essential for monitoring how well different members of the team work with individuals, including the approaches and techniques used, and to ensure that agreed ways of working are being followed consistently by everyone. It will also be a good opportunity for you to provide individuals and others with positive and constructive feedback.

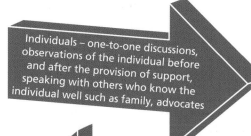

Individuals – one-to-one discussions, observations of the individual before and after the provision of support, speaking with others who know the individual well such as family, advocates

Team members – supervision, shadowing of team members while supporting individuals, working alongside team members, modelling of good practice to the team, holding team meetings

Figure 16.4 Evaluation methods

Key term

An **organic action plan** is a plan of action that is updated regularly to meet an individual's changing needs or preferences.

Time to think

4.2 Are you an evaluator?
- What methods do you use for evaluating progress towards goals? Why?
- How effective are you in using these? What improvements can you make?

Carrying out your agreed evaluation role effectively will involve using the widely accepted framework of being SMART, which you learned about in AC 2.2.

Organic action plan

Ensuring that you are fully committed to carrying out your role will be essential to successfully evaluating an individual's progress towards goals and the effectiveness of the methods used. Working in partnership with others such as the individual, a member of the team or another professional and sharing the evaluation process with others will enable you to put together an **organic action plan** that reflects the individual's priorities and goals as well as their abilities and skills.

AC 4.3 Agree revisions to the plan

It is a legal requirement under the Care Standards Act that plans of care and support are updated regularly to reflect changes in the individuals' needs or circumstances, for example that the individual has learned a new skill such as preparing a hot drink.

Once you have agreed with the individual and others the **objectives** that have been achieved and those that have not, you must then all work together to identify the changes that need to be made to the plan of support to enable the individual to meet their goals for developing or maintaining their skills. It is important that what is agreed is:

- documented
- produced in a format that can be understood by all those involved
- accurate
- factual
- signed and dated.

Revisions

The revisions that are made to an individual's plan must also be in line with the scope of your job role and responsibilities and your work setting's agreed ways of working.

Revisions may occur on more than one occasion and may be due to a number of reasons, including closing the plan if all objectives have been met, reducing the level of support to reflect increased independence, increasing the level of support to address unmet needs, changing the type of support or changing the method of delivering support.

Read through these **good practice guidelines** for agreeing revisions to an individual's plan of support:

- Always provide individuals with the opportunity to be involved.
- Seek an individual's permission to ask the views of others involved in their lives.
- Use or represent the individual's own form of communication when agreeing revisions, i.e. use words or phrases that the individual uses.
- Ensure all revisions are clearly understood.
- Ensure revisions reflect the individual's changing needs.
- Maintain confidentiality.

AC 4.4 Record and report in line with agreed ways of working

Good communication is the basis of recording and reporting in line with agreed ways of working which will also include policies and procedures where these exist.

- **Recording** – it is important to record all discussions, decisions and actions agreed or not agreed, including any referrals made for additional services, information or advice. Full details must be recorded so that all those involved can be consistent in their working approaches with the individual. All records kept must be clear, legible and relevant so that they can be understood easily by all those involved.

- **Reporting** – it is important to report on revisions agreed to an individual's plan at a forum where the whole team can be involved, i.e. at a team meeting, so as to:
  - ensure a consistent approach

- consolidate the team's understanding of what has been agreed
- celebrate achievements together
- provide opportunities for team members to clarify areas of support being provided and to ask any questions they may have.

Reporting in this way to the whole team will also be an opportunity for the team to raise any difficulties they may be having, and to share approaches that seem to work well that can be used to overcome these difficulties.

This is integral to enabling all team members to feel supported and encouraged to continue providing high-quality support for developing or maintaining individuals' everyday skills.

Maintaining confidentiality and promoting the active participation of individuals must underpin all support provided.

Research and investigate

4.4 Evaluating support
Find out about your work setting's agreed ways of working for evaluating support for developing or maintaining individuals' skills for everyday life.

Case study

4.1, 4.2, 4.3, 4.4 Charlene

Charlene is a senior support worker providing support and supervision to a team of support workers who provide support to individuals who have learning disabilities to develop and maintain their skills for everyday life. Charlene mentors all existing staff and inducts all new staff members who join the team. This morning Charlene is supporting an individual in the review of their support plan. It has been agreed with the individual and the others present for a recently recruited support worker, Jo, also to be present so that she can learn more about how to evaluate the effectiveness of support provided.

1 What methods can Charlene demonstrate for working with an individual and others to agree the criteria and processes for evaluating support?

2 How can Charlene ensure that she carries out her agreed role to evaluate progress towards goals and the effectiveness of the methods used?

3 What agreed ways of working for agreeing revisions to the individual's support plan might Charlene explain to Jo?

4 What best practice guidelines for recording and reporting must Charlene follow and role model to Jo?

Evidence activity

4.1, 4.2, 4.3, 4.4 **Evaluating support**

Reflect on an occasion when you worked with an individual and others to evaluate the support provided for developing or maintaining their skills for everyday life. Provide details of:

- how you agreed with the individual and others the criteria and processes to use for evaluating support
- your agreed role in evaluating progress towards goals and the effectiveness of methods used
- how you agreed revisions to the individual's plan
- how you record and report in line with agreed ways of working.

You will also need to be observed by your assessor working with an individual and others to agree criteria and processes to use for evaluating support, to carry out your agreed role in evaluating progress towards goals and the effectiveness of methods used, to agree revisions to the individual's plan, and to record and report in line with agreed ways of working.

Legislation

- **Care Standards Act 2000**
- **Data Protection Act 1998**
- **Human Rights Act 1998**
- **Mental Capacity Act 2005**
- **Mental Health Act 1983 (amended 2007)**

Useful resources

Websites

Alzheimer's Research UK

www.alzheimersresearchuk.org

Care Quality Commission

www.cqc.org.uk

The Health & Social Care Information Centre

www.hscic.gov.uk

Skills for Care

www.skillsforcare.org.uk

Skills for Health

http://skillsforhealth.org.uk

Stroke Association

www.stroke.org.uk

Publications

Mansell, J., Beadle-Brown, J., Ashman, B. and Ockenden, J. (2005) *Person-centred Active Support: A multi-media training resource for staff to enable participation, inclusion and choice for people with learning disabilities.* Brighton: Pavilion Publishing.

Mansell, J. and Beadle-Brown, J. (2012) *Active Support: Enabling and empowering people with intellectual disabilities.* London: Jessica Kingsley Publishers.

Unit HSC 3020

Facilitate person-centred assessment, planning, implementation and review

This unit is worth 6 credits

What are you finding out?

It is vital that people have the right care to meet their needs. It is important therefore that procedures are followed to ensure that needs are met. Further, it is important that individuals are at the centre of this process so they feel that they are actively involved in their own care. Good, effective care planning can ensure all these criteria are met. Care packages should never be designed for the ease or convenience of care workers.

By the end of this unit you will:

1 Understand the principles of person-centred assessment and care planning.
2 Be able to facilitate person-centred assessment.
3 Be able to contribute to the planning of care or support.
4 Be able to support the implementation of care plans.
5 Be able to monitor a care plan.
6 Be able to facilitate a review of care plans and their implementation.

LO1 Understand the principles of person-centred assessment and care planning

AC 1.1 Explain the importance of a holistic approach to assessment and planning of care or support

Individuals may need care at various times in their life. There are a number of reasons why individuals may need care. These can include:

- physical disability
- learning difficulty
- memory problem
- lifestyle issues
- bereavement
- addiction issues
- family issues or breakdowns
- mental health issues
- their (young or old) age.

Because there is such a range of individuals, it follows that there is a range of reasons they may need care. To meet all these individual and specific needs, care planning is vital.

A Holistic approach

Holistic health approach means seeing the whole person, not just their physical health but also their emotional, sexual, social, intellectual, mental and spiritual health. When we care for someone, we need to consider all these needs, which can be interlinked.

Traditionally, health has been seen as mostly physical but, increasingly, it is the norm and good practice to consider an individual's holistic health. Only concentrating on physical aspects of care could miss key needs. A consequence of this could

be that as well as not caring for that aspect of their health needs, the physical side of their health may worsen too.

It is important that an individual is looked at holistically, acknowledging all their facets, otherwise important aspects of the person will not be recognised. An individual needing care is more than a 'service user'; they are a person with a history, a life and an identity. Ignoring this could be detrimental to the quality of care delivered.

Being person-centred is about listening to and learning about what individuals want from their lives, and helping people to think about what they want both now and in the future. Family, friends, professionals and services work together with the individual to make this happen. The case study of Robert below shows how detrimental ignoring an individual's holistic needs could be.

Key term

Holistic means acknowledging the person as a 'whole' and not just focusing on one aspect of their health and well-being.

Case study

1.1 Jean

Jean is 76 and is continually being admitted to hospital after falling. She is given pain relief, has her wounds dressed and has any broken bones cast. Her physical care needs are assessed and supported and, between them, her carers 'fix' her.

Jean is, however, unhappy, lonely and depressed. She always falls at the same place, getting in and out of her house. As she explains, 'That step will kill me one winter!' Because of this, she now avoids going out as much as possible. She rarely goes to the shops, and when she does she stocks up on frozen, processed foods. She has stopped going to the library and the day care centre entirely. She rarely sees her friends. She is also now putting on weight.

1. In what ways are these assessments failing?
2. What are the consequences of this on her holistic health?
3. What simple action could improve Jean's life significantly?

AC 1.2 Describe ways of supporting the individual to lead the assessment and planning process

The role of clients in their care planning is recognised in legislation such as the Care Act (2014), the Health and Social Care Act (2012) and the Human Rights Act 1998, which prioritised it as best practice and marked a way forward for all future care planning. Since these Acts, the idea has evolved that individuals requiring care should be involved in every stage of the planning process (see Figure 17.1).

Consider the reasons why people need care, as outlined in AC 1.1. Such a range of reasons results in a wide range of needs. To meet all these individual and specific needs, care planning is vital. Usually the planning process involves the stages outlined in AC 1.1. This process needs to be a continuous cycle, as needs can change. A care plan that meets needs when implemented may not still be meeting them six months later so on-going monitoring and reviews are vital.

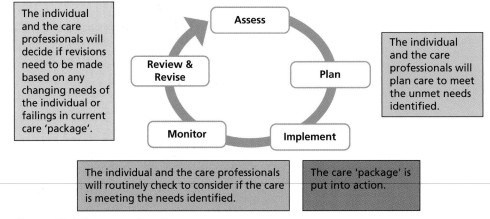

Figure 17.1 The care planning process

When assessing and planning, it is vital that the individual leads the process. This may sound obvious, but it is surprising how often this is overlooked as care professionals think they 'know what's best' for the individual. Care professionals must remember that the individual is the foundation of care planning; it is their body, their discomfort, their life and, fundamentally, their care. Care planning that is not person-centred is meaningless. It is not acceptable to merely 'go through the motions', care workers must value an individual's role in this process – that is best practice. It is essential to **empower** people in their own care.

Direct payments

Direct payments can support empowerment. They are payments given to individuals in place of the care services they have been assessed as needing. Direct payments are intended to give individuals greater choice in their care. The payment must be enough to enable the individual to purchase services to meet their eligible needs, and must be spent on services that meet these needs.

Tips to support an individual to lead assessment and planning

- Ask the individual what they want and what they consider their needs to be. Leading questions – such as 'Your current hygiene

arrangements are fully meeting all your needs, aren't they?' – should be avoided as they may lead to agreement when it may not actually be the case. Also, **open questions** are preferred to **closed questions**, so instead of asking 'Are you happy?' try 'Tell me about how you feel at the moment.'

- Care workers should meet individuals face to face. Assessment is not best done by telephone or email. Individuals need to feel valued enough to be met in person.
- Care workers should make clear that everything will be kept **confidential**. This will reassure the individual that it is okay to divulge necessary information.
- Discussions should be in a simple format. Bamboozling individuals with **acronyms**, jargon and technical terminology will not help them to lead the assessment. On the other hand, care workers should avoid patronising individuals by using language that is too simplistic. Using a balance of detailed information that is clear and simple is important.
- Employ **empathy** throughout. It is vital that care workers consider how the individual feels, which will help strengthen the care worker–individual relationship.
- If anything needs repeating, this should be done patiently and clearly. At the end, care workers should clarify and summarise to ensure that everything is understood and to minimise mistakes. Any terminology should be clarified, as an individual's interpretation of 'priority', for example, may differ from yours or that of another organisation.
- Check with the person who they would like to be involved in this process.
- Revisit the plan and ask the person if it is what they want and need.
- Use additional sources of information such as previous records, ensure the person knows their options.
- Support individual, family and carers to feedback.
- Support people to say what they want to say.
- Give copies of documents to everyone. Allow time for individuals to read them and ask

Key terms

Open questions can, in theory, result in any answer and can be better for getting people's opinions than closed questions.

Closed questions are questions that result in set responses, e.g. a question will get the answer 'yes'/'no'.

Confidential information is given in private and intended to be kept secret. You must restrict access to this information and respect its privacy.

Acronyms are formed from the initial letters of words, e.g. NHS is an acronym for the National Health Service.

Empathy is the ability to view a situation from another individual's perspective.

To **empower** means to give someone control over their life and decisions.

Key term

Active participation recognises an individual's right to participate as independently as possible; the individual is regarded as an active partner in their own care, rather than a passive recipient.

questions, then ensure that documents are signed. This is an opportunity for any mistakes or disagreements to be highlighted, and is a record if there are any future queries.

Advocates

Not every individual is in a position to lead fully in the process (due to age, communication difficulties, sensory impairments, mental health problems, learning difficulties) and so the use of an advocate may be needed. An advocate is someone who represents another. Advocates do not make decisions on an individual's behalf, but do seek information, ask questions and present information to the individual in an unbiased way, allowing the individual to be informed and hence make decisions. Advocates ensure that individuals' rights and interests are supported.

SEAP states that advocacy in all its forms seeks to ensure that people, particularly those who are most vulnerable in society, are able to:

● *Have their voice heard on issues that are important to them.*

● *Defend and safeguard their rights.*

● *Have their views and wishes genuinely considered when decisions are being made about their lives.*

(Source: www.seap.org.uk)

Carers should aim to allow **active participation** when assessing and planning care. This not only leads to better care, but will also aid ownership of any care packages and help an individual's self-esteem and make them feel valued and respected.

Often an individual may not feel they are being listened to or that they are important. They may

Evidence activity

1.2 The importance of supporting an individual to lead assessment and planning
Produce a report on the ways you would support the individual you described in Evidence Activity 1.1 to lead their assessment and planning process.

not feel able to question this or to challenge what has been said or decided.

One of the ways of ensuring individuals are at the centre and are able to lead are personal budget or an Individual budget. This is the money individuals are given from the Council and other funding streams to spend on their choice of Self-Directed Support.

AC 1.3 Describe ways the assessment and planning process or documentation can be adapted to maximise an individual's ownership and control of it

There is little point involving individuals if they cannot access the process or documents. If individuals have issues affecting their abilities, they will feel little or no ownership over the process. Consider Table 17.1.

Key terms

Active listening requires the listener to feed back, acknowledging they have understood what is being said.

Lip reading is a visual form of communication that involves observing a person's lip shapes, gestures and facial movements.

Makaton is a visual form of communication for individuals who have learning disabilities and communication difficulties, in which gestures are used in combination with pictures and symbols to communicate messages.

One-page profile is a summary of what is important to someone and how they want to be supported.

These are addressed on the following page.

Meetings	Effective verbal communication
Care workers need to consider the logistics of meetings. Meetings should be arranged in a suitable location. If an individual has to travel long distances, possibly at cost to themselves, they may not feel they are a priority. Arrange meetings at times that are convenient, showing flexibility and openness. Make sure everyone is comfortable; ensure that chairs, tables, refreshments, etc., are available. If the individual has any disabilities, make sure that facilities meet these needs, for example by ensuring there is wheelchair access, disabled parking and toilets. Ideally, arrange meetings in the client's own home, fully working the process around them.	Care workers should employ effective verbal communication skills. Language should be appropriate to the age, ability and understanding of the individual. Being confused or embarrassed because they do not understand is not a positive outcome. If the person speaks a language other than English, ensure that interpreters are available, thus respecting the right of the individual to fully participate.
Effective non-verbal communication skills	**Communication aids**
Effective non-verbal communication skills will make individuals feel more comfortable. Care professionals need to consider their facial expressions, eye contact, posture (whether sitting or standing), gestures, etc. A smiling, friendly face, nodding when an individual is talking, shows that the care worker is respecting what the individual has to say. A scowling, slouching care worker may not make an individual feel that what they are saying is important. One strategy to use is **active listening**.	Communication aids can be used to assist discussions (see Figure 17.2). For individuals with visual impairments, Braille and the spoken word could be used. For individuals with hearing impairments, hearing aids, sign language, a signer, **lip reading** and the written word could be used. For those with emotional difficulties or behavioural issues, **Makaton**, picture aids, photographs, visits, plans, flash cards, etc., could be used to help. These are effective at ensuring inclusiveness and allowing individuals to participate fully in all stages of care planning.

Table 17.1 Actions to help individuals take ownership of the care planning process

Research and investigate

1.3 Active listening

Find out about active listening. In particular, find out about Egan's steps to active listening, and the use of the SOLER strategy.

Evidence activity

1.3 Adapting planning and documents

Produce a detailed list of 'top tips' for a new care worker on the ways in which assessing and planning documents can be adapted to maximise an individual's ownership and control.

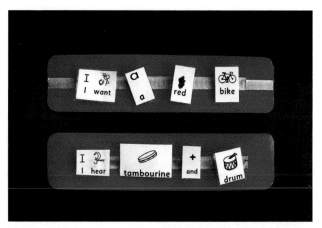

Figure 17.2 Images can be used to assist communication

LO2 Be able to facilitate person-centred assessment

AC 2.1 Establish with the individual a partnership approach to the assessment process

Alongside the individual, there are many people who can be involved in assessment, who are all able to give their opinion and professional expertise. A partnership approach is effective when professionals from different disciplines work together. It can be most effective where there is a key worker (sometimes referred to as a care co-ordinator, facilitator, care manager or similar) who can assist individuals in managing their care planning process. It is important that they co-ordinate assessment, request written reports and professional opinions, and invite others to case meetings.

It is vital that the key worker explains the process of a partnership approach to the individual, outlines the benefits to them and reassures them of any confidentiality issues, etc. It is imperative that the individual is comfortable with a partnership approach and does not feel intimidated or that everyone is 'ganging up on them'.

AC 2.2 Establish with the individual how the process should be carried out and who else should be involved in the process

The individual and the key worker should consider who may be involved in the process. This could potentially be an exhaustive list as each individual's needs are unique and complex. These care professionals may include counsellors, key workers, social workers, police, physiotherapists, GPs, nurses, **domiciliary workers**, care workers and hospital consultants.

The individual needs to consider how the process should develop, which will depend on the urgency or complexity of care needs. Whichever method is chosen, best practice is assessment through a **Single Assessment Process**, which means individuals' needs are assessed without procedures being needlessly duplicated by different agencies. Then, with the individual's permission, the information is shared with the other professionals involved. Decisions should

be made as to the format in terms of weight of opinion, time allocated, themes, care setting, etc.

AC 2.3 Agree with the individual and others the intended outcomes of the assessment process and care plan

Outcomes are what someone wants to achieve at the end of the care plan, the desired results or consequences of actions. First, outcomes must be identified; a **care plan** without outcomes is not as effective. Second, ensure that outcomes are agreed throughout the partnership. It would be ineffective to have a partnership approach to assessment that had separate intended outcomes. The individual and others such as carers, friends, relatives and professionals can all have useful input into appropriate intended outcomes.

SMART targets

To make these outcomes as useful as possible, they should be:

S   **S**pecific
M   **M**easurable
A   **A**chievable
R   **R**ealistic
T   **T**ime related

SMART targets ensure that there is less confusion, and you can see whether or not they have been achieved. Intended outcomes must be formally written into care plans, so success at meeting them can be judged. It may be useful to prioritise intended outcomes or to break them down into more manageable, attainable results.

AC 2.4 Ensure that assessment takes account of the individual's strengths and aspirations as well as needs

The aim of any person-centred assessment is to focus on and identify the strengths and work on building those, to ensure that the individual

has the best quality of life and **optimum** health and well-being. This does not just mean helping an individual to *not be* ill, *not be* in pain, *not be* disadvantaged; it is about helping them to be the best they can be.

A positive definition of health is when something is achieved or gained; being as fit and healthy as you can be, having the best health, wanting to add 'life to years and years to life'. It focuses more on well-being than just on health for the sake of 'getting by'.

The World Health Organisation's definition of health takes a positive view: 'Health is a state of complete physical, mental and social well-being and not merely the absence of disease or infirmity' (WHO, 1946). This definition includes mental and social well-being, so is also a more holistic definition of health.

This principle is just the same for assessment and meeting an individual's needs. It is not enough just to assess and deal with all the areas where they are in need. It is about their total well-being being as good as possible; allowing people to do what they can do (their strengths) and what they'd like to do (aspirations). Ensuring that individuals remain independent and autonomous is essential for their self-esteem and feelings of worth.

AC 2.5 Work with the individual and others to identify support requirements and preferences

It is important that individuals are able to highlight their support requirements and preferences. Using a good written template for this is best practice, as this ensures that:

● all assessments are standardised, limiting variations between individuals

● it identifies what any extra paid support will be needed can do; and what the individual can do family and friends

● nothing is missed out by any assessor.

Many examples of care assessment documentation can be found online (see Figure 17.3 for an example). It is important to ensure that templates allow room for comment, otherwise their use is not person-centred.

The document should be worked through, remembering any issues discussed earlier in ACs 1.2 and 1.3. It is often a good idea to allow the individual to consider their assessment beforehand, instead of it being 'sprung upon them'. Ideally, offer the individual a document beforehand, to record any reflections on their own needs. Doing this means that they can really consider their care needs beforehand, so the process can be more person-centred.

When individuals and others are assessing, they may do this at two levels, general and specialist. The general level may deal with everyday aspects, such as day-to-day needs. Specialist assessment would be through an appropriate specialist, such as a nurse, GP, occupational therapist, psychologist or physiotherapist. Specialists will assess specific needs, as they have expert knowledge and opinion. All assessments will be facilitated and put together by the key worker. Although getting specialist assessment is vital, however, individual opinions or judgements should not be disregarded or seen as 'supplementary'.

	Fully Independent	Independent with support	Completely dependent
Physical Health Needs			
Mobility	☐	☐	☐
Breathing	☐	☐	☐
Pain	☐	☐	☐
Skin	☐	☐	☐
Sexual needs	☐	☐	☐
Foot care	☐	☐	☐
Eating, drinking and swallowing	☐	☐	☐
Lifestyle changes desired(diet/alcohol/smoking etc)	☐	☐	☐
Medications	☐	☐	☐
Personal Care			
Getting in/out of bed	☐	☐	☐
Washing	☐	☐	☐
Bathing/showering	☐	☐	☐
Toileting	☐	☐	☐
Hair care/personal hygiene	☐	☐	☐
Dressing	☐	☐	☐
Oral health	☐	☐	☐
Cooking/food preparation	☐	☐	☐
Housework/laundry	☐	☐	☐
Shopping	☐	☐	☐
Worship	☐	☐	☐
Emotional Well-being			
Sleeping	☐	☐	☐
Confidence and disorientation	☐	☐	☐
Memory	☐	☐	☐
Depression	☐	☐	☐
Bereavement or loss	☐	☐	☐
Social Well-being			
You, your family, and friends	☐	☐	☐
Carer support	☐	☐	☐
Pets	☐	☐	☐
Social contacts	☐	☐	☐
Childcare/parenting/other caring responsibility	☐	☐	☐
Accommodation			
Location	☐	☐	☐
Accommodation	☐	☐	☐
Warmth	☐	☐	☐
Access to and around the accommodation	☐	☐	☐
Amenities of the accommodation	☐	☐	☐
Security & safety	☐	☐	☐
Education & Employment			
Help finding work or training	☐	☐	☐
Studying or qualifications	☐	☐	☐
Your leisure activities (pastimes and hobbies)	☐	☐	☐
Financial Well-being			
Benefits	☐	☐	☐
Management of personal finances	☐	☐	☐
Help with debt	☐	☐	☐
Miscellaneous			
Use this space here to tell us of any issues or problems or questions you have	☐	☐	☐

Figure 17.3 An example of a simple assessment form

Evidence activity

2.5 Identifying support requirements and preferences

Using the same individual as for Evidence Activity 2.2, assess your individual using a form similar to the one shown in Figure 17.3 (or any other you have found).

LO3 Be able to contribute to the planning of care or support

AC 3.1 Take account of factors that may influence the type and level of care or support to be provided

Once an individual has been assessed, the next stage is to decide what care and support is required to meet their needs. Many factors will influence this.

How feasible or possible are the aspirations?

If something is feasible, this means it is possible. Sometimes, with the best will in the world, certain aspirations are not achievable. Reasons why this may be so include:

- **Time** – there may not be enough time to organise certain care or support, or by the time it has been organised it may be too late.
- **Money** – resources in health and social care are **finite**, and sometimes individuals cannot have what they would like or, unfortunately, what they need. Care organisations that are funded by the government have budgets and have to prioritise how they spend their money. Equally, charities have limited funds and are dependent on donations from government and individuals. On occasion, individuals themselves may have to fund services and obviously, if they cannot, then they may not be able to access that support.
- **Staffing** – some care may require a certain quantity and quality of staff. As with money,

Key term

Finite means limited, cannot be exceeded.

Case study

3.1 Margaret

Margaret is living in a nursing home. She has trouble communicating. Every time the care worker helps Margaret to wash, she runs a bath even though Margaret prefers a shower. Her carer also gives Margaret 'a little treat' by putting bath salts in, but Margaret hates these as she thinks they scratch her legs and bottom as they don't dissolve properly. If she must have a bath, she prefers bath oils. The care worker then washes Margaret's hair with a supermarket's own brand shampoo and doesn't use a conditioner; she rinses her hair with bath water, not clean water. This upsets Margaret, as she liked having nice, shiny hair.

1 Consider how something as simple as this washing practice is not respecting Margaret's values and preferences.

there may not always be enough staff to meet the needs of the individual and, clearly, staff need to be paid so this links to money too.

- **Health/ability of individual** – there may be times when the individual's health or abilities may make their preferences or aspirations difficult, and it may be that these cannot be met as a result of this.

The individual's beliefs, values and preferences

Beliefs, values and preferences have to be taken into account when planning to meet an individual's needs. This could be something simple, such as preparing food a certain way; for example, an individual may prefer grilled bacon with the fat cut off. If bacon was instead fried with the fat left on and extra lard used in the pan, the individual may not eat it and hence may miss a meal. This preference would mean that a need would therefore be unmet.

As well as preferences in day-to-day activities, it is vital that an individual's religious, spiritual or lifestyle beliefs are also respected and promoted. An individual's religion will affect the day-to-day care they receive – their diet, dress, washing rituals, prayer routines, etc. A carer not actively promoting any beliefs in the planning of care would not be ensuring that rights to equality and diversity are being met; indeed, the care plan could even be discriminatory. All aspects of care planning need to be anti-discriminatory – including the language used, the resources available, the staff employed, the locations, etc.

Risks associated with achieving outcomes

Occasionally there may be risks involved in achieving outcomes, and this may affect the ability to provide the required type and level of care. These could be general health and safety risks, or specific risks to the individual's well-being. For example, an individual's desired outcome – that they are able to live independently without support – may not be possible if carers, family, friends and others believe that they may be at risk. Service providers have a duty of care to ensure all individuals are safe and free from harm. If anything were to happen to an individual, they may be deemed responsible for poor-quality care and mismanagement of the situation. It may be that a long-term target can be established for a desired outcome, but that short-term targets are also needed in order to judge how risk-free or feasible the intended outcome would be in the future.

This needs to be balanced with the rights individuals have to the life they choose, however. This can sometimes be an ethical dilemma for care workers.

Availability of services and other support options

If a service is not available, it is clearly not possible for an individual to access it. Often, services are not equally spread out across the nation, and an excellent service that someone has accessed in one place may not be available elsewhere. Also, there may be travel involved even if such a service is available, or its opening hours may not match the times when an individual needs it.

Key term

Anti-discriminatory means to treat everyone equally and fairly.

Evidence activity

3.1 Factors that may influence the type and level of care

Using the same individual as for Evidence Activity 2.2, describe any factors that can change the support needs of the individual.

AC 3.2 Work with the individual and others to explore options and resources for delivery of the plan

All options for delivery need to be explored with the individuals and others involved, to consider the most effective and efficient ways to deliver the plan. Working together, sharing ideas, considering all the benefits and disadvantages of the options and generally considering the **logistics** of a plan's delivery is ideal. This will involve the person in their care and continue to be person-centred, and will also highlight any potential downfalls before they occur.

Once options are decided, the specific details need to be established, i.e. frequency, times, duration and staffing. Sometimes, the full plan is referred to as the macro-plan, whereas the day-to-day, more specific care plan is often called the micro-plan. It is essential that all are clear on the details, as the misunderstanding of these could lead to problems.

Care could be provided from the following options and resources:

- **Informal support** – unpaid non-professionals, often spouses, parents or siblings.

Key term

Logistics refers to the full management of a task or procedure, from beginning to end.

- **Formal support** – paid, qualified staff whose job is to provide care.
- **Care or support services** – the range of services available from health and social care.
- **Community facilities** – communities often have a wealth of services for individuals. Libraries, day centres, town halls, community centres, etc., all have facilities that could have a positive effect on an individual.
- **Financial resources** – some services are offered by private organisations at a cost. Some individuals have to use these services because they are only available privately; others may choose a private service in the belief that it provides better choice and quality. This would obviously draw on an individual's finances.
- **Individuals' personal networks** – individuals may be part of teams, clubs, societies or religious groups that could impact positively on their lives.

A good care plan would draw on all of these to provide the right 'package' of care designed by, and right for, the individual.

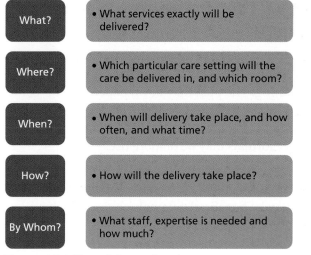

Figure 17.4 Care delivery details

> **Key term**
>
> **Component parts of a care plan** may include physical needs, care needs and how these are all going to be met.

> **Evidence activity**
>
> **3.2 Exploring options and resources for delivery of the plan**
>
> Using the same individual as for Evidence Activity 2.2, describe any options and resources the individual may have to support delivery of any plans.
>
> Think about the personal networks individuals may have. What are the benefits of these, and why would it be bad if a care plan did not acknowledge these?

> **Evidence activity**
>
> **3.3 How component parts of a plan will be delivered and by whom**
>
> Using the same individual as for Evidence Activity 2.2, describe some suggested plan components and who could deliver these.

AC 3.3 Contribute to agreement on how component parts of a plan will be delivered and by whom

Agreeing delivery

Problems can occur if it is not agreed at the outset what will be delivered and by whom. These include:

1 **Duplication** – if it is not stated who is responsible for a task then more than one person could assume that they are, and so it could be delivered more than is needed. This

is clearly inefficient and a waste of resources, as well as potentially being intrusive in someone's life.

2 **Omissions** – a potentially worse situation would be if it is not stated who is responsible for a task and everyone assumes it is not their responsibility, so no one delivers. This would mean that the individual would not receive the care they need.

The need to agree and formalise how components of the plan will be delivered (see Figure 17.4) is even more important when single assessment and working in partnerships is being practised. If it is made clear who is responsible for what then this also highlights who is accountable for any failings in the care plan or provisions, so no one can claim later that 'I didn't know'!

AC 3.4 Record the plan in a suitable format

As when assessing, consideration may need to be given to needs and preferences when planning. The plan may be on paper and, for some individuals, this may be the most appropriate format. For some groups of individuals, however, other formats may be of more use.

- For people with **learning difficulties**, simpler language and avoiding technical language may be beneficial. Symbols or signs, such as Makaton, could be used.
- For the **visually impaired**, braille, large font or Makaton symbols can all be helpful. Or the care plan could be presented in an audio format.
- For the **hearing impaired**, the use of sign language, a signer or lip reading may help when explaining the plan or when the individual has questions. The individual may also benefit from a hearing aid.

Present the plan in a way that is appropriate to the age, needs, ability and preferences of the individual and, if in doubt, ask them! It is not offensive to ask someone how they would like the documents to be presented, but it is offensive *not* to ask. Whatever format is chosen, however, it must be clear and easy to follow with good standards of English.

The plan should include the views of all concerned, including the person's/child's, family/carers, identification of the areas of need, priority areas, goal setting, action planning and risk management; how can workers make the care as safe as possible?

Evidence activity

3.3 Recording the plan in a suitable format
While at your work setting, record any plans you have in a suitable format for the individual in question.

LO4 Be able to support the implementation of care plans

AC 4.1 Carry out assigned aspects of a care plan

This can often be seen as the simplest part of the planning process and, if good assessment and planning have taken place, it can be. Quite simply, this is where the care plan is put into effect.

Success at this stage is more likely if:

- assessment has been person-centred
- you have done a holistic examination of needs and preferences
- planning of delivery has been person-centred
- a partnership approach has been applied
- there have been opportunities for the care plan to be checked and amended.

If this has occurred, implementation *should* be fairly straightforward (see Figure 17.5). This is not guaranteed, however, and communication still needs to happen to ensure that any issues are highlighted immediately.

This is a key stage, when the care workers who are appointed to deliver particular aspects are deployed, at which in theory the needs of the individual start to be met for example the provision of practical support or personal care for certain aspects of daily living.

This could be an emotional time. On the one hand, the individual and others around them may be anxious about how the care plan will work, whether it will be successful and whether or not needs will be met. On the other hand, the individual and others around them may also be excited and pleased about the implementation of positive changes to their lives for which they have been waiting. Therefore, sensitivity and patience may be needed with the individual to ensure that they cope with this transition.

Figure 17.5 And… action!

AC 4.2 Support others to carry out aspects of a care plan for which they are responsible

One essential role for a key worker is to oversee implementation of the care plan and to support others in their roles. Key workers will often be the first port of call for any questions, not just from the individual but also from any of the partnerships involved in provision and delivery of the care plan.

It is important that key workers deal with any issues quickly, patiently and in a way that is supportive. If a key worker is unapproachable, reprimanding or judgemental, anyone involved in the delivery of the care plan, including the individual, may not feel confident to seek clarification, request guidance or ask for assistance.

If those responsible for the care delivery are not performing, however, then the key worker must ensure that they are challenged. This must be dealt with in a professional, supportive way. But equally, if someone is not providing the care that they should be, key workers need to have the authority and the ability to report this and deal with it. If necessary, disciplinary action needs to be taken. Everyone needs to be accountable for their role. Carers also need support and guidance to ensure they are able to carry out their role safely and with confidence.

Time to think

4.2 Could you?

What characteristics make a good, supportive key worker?

Evidence activity

4.2 Supporting others to carry out aspects of a care plan

While in your setting, support others to carry out the aspects of the plan for which they are responsible. Collate witness statements and any documentation as evidence.

AC 4.3 Adjust the plan in response to changing needs or circumstances

At the outset it may be noted that the plan needs immediate changes, before the scheduled review date. In this case, the plan needs adapting to take account of this. Clearly, this needs to be done immediately.

Reasons a plan may need changing could be because:

- a need was missed
- the individual's needs alter
- the individual changes accommodation, possibly even geographical area (which may result in a different local authority or service providers becoming responsible for their care)
- services open or close, or opening hours change
- there are care worker problems, e.g. staff sickness, industrial action or redundancies.

Evidence activity

4.3 Adjusting the plan in response to changing needs or circumstances

While at your work setting, adjust a care plan in response to changing needs or circumstances. Collate witness statements and any documentation as evidence.

Case study

4.3 Harpreet and Avaninder

Harpreet has mobility problems due to a recent hip and knee replacement. His main caregiver is his wife, Avaninder, who assists with all his dietary, hygiene and toileting needs. Harpreet has a care plan in place, which details services provided by others, e.g. transport, physiotherapy, medical care. When returning home from shopping one day, Avaninder slips and damages her back. An ambulance is called and, after a short period in hospital, she is sent home to rest in bed for approximately a week to allow her bruised and tender back to heal.

1 Why will Harpreet's current care plan no longer be effective?
2 Imagine you were the key worker for this household. What adjustments would you make to Harpreet's care plan?

LO5 Be able to monitor care plans

AC 5.1 Agree methods for monitoring the way a care plan is delivered

Once a care plan is being implemented, everyone needs to be aware of how it will be checked and monitored. Methods for monitoring need to be agreed with the individual and the care team, as detailed below.

- **How often?** This may depend on the severity of the individual's needs, as well as the level of changes being made. The more severe the needs or the greater the level of change, the greater will be the need for frequent monitoring. Monitoring may be at set, frequent points, or the care delivered may be so simple that there needs to be monitoring only if an issue arises.
- **How?** What method should be used to feed back on whether the care plan is effective or not? This could be in person if that is most suitable, or case meetings may be needed. It may be judged that face-to-face feedback isn't required and that written reports are sufficient. Verbal feedback on its own should be avoided under all circumstances, as there is no record of this.

Key term

Being on the **periphery** means being on the edge, or having only minor involvement in something.

Evidence activity

5.1 Agreeing methods for monitoring the delivery of a care plan

Using the same individual as for Evidence Activity 2.2, produce a poster describing methods that could be used to monitor the way a care plan is delivered.

- **Who will feed back?** Clearly, the more care workers, family members and friends who feed back, in addition to the individual, the more evidence there will be on the effectiveness of the delivery. This has to be balanced with information overload, however. A line may need to be drawn at people who have very minor involvement in the care delivery.

Whatever is decided, it must be discussed with the individual and using the methods they desire and feel are suitable. On-going monitoring and review is important to ensure a person's needs are met at all times. Needs can change, a person can become more mobile so need less support, for example.

AC 5.2 Collate monitoring information from agreed sources

It is the key worker's role to collate (i.e. collect) all the monitoring information from the agreed sources, allowing an overview of the expert perspectives of all those involved. The key worker needs to ensure that the information they collate from the agreed sources follows essential guidelines (see Figure 17.6), which will ensure that monitoring is as effective as possible. Information collected must be recorded and stored using agreed ways of working. For example, records must be securely stored. Any changes observed or passed on to you by the individuals or their family or carers must be recorded. Make a note of what they say, sign and date it.

Rule 1 – Accuracy. When care workers report their observations, they should ensure they are as accurate as possible. This ensures there is little doubt over the meaning of what they are saying. Information could be used to alter a care plan and the care an individual gets, it could be used in any investigations or tribunal and could also be read by any of the parties involved, including the individual themselves, so every statement needs to be accurate and true.

Rule 2 – Objectivity. Although it can sometimes be difficult to not put one's own viewpoint or opinion on what one sees, hears or thinks, it is vital this is avoided. When reporting on an individual's care all elements of subjectivity need to be removed. Avoid 'I think' and 'I believe'. Waffle should also be avoided as this could cloud judgements.

Rule 3 – Facts. It is more effective to comment on a *measured* difference. Instead of reporting 'It looks like Hilda has lost weight since she moved into the residential home, it might be more beneficial to say 'In the two weeks since Hilda moved into the residential home, her weight has reduced by 7lbs'. Comments making clear how many meals eaten, hours spent sleeping, fluids consumed, and exercise done, etc. will lead to better monitoring.

Figure 17.6 Rules for collating information

Evidence activity

5.2 Collating monitoring information from agreed sources

While in your setting, collate monitoring information from agreed sources. Provide documentation as evidence.

AC 5.3 Record changes that affect the delivery of the care plan

Any changes made to the plan as the result of any monitoring need to be recorded in as much detail as the initial plans were, to ensure that all parties are in full support and have knowledge of the changes.

It is also important to remember that changes in the individual can be exceptionally subtle. Not all changes are obvious, and they may not even be acknowledged by the individual. Changes such as increasing feelings of depression, isolation or lower self-esteem may not be apparent.

Changes may be rectified by something as simple as adapting somebody's pain relief. Good care workers will not only make a conscious effort to monitor these changes, but will record them also.

Information needs to be stored in one place, and kept easily accessible. Changes need to be recorded immediately and information should be shared with the individual and others, so they are kept up to date.

LO6 Be able to facilitate a review of care plans and their implementation

AC 6.1 Seek agreement with the individual and others about who should be involved in the review process and criteria by which to judge effectiveness of the care plan

When the care plan is ready to be reviewed at the scheduled time, the individual should discuss the success of the plan from their perspective. Individuals should be given the opportunity to reflect on how they feel their care plan has met their needs before any meeting, to ensure they have time to consider, articulate and prepare for any discussions. This again is about making the process person-centred, not just in the assessment and planning, but throughout.

Who should be involved?

Once a review is in place, individuals and others involved should be asked about who should be involved in the review process. A balance needs to be made between the range of information received and its relevance. One course of action is to speak with the individual about who they would like to be involved in the review process.

- Many of the people involved in the assessment stage, such as relatives or carers, may be called upon. They may be able to provide feedback that can be more comparative, i.e. they can talk about the individual's needs both before and after the care plan.

- The individual may have friends or family who they believe can provide useful feedback.
- The individual may have care workers to whom they have become particularly close or with whom they have spent significant amounts of time. They may feel they would like them to be consulted about their progress.
- There may be care workers with whom relationships have been poor and the individual may not respect or trust any comments from them.

Clearly, the key worker needs to bear any of these reservations in mind, but they also have to weigh up an individual's personal feelings against the goal of getting the most accurate picture of whether the care plan has been successful.

Judging the effectiveness of the plan

In theory, the criteria by which to judge the effectiveness of the care plan should have been decided with the individual at the outset, as one could argue that the goalposts have been moved if these are put in place at the end of the plan. If significant changes have occurred, however, then new criteria against which to judge the success of the care plan need to be established with the individual that take these changes into account.

For example, you will need to ask has the person achieved any steps towards their goals? Have their needs or abilities changed? Have their skills or abilities improved so they require less support?

Outcomes or goals can be set and amended as they are achieved or when the person's needs change.

AC 6.2 Seek feedback from the individual and others about how the plan is working

As with monitoring, it is vital that the individual and everyone involved in their care is able to

Evidence activity

6.2 Feeding back about how the plan is working

While at your work setting, seek feedback from an individual and others about how the plan is working. Provide witness statements and documentation as evidence.

comment on how the plan is working, whether it is being successful and where there may be room for improvement.

Three possible problems may arise if the individual or care workers do not highlight successes or failures:

1 If another care plan is designed, it will continue with the same inappropriate care.
2 The care plan may continue when it is not needed any more.
3 The care plan may end when it is still needed.

Care workers may believe that only small 'tweaks' to the care plan may be needed, for example more frequent trips to the dentist to assist with denture care. On the other hand, more significant changes may be reported as being needed, e.g. a belief that a move from living in the individual's own home to nursing care would be suitable. Whatever the feedback, it is vital that it is recorded and shared.

Checklists could be used to identify if any, or all of the steps towards agreed objectives have been met.

AC 6.3 Use feedback and monitoring/other information to evaluate whether the plan has achieved its objectives

At the 'end' of a care plan, it is good practice to consider whether the plan has met its objectives. The worst situation would be if the plan were just to 'fizzle out' with no reflection, discussion, review or agreement. It will not be possible to make any revisions to the plan if this stage is not considered.

Case study

6.3 Mark

Mark is a nine-year-old child with a combination of visual and hearing impairments. Mark and his parents want him to move to a mainstream school. His care plan for the last year has targeted how he could cope with the move. His care plan is due for review and there is a variety of reports and monitoring to be consulted.

The feedback from his parents details how Mark has gained in confidence in the last year, how at times he reports feeling bored at the school and wanting to take part in more challenging activities. They say he is a bright boy and feel he would be better suited to and challenged by a mainstream school.

Most importantly, a review from Mark explains that he loves his current school, but that he sometimes finds the work easy and that while he is at school he misses his friends from his street, whom he socialises with at evenings and weekends. He knows going to the local primary school will be tough, but says he is determined and wants to give it a shot. He really wants to go to the local high school at the same time as his friends and sit as many GCSEs as possible.

1 Why is it useful to have reviews and feedback?
2 What would the problem be if all of the monitoring was requested *apart from* Mark's?
3 Do you think Mark's objective of transferring to his local mainstream primary school is possible?

Evidence activity

6.3 Using feedback and monitoring to evaluate the success of the plan

While in your setting, use feedback and monitoring/other information to evaluate whether an individual's plan has achieved its objectives. Provide witness statements and documentation as evidence.

AC 6.4 Work with the individual and others to agree any revisions to the plan

Once feedback has been received and examined thoroughly, the next stage is for the individual and others to decide on and agree any revisions to the plan. There are five outcomes that could be agreed upon.

1 **Closing the plan if all objectives have been met** – some people may need care provision for a set period of time only; maybe their condition wasn't chronic (e.g. they had broken a bone) or they have recovered from an illness. In such cases, the care plan may come to a natural end if the individual becomes independent and no longer has any unmet needs.

2 **Reducing the level of support to reflect increased independence** – if an individual is improving, or is able to take on more tasks for themselves, it may be possible to reduce the care delivered.

3 **Increasing the level of support to address unmet needs** – sometimes, an individual's care needs increase; they may have become more ill or weaker, or the level of informal care available may have decreased. In this case the revised care plan will need to reflect this and the level of care delivered will need to increase. It may be that as an individual has aged, future needs have become more apparent, e.g. a woman showing signs of the menopause may now need support in this area.

4 **Changing the type of support** – an individual may have become more independent in one area but more dependent in another, or the support originally offered wasn't in the right style. In these cases, the type of care may need to be altered.

5 **Changing the method of delivering the support** – a service provider may not be deemed the most appropriate for the needs of the individual; it may be too far away, not suitable, or a more suitable service may have become available. It may be that the same support is delivered in a different setting. For example, if care was required when an individual was in hospital, the same care may need to be arranged at the individual's home on their discharge or at another care setting if they are transferred.

It is worth noting that for some individuals, care plans may never actually finish – an individual may have a care plan all of their life, so it will always need to be monitored, reviewed and adapted. The key principle here is that care plans are not only reviewed and amended as necessary but that, at each stage, the individual is central to this.

Evidence activity

6.4 How to support an individual to lead assessment and planning

Produce a report on the ways you would support the individual you described in Evidence Activity 1.1 to lead their assessment and planning process.
- How could you work with them to agree revisions to their plan?
- How should any changes be recorded?
- How can colleagues be informed of any changes?

AC 6.5 Document the review process and revisions as required

Due to the importance of the care planning process, it is vital that all revisions are documented appropriately and are clear. It may be best to draft a complete new copy, dated to ensure there is no confusion as to which care plan everyone is working to. Copies of the new care plan need to be circulated to the appropriate people.

It is vital that the individual's or others' opinions on the revisions are noted. If anybody has any reservations or disagreements about any changes, these need to be recorded.

The storage of and access to documents also need to be considered.

- **Storage** – all care plans should be stored securely. Paper documents and electronic documents need to be organised, tidily and **chronologically**, in a way that means they can be found easily if they need to be referred to. Both paper-based and electronic data needs to be stored in line with the Data Protection Act 1998.
- **Confidentiality** – when documents are stored, confidentiality must be of utmost importance. Only those with the authority to access the information can do so. This

will ensure that the individual trusts service providers. Care workers need to ensure that individuals understand that confidentiality will be upheld. Written documents need to be stored in a place that is secure, restricted or locked, and not left where anybody else could view them. Electronic documents need to be stored in places that are password protected, on personal user areas (shared areas should be avoided) and not on removable storage (e.g. USB memory sticks), as these could be lost.

Having excellent documents and exemplary recording and storage of notes is clearly the best way to give quality care to the service user. It will also support care workers, however, especially if there are any questions, complaints or investigations into the quality of care. Good documentation will:

- protect those care workers who are doing their work properly
- highlight any care workers who are not doing their work properly.

Key term

Chronologically means in order of time or occurrence.

Research and investigate

6.5 Data Protection Act 1998

Find out as much as you can about the Data Protection Act 1998: its purpose, principles, etc.

Case study

6.5 Shanice

Shanice is an elderly lady who has no known conditions or impairments other than what would be expected for a woman of her age. Her children are very concerned about the care she has received over the last 15 years; for example, she has had unmet needs and has been left for days at a time without scheduled visits. She first moved into a residential home to assist with her social and emotional needs four years ago, but since then she has had to move twice, once because the home was too far away from her home town and her friends and family, and again because the care home closed. In the new care home, her children are very concerned about the standard

of personal care. Shanice's clothes are sometimes dirty, especially her underwear, although there is no evidence that Shanice has any issue with bowel or bladder control. She has lost weight, become increasingly anxious and at times seems nervous. She has aged faster than would be expected from developmental norms.

Her children have reported Shanice's care to the Care Quality Commission and it is being investigated. Her files, case notes and care plans since she first started receiving care are being requested.

- Why is it important to look at all the documents relating to Shanice's care over the last 15 years?

Evidence activity

6.5 The importance of supporting an individual to lead assessment and planning

Explain the requirements of reporting and recording personal information.

What must you be aware of?

Legislation

- **Carer (Recognition) Act (1995)**
- **Children Act (1989)**
- **Data Protection Act 1998**
- **NHS & Community Care Act (1990)**
- **The Care Act 2014**
- **Health and Social Care Act 2012**
- **Human Rights Act 1998**

Useful resources

Websites

Makaton

www.makaton.org

Photosymbols

http://photosymbols.org.uk

SEAP

www.seap.org.uk

World Health Organization

www.who.int/en

Reports

Social Policy Research Unit, York University (2000) 'Introducing an outcome focus into care management and user surveys'

Support individuals to live at home

This unit is worth 4 credits

What are you finding out?

The saying 'one's home is one's castle' highlights how individuals view their homes as invaluable or priceless. Various places can be a 'house', a 'shelter' or 'accommodation', but having a 'home', somewhere to call your own, is something many people value highly. If an individual needs care and support to meet their needs, then for many the best option is to assist them to remain at home for as long as possible. Moving a person away from their own home is often the last resort. Any care organised to support individuals to live at home must be co-ordinated in a formal structure, however, with the individual leading the process.

By the end of this unit you will:

1 Understand the principles of supporting individuals to live at home.
2 Be able to contribute to planning support for living at home.
3 Be able to work with individuals to secure additional services and facilities to enable them to live at home.
4 Be able to work in partnership to introduce additional services for individuals living at home.
5 Be able to contribute to reviewing support for living at home.

LO1 Understand the principles of supporting individuals to live at home

AC 1.1 Describe how being supported to live at home can benefit an individual

Living at home can have many benefits for an individual – see Figure 18.1.

Physical benefits include:

- There are facilities to meet physical needs – bathroom, kitchen, bedroom, etc.
- Individuals may have all the physical comforts they like around them.

Intellectual benefits include:

- Individuals are more likely to know where everything can be found in the home.
- The individual knows their way around the house.
- The individual knows the geographical area better, so is more likely to know how to get around.

Emotional benefits include:

- Feeling proud that they are remaining at home.
- Improved self-esteem and self-worth.
- Feeling happy and content that they are in their own home.

Social benefits include:

- Maybe sharing a home with parents, siblings, children, etc.
- Friends and family are more likely to live locally.
- They are able to invite friends and family to their home for social events.

> ### Time to think
>
> **1.1 Home is where the heart is**
> Think about your home.
>
> - Why do you like it?
> - How would you feel if you had to leave it?

Figure 18.1 Home comforts

It is usually preferable for an individual to remain living in their own home rather than moving to residential care, regardless of age and ability. Most people want to live where they feel safe and secure. The saying 'home is where the heart is' means that home is where a person experiences happiness, love or well-being. It may be a place where someone has lived most of their life, where their family has lived (or still does), where they have memories and experiences. Moving to another setting could be upsetting and distressing, and lead to a lot of anxiety and fear. It may also mean moving away from their friends, family and local networks.

> ### Evidence activity
>
> **1.1 How living at home can benefit an individual**
> Describe the benefits of living at home.

AC 1.2 Compare the roles of people and agencies that may be needed to support an individual to live at home

There are many people and agencies that may be needed to support an individual to live at home, including a range of health, social and early years services. Often the roles and responsibilities can overlap due to provision increasingly being delivered in multi-disciplinary teams and funded through a 'mixed economy of care' or from several sources.

People or agencies that may be needed to support an individual to live at home include:

- GP
- district nurses
- dietician
- optician
- physiotherapist
- chiropodist
- dentist
- psychiatric nurses
- occupational therapist
- social worker
- care assistants
- domiciliary care worker
- housing officers
- counsellor
- home tutor
- educational welfare officers.

Research and investigate

1.2 Comparing roles
Choose three roles from the list above. Research the roles and responsibilities of each and compare them.

These people and agencies are often co-ordinated by one care worker. This may be a social worker, but increasingly roles are being created solely to co-ordinate care. This role may also be referred to as a key worker, care co-ordinator, facilitator, care manager, case manager or similar, but for ease, the term key worker will be used throughout this chapter.

There are many roles that people and agencies can take:

- **Supporting** – some roles, like **advocates**, may support individuals with the services and

Key term

Advocates represent individuals or speak on their behalf to ensure their rights are supported.

Research and investigate

1.2 Mixed economy of care
Find out what 'mixed economy of care' means.
What are the benefits of services being delivered in this way?

benefits to which they are entitled. They may help individuals to organise their finances, education or support. Individuals may need support regarding rights, benefits, electoral roll forms, insurance, tax, etc. The key worker's role is not usually to advise, but to provide information, to outline advantages and disadvantages, and to assist individuals to make their own informed decisions. This will help to empower individuals.

- **Educating** – some roles involve helping individuals to gain knowledge or experience. For a child, this could be at school. For an adult, this could be through training or courses. It could also, however, mean education in life skills, such as how to manage finances, use a cash machine, etc. It could also mean educating an individual about their health condition or the equipment they now need to use.
- **Healthcare** – some roles may involve delivering medical care to individuals. This could be pain relief, dressings, medication, immunisations, treatments, health education, etc.
- **Social care** – some roles may involve providing social care. This could be providing individuals with company, preparing meals, domestic support, travel assistance, counselling, welfare, etc.
- **Planning** – some roles may involve the co-ordination of care. This may mean not actually delivering or providing care, but instead managing an individual's care so that the people who are delivering it provide the best quality care.

- **Adapting/decorating** – some roles may involve adapting the home to make it more accessible for the individual, e.g. putting in ramps, hand rails or stair lifts, lowering cupboards or switches. Some roles may help people with any task involved in the upkeep of their home, e.g. painting and DIY.

The roles of these people and agencies will not always be performed in the individual's own home, but could be delivered in another setting.

Case study

1.2 Peter

Peter has spent most of his life being cared for by the women in his life. As a child his mother looked after him, and when his mother was at work his older sister looked after him. He married at 19 and then his wife cooked, cleaned, washed and ironed for him. Peter did his share of the chores in the home, but tended to do traditional gender-specific roles, meaning he did the manual work like DIY, gardening, decorating, etc. When his wife passed away last year, Peter struggled. He lived on sandwiches and cold food. He became unkempt and his clothes became soiled. The house became increasingly dirty. Neighbours called social services as they thought Peter needed to go into a home.

On assessment, it was clear to all that Peter was a bright, able man. It was decided that he would benefit from being educated and receiving support on skills to live on his own. He was shown how to use the washing machine, microwave and cooker. Some support was organised so that he always gets some hot meals each week. Once a week a care worker visits Peter to check on him and give him any extra help and support his needs.

1 How has this support benefited Peter?
2 Do you think Peter should have gone into a home? Justify your answer.

Evidence activity

1.2 Supporting an individual to live at home
Write a report comparing the role of a selection of people and agencies that could support an individual to live at home.

AC 1.3 Explain the importance of providing information about benefits, allowances and financial planning, which could support individuals to live at home

In September 2014 it was reported that benefits worth up to €16.8 million – ranging from pension credit to Jobseeker's Allowance – go unclaimed each year. The fact that each year there is such a huge amount of unclaimed benefits, when so many people are disadvantaged and living in poverty, is not only ironic but also tragic. Resources matter to everyone, but if an individual is vulnerable, every resource can contribute to helping their care needs to be met.

A small change to an individual's resources, allowances and financial planning could make a significant difference to their independence if they are then able to organise resources to do more things for themselves. This can also make a difference to **autonomy**, as individuals will have more control over their life. It can be **empowering**.

It can be difficult to discuss money as it is an area about which individuals might be embarrassed, reserved or private. Some people may even find it vulgar to discuss finances. It is vital that care workers discuss the subject with sensitivity and tact so that they do not cause any offence.

Benefits and allowances
There is a whole range of benefits that could be claimed or monies reimbursed, as shown in Table 18.1.

Key terms

Autonomy means having personal freedom and the ability to be independent.

To **empower** means to give someone control over their life and decisions.

In retirement	• State Pensions (dependent on whether eligible for married or single pension allowance) • Pension Credit and Savings Credit • Cold Weather Payments
Employed on a low income or looking for work	• Income Support • Jobseeker's Allowance • Housing Benefit • Council Tax Reduction • Working Tax Credit • Child Tax Credit
Ill or injured	• Statutory Sick Pay • Employment and Support Allowance • Healthcare Travel Costs Scheme • Prescription assistance
Expecting or bringing up children	• Maternity Allowance • Statutory Maternity Pay • Child Benefit • Child maintenance
Disability	• Disability Living Allowance • Attendance Allowance • Independent Living Fund • Carer's Allowance
Bereavement	• Funeral Payments • Bereavement Allowance • War Widow or Widower Pension
In education	• Education Maintenance Allowance (EMA) (Northern Ireland, Scotland and Wales) • 16–19 Bursary Fund (England) • Student loans • Bursaries

Table 18.1 Possible benefits and allowances available

These are correct at time of going to press, but the names of benefits and eligibility criteria may alter due to changes in government policy. For up-to-date information on benefits and allowances, www.gov.uk is an excellent website.

Financial planning

Individuals can draw on any inheritance, savings and private pensions to support them to live at home. If an individual has resources, they should be guided as to how best to use them. Individuals may have savings, stocks or shares or, if not, this may be something they would like to start. They may also like guidance on what tax they should be paying.

It is also worth considering how they pay for services, e.g. utilities. Direct debits and standing orders can be simpler and often cheaper than paying bills by cheque or cash, but some people are cautious about setting them up.

If an individual is struggling with debt, support and guidance should be offered to help reduce it. Also, there should be guidance on how to spread costs, using monthly payments, etc.

Helping individuals to save to prepare for any unexpected costs or future care needs is also good practice.

Case study

1.3 Pound Avenue

There are two individuals on Pound Avenue who are receiving support to assist them to live at home. They have just divulged their financial situations to their care workers.

Rich has been saving up for many years. He does not trust banks or anyone else with his money – he keeps it 'safely' secured around his house in tins, under floorboards, under his mattress and in suitcases. He estimates there is around £20,000. He has seen local youths hanging about close to his house and is worried.

Paul lives next door to Rich. He was made redundant a few years ago, but never found another job due to his poor health. He never really saved any money when younger and then mismanaged some of his money in his fifties. He struggles to get by every week and is sure he does not get the benefits to which he is entitled. He recalls putting money into a pension when he worked as a miner in his twenties. He has numerous credit cards, which he depends on to get by each week, because, 'Well, everyone does, don't they?' But he is worried. He estimates that he is around £20,000 in debt.

1 In what ways are Rich and Paul each putting themselves at risk?
2 What support would you offer to Rich and Paul?

Sources of help

These include:

- Citizen's Advice Bureau
- local debt organisations
- credit card companies
- financial advisors
- National Debtline.

Evidence activity

1.3 The importance of providing financial information

Produce a report for a key worker starting work, explaining why it is important to provide individuals with information on benefits, allowances and financial planning.

AC 1.4 Explain how risk management contributes to supporting individuals to live at home

Risk management is examining a care setting to recognise and redress any potential risks that may occur, in the hope that the risk can be either removed or reduced. Apart from being best practice, it is also a legal requirement under the Health and Safety at Work etc. Act 1974 (HASAWA) to make sure that individuals and their carers are kept free from risk.

Under the Act, an 'employer' must carry out risk assessments and take action even if the care is being delivered in an individual's own home. Sometimes, however, the hazard cannot be removed, e.g. if it is in the individual's home. In this case, all that can be done is to make the individual aware of the risk, make suggestions and support them in how it could be removed. Care workers cannot go into an individual's home and start replacing, changing or moving their possessions without their permission.

In simple terms, risk management means:

1 Identifying risks and hazards.
2 Implementing changes or measures to reduce or eliminate those risks. This could be carried out by:
   - **area** – particular areas have particular hazards, e.g. kitchen, bathroom, bedroom, garden, etc.
   - **activity** – particular activities have particular hazards, e.g. personal hygiene, climbing stairs, housework, clothes (washing, drying and ironing), etc.
   - **hazard** – e.g. fire, falls, burns, scalds, electrocution, intruders, security, etc.

Having identified the risks, it is vital to apply risk control measures.

By removing risks, which may require only simple changes, individuals are more likely to be able to remain in their own home and be safer. If this is explained to them, and they understand how it will not only assist them to remain in their own home but will also allow them to do so safely and more independently, they are more likely to accept and welcome your actions.

Figure 18.2 How could this pose a risk in the home?

LO2 Be able to contribute to planning support for living at home

AC 2.1 Identify with an individual the strengths, skills and existing networks they have that could support them to live at home

Identifying with an individual the strengths, skills and existing networks they have will not only allow any support to be person-centred, it will also help individuals to maintain their independence.

Strengths and skills – what an individual can do competently

Different people are good at different things, and a good care worker will recognise and encourage the things at which someone is good. These could be part of their character – for example, an individual may be articulate, able, organised, energetic, positive thinking – or they could be practical accomplishments, such as sewing, dressmaking, cooking, DIY, gardening, decorating, painting, being creative, etc.

Care workers must recognise what an individual can do, not what they cannot do, as is too often the focus. Value every individual – they should never be undermined. Everyone needs to be proud of their successes and accomplishments. Disregarding someone's strengths and skills does not value the person, and care workers 'taking over' and performing tasks instead could lead to increasing dependence and loss of autonomy.

Existing networks – networks of which an individual may already be part

People may belong to many networks based on their neighbourhood, religion, day centres they attend, public houses they visit, clubs, medical conditions, support groups, trade unions, past employment, etc. It is a waste of resources if care is planned to support an individual when the same support is already available and provided elsewhere. Furthermore, it is likely to be less effective if the support is arranged as an 'add on'. The care that is already in place may be more relevant and appropriate for the individual as they have arranged it themselves.

Case study

2.1 Adam

Adam is a young man in his mid-thirties who lives at home. He has used a wheelchair since an accident. His carer has arranged for him to have a Christmas meal with a local support group, where Adam does not know anyone. Adam is disappointed, as the meal is on the same evening he has arranged to go out with his old football team for a Christmas meal. He knows lots of people who will be there and is looking forward to it. His care worker gets cross with Adam, explaining that he has arranged the meal with the support group and it has already been paid for! The care worker has also arranged for the Access Bus to pick Adam up to take him there and return him home, whereas Adam prefers to book taxis for his evenings out as he likes the flexibility they offer.

1 Explain where the care worker has failed Adam in this situation.
2 What should the care worker do in future to support Adam?
3 How can support be accessed to enable Adam to carry out the activities of his choice, while still living at home?

AC 2.2 Identify with an individual their needs that may require additional support and their preferences for how the needs may be met

Just as anyone moving into a new residential setting would have their needs assessed, an individual residing in their own home must also have their needs assessed. This can be done using many methods and formats, but assessment of the following factors is essential:

- **personal** – what needs do they have in relation to wishes and preferences.
- **physical** – needs about access or equipment which may be required for their mobility.
- **financial** – do they have finds, or a budget or do they need support accessing these.
- **social** – do they have activities or events they like to attend.
- **environmental** – needs in relation to where they live.
- **safety** – does a risk assessment need to be carried out to ensure they are safe.

In each of these areas, individuals will need to assess their abilities on a spectrum similar to that shown in Figure 18.3.

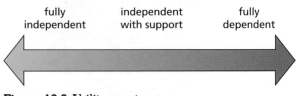

Figure 18.3 Ability spectrum

Clearly a full assessment with an individual will be more detailed and will fully document all the reasons why they feel the way they do about their abilities. The whole process has to be person-centred and led by the individual themselves. Care workers should not assume anything. All assessment must empower an individual. Individuals should lead discussions about how these needs should be met.

Some of the support required may relate to:

- training
- adaptations
- equipment
- social interactions
- professional support
- respite care
- transport.

Decisions should focus around:

- with what individuals feel comfortable
- how intrusive it may be in their life
- how significantly, or soon, it may need adapting if future needs change
- what can be afforded
- how it ties in with any informal care or existing networks of support.

All the options for support need to be discussed with the individual, allowing them to state which they prefer. Then a 'package' of support can be drawn up for them to live at home.

AC 2.3 Agree with the individual and others the risks that need to be managed in living at home, and ways to address them

Living in one's own home may be the most preferred option, but there may be risks with this. Once a home has been assessed, individuals need to be made aware of risks so that they can either be dealt with or so the individual can make informed decisions about whether they are able to remain safely in their own home.

Table 18.2 explains some of the risks associated with living in your own home. Many of these risks may increase if the individual lives on their own, or if they live with another person who is also vulnerable.

Once all risks have been identified, it is vital that this information is shared with individuals so that

they, along with others, can agree the risks that need to be managed and ways to address them. The others involved in this process could be:

- family
- friends
- advocates
- others who are important to the individual's well-being.

These could be people either living in the same home, providing informal care, or who care about the individual and whose support and involvement are therefore vital.

All the options need to be discussed, in detail, along with the consequences, e.g. costs, disruption, etc. Some risks may be less significant and can be addressed as soon as they are highlighted, for

> **Key term**
>
> **Accentuated** means emphasised.

Risk	Examples
Inappropriate care	Equipment to enable care in the individual's own home may not be sufficient.
	Individuals may have to use equipment themselves and they may make mistakes.
Isolation or depression	There could be a risk of isolation and depression from being alone in one's own home.
Medical care	Care may not be available 24/7; the individual may need support when it is not available.
	When support is arranged, it may be rushed and unsupervised.
Security	Potentially more vulnerable to intruders or crime if on their own.
	Less extensive security systems and maybe less secure windows and doors.
Forgetfulness	Individuals, especially if they have memory issues, may forget to take medication, fulfil daily chores or turn off equipment.
	There may be risks of forgetting to secure the property.
Abuse	If individuals are on their own, there may be less supervision and protection so there may be more opportunity for abuse to occur.
Accidents involving the individual	As individuals are more likely to be performing daily activities on their own, there is more likelihood that their condition or age may lead to an accident.
	Consequences of an accident could be **accentuated** as it may take longer to get support or treatment.
Accidents involving the accommodation	Equipment and resources may not be professionally monitored and therefore may be more at risk from electrical fault, fire, failure, food or breakage.

Table 18.2 Potential risks associated with living at home

Research and investigate

2.3 Abuse
Unfortunately, abuse can happen to anybody, including an individual in their own home.

- Research the types of abuse that can occur and the possible symptoms of abuse.
- What systems could be put in place to prevent abuse?

example by purchasing a multi-way plug to deal with any overloaded sockets.

Many of these hazards can also be reduced by systems that care organisations have in place, including:

- police checks, protocols and supervision
- named wardens and supervisors
- regular safety audits
- regular checks of equipment.

LO3 Be able to work with individuals to secure additional services and facilities to enable them to live at home

AC 3.1 Support the individual and others to access and understand information about resources, services and facilities available to support the individual to live at home

Accessing and understanding information is key if an individual and others involved are to feel any sense of ownership over the support. If necessary, documents must be adapted – if there is any doubt, check whether this needs to be done.

There is a variety of ways to make information accessible and easier to understand.

Key term

Accessing means finding and using.

Case study

2.3 Edward
Edward has early onset dementia. He sometimes forgets to heat up food and will often eat cold baked beans, for example. Sometimes he forgets to turn the heating on when it is cold or off when it is hot. The wiring throughout the house is loose and the fire alarm has not been checked for years. One day, Edward starts to run the bath, but then gets side tracked by the snooker on the television. He is only made aware of the flooding when a neighbour comes into his house and alerts him to water dripping through the overflow. On examination, his whole bathroom is flooded and water is leaking through to the kitchen.

1 List the hazards from which you feel Edward is at risk.
2 Start to think about any measures that could be put in place to ensure that Edward can stay in his own home.

Use **communication aids**:

- For individuals with visual impairments: larger type, **Braille** and putting the information into an audio format could be beneficial.
- For individuals with hearing impairments: hearing aids, sign language, signers, lip reading and the written word could be used.
- Electronic and technological developments are also increasingly effective at aiding communication and should be employed where appropriate.

Use a **simple format**:

- Ensure that language is appropriate to the age, ability and understanding of the individual. It is vital that individuals are clear about the information and not confused.
- If the person speaks a language other than English, ensure that interpreters and translators are available, thus respecting the right of the individual to participate fully.

Use **communication systems**:

- For individuals with emotional difficulties, learning difficulties or behavioural issues:

Key terms

Makaton is a visual form of communication for individuals who have learning disabilities and communication difficulties, in which gestures are used in combination with pictures and symbols to communicate messages.

Photosymbols is a collection of pictures for making EasyRead information. They are designed to be placed alongside words to make information easier to understand.

Braille is a tactile form of communicating that involves touching a series of raised dots that represent letters and numbers.

Evidence activity

3.1 Accessing and understanding information about resources, services and facilities

Produce a poster to show how information can be made accessible and understandable.

picture aids, photographs, visits, plans, flash cards, etc. may be of use.

- **Makaton** could be used; this is a system of signs and gestures.
- **Photosymbols**, which use images to send a message, could be used.

It is important to present information about resources, services and facilities available to support the individual to live at home in a way that is appropriate to the age, needs, ability and preferences of the individual and, if in doubt, to confirm with the individual how they would like details to be presented. Inclusiveness should be paramount and individuals must be encouraged to participate fully if the support is to be person-centred.

Information provided to the individual and others must be in a format they can easily understand. For example Braille or audio formats. You should be able to explain key points and support them with any queries or concerns they have.

AC 3.2 Work with the individual and others to select resources, facilities and services that will meet the individual's needs and minimise risks

Individuals must decide, with the others involved, which resources, facilities and services will meet their needs and minimise risks. These must be included in a care plan that formalises the decisions the individual and others make.

Individuals could consider whether any of the following would be of use to assist them to live at home safely.

- **Training** – this could be training on how to use everyday equipment such as the cooker, microwave or washing machine. Training could also be on how to use any equipment that has been installed, e.g. hoists.
- **Adaptations** – it may be necessary to adapt the home to enable a person to live there comfortably and safely. This could mean external changes (e.g. ramps) or internal changes (e.g. a stair lift, lowered units, widened doors).
- **Equipment bought** – a vast range of equipment can be bought from various outlets online or from shops and catalogues to allow individuals to be as independent as possible, as shown in Table 18.3.
- **Social interactions** – whether arranged within the home or out of it, social interactions may be needed to ensure that individuals have a good range of relationships and are not isolated. Visits to day centres and clubs, trips out and visits by others to the individual's home may all be useful.
- **Professional support** – this could mean nursing care, social care, education, therapy, counselling, treatment, medication, etc. All will deliver specialist support that can ensure individuals are as physically and emotionally healthy as possible.
- **Respite care** – this type of support can help individuals to live at home, as it allows informal carers to have a 'holiday' from care. Without this break, care for an individual may suffer indirectly because carers may become stressed

Mobility aids	Walking frames
	Walking sticks
	Scooters
	Wheelchairs
Eating aids	Angled cutlery
	Non-slip plates
	Cups with handles
Cooking aids	Electronic knives and accessories
	Tap turners
	Kettle tippers
Sleeping aids	Raised beds
	Lowered beds
	Adjustable head rests
	Bed trays
	Angled pillows
Bathing aids	Non-slip mats
	Rails
	Dry shampoo
	Hair rinsing trays
	Walk-in showers and baths
Personal aids	Commodes
	Continence pads
	Raised toilet seats
Memory aids	Alarms
	Tablet boxes
	Thermostats
	Orientation sheets
	Checklists
	Reminders
Dressing aids	Button fasteners
	Velcro
	Shoe horns
	Sock and stocking aids
	Zipper pulls
Transfer aids	Hoists
	Transfer boards
	Monkey pole/lifting handle

Table 18.3 Aids to assist living at home

Evidence activity

3.2 Selecting resources, facilities and services

Choose a condition, impairment or illness. Produce a report on the resources, facilities and services that may meet the needs of an individual with that condition, impairment or illness.

and tired. Supporting informal carers helps to support individuals.

- **Transport** – having transport arranged to allow individuals to access support may be all that is required. Taxis, cars or minibuses could all be arranged to promote an individual's ability to live at home.

AC 3.3 Contribute to completing paperwork to apply for required resources, facilities and services, in a way that promotes active participation

Active participation allows individuals more control over their support. Examples of types of paperwork that might need to be completed include:

- applications
- assessments
- requests
- feedback
- finance forms
- agreements (which may need to be read and signed).

It is vital that paperwork is completed accurately and within deadlines. Poor

Key term

Active participation is a way of working that recognises an individual's right to participate in the activities and relationships of everyday life as independently as possible; the individual is regarded as an active partner in their own care or support, rather than as a passive recipient.

completion of paperwork may lead to refusal of applications. Individuals may need support in this process, but ideally it should be the individual who applies.

If individuals need assistance either with the practicality of completing the application (with writing, reading, etc.) or with the knowledge of what to submit (content, how to answer questions) then the care worker should assist in a way that is empowering. The care worker should not take over and complete the paperwork themselves. Possible ways in which to involve an individual include:

- reading out the questions
- explaining the questions
- filling in answers given by the individual
- providing a selection of answers, to which the individual can point to indicate their selection
- using audio formats
- using electronic forms
- using magnifiers and other reading and writing aids
- allowing sufficient, dedicated time for an individual to be fully involved.

Initially, completing paperwork can seem daunting. With time, however, individuals may become more fluent with terminology, calculations and requirements and become more confident in completing paperwork independently.

Time to think

3.3 Involved?

Anthony is a busy care worker, with lots of individuals to see in his schedule. He often has to help individuals to apply for things such as car tax rebates, housing benefit, new equipment or adaptations. There are times when Anthony is so rushed, he just takes the forms and completes them himself. 'No problem,' he says. 'At least they get done!'

Why is Anthony's practice a problem?

Evidence activity

3.3 Contributing to the completion of paperwork

Produce a brochure detailing ten 'top tips' for promoting active participation when contributing to the completion of paperwork.

AC 3.4 Obtain permission to provide additional information about the individual in order to secure resources, services and facilities

In organising support for individuals there are times when care workers may need to divulge information about them. This must be discussed with the individual prior to any disclosure, and they must give their permission. A key principle in providing person-centred care is that permission is gained *before* information is shared. Information belongs to an individual; it should not be given out unless they allow it.

Individuals often share information with care workers as they have a relationship built on trust. They may feel betrayed if they later find out that this information has been shared with others without their permission. Discussing the need to share information, and explaining how it will remain confidential and will assist in getting them the required support, should help an individual to make decisions about their information.

Clearly, if an individual is at risk, or putting others at risk, the boundaries of confidentiality become more blurred and the care worker needs to make a judgement about whether to **breach** (see page 334 for definition) confidentiality without the individual's permission. This would need to be done in line with procedures, however, and the care worker should divulge the information privately to their line manager only and not to other staff.

Evidence activity

3.4 Obtaining permission to provide additional information about the individual

Produce a statement outlining the importance of gaining permission to provide additional information and how this should be done.

Permission should always be gained in writing once the individual fully understands with whom the information may be shared. This should all be done in line with the Data Protection Act 1998.

LO4 Be able to work in partnership to introduce additional services for individuals living at home

AC 4.1 Agree roles and responsibilities for introducing additional support for an individual to live at home

Once it has been agreed which resources, services, facilities or support are to be employed to support an individual to live at home, it is important that everyone is clear about their roles and responsibilities. Otherwise there could be problems, such as duplications and omissions. Roles could include the person responsible for accessing funding, or renewing care needs and plans.

Everyone must be clear about what their role is and what responsibilities they have, to ensure that no one has misunderstood. Good care planning, with clear, detailed documents that are shared with all partners, is best practice.

Case study

4.1 Agreeing roles and responsibilities for introducing additional support

Arthur lives in his own home with support. He is frail, with severe arthritis, and also suffering from depression. He does not enjoy social interactions, preferring his own company. During the week, four people visit him to support him. On a Monday, two people support him: his counsellor and a care assistant (who is there to tidy his house and prepare food). On Tuesday, he is supported by a care assistant (who washes and irons his clothes and prepares food) and a nurse (who helps with his pain relief). Nobody then supports Arthur from Wednesday until the following Monday.

All four staff know that Arthur has 'poor social relationships' and yet all try to converse with him. Arthur moans that they all try to engage him in conversation, and says: 'Damned busybodies, always asking the same irrelevant questions. Where's that woman I saw at the beginning? She was nice.' One Tuesday, while upstairs, the nurse brings some of his washing down and puts it in the washing machine. When the care assistant arrives, he is annoyed that the nurse has done this and starts to argue with her. They have a full-blown argument in front of Arthur, which upsets him greatly.

- Identify the areas where support being delivered to Arthur has not been managed correctly.
- Produce a detailed plan for those providing care for Arthur, making clear days, times, roles and responsibilities that would support him best.

Evidence activity

4.1 Roles and responsibilities

Agree roles and responsibilities for introducing additional support for an individual to live at home.

AC 4.2 Introduce the individual to new resources, services, facilities or support groups

Individuals use support about which they know. If they do not know about available support, it is unlikely to be used. As people develop needs or recognise that they require support for current unmet needs, they may need to find new resources, services, facilities or support groups.

For example they may need additional resources such as a stair lift at home, or they may benefit from accessing a local support group to meet people of their own age or ability.

There are many reasons why it is sometimes difficult to know exactly what is available:

- Support available can change frequently due to governments, funding and policies changing.
- Different services may notify people only about their own support, e.g. the NHS may only publicise services it provides, and social services may do the same.
- Some services are provided voluntarily and so are not publicised within the local service frameworks.
- Support is not always easy to find in directories such as the Yellow Pages or Thomson Local, or online.
- There can often be duplication with other services.

In an ideal world, an individual could research support for a condition and have a full, up-to-date and accurate list of services available to them in their local area. This is not always possible, however.

The growth of the internet has made researching support much easier. The individual may need to be assisted to use the internet to find suitable support. The local library could also be useful, because it is often possible to use the internet there and it may also have information about local services.

Once one source of support is found, finding others can become easier, as word of mouth is often one of the best ways to find out about local support available. The care worker can support the individual and help them to lead this and decide which support is right for them, and then support the individual to apply for, attend or request the support should they wish to do so.

Time to think

4.2 Where would you go?

Imagine that one day you found out you had dementia.

- Where would you go to receive support?
- How would you find out from where support was available?

Evidence activity

4.2 Introducing the individual to new resources, services, facilities or support groups

Choose one condition, disability or impairment.

Produce a directory of all the resources, services, facilities or support groups available in your local area that may help to support individuals with this condition, disability or impairment.

AC 4.3 Record and report on the outcomes of additional support measures in required ways

If an individual receives or attends any additional support, it is useful to be able to measure its success. If it is not effective, other support may be needed as well or instead.

All outcomes need to be recorded and reported (e.g. through reports, charts, graphs, scales, discussions, **anecdotal** evidence, medicals, etc.) so that any support can be reviewed and finished, adapted or improved. The support can then continue to meet the individual's needs in the best way possible.

Key term

Anecdotal means based on personal recollections rather than on facts or research.

Research and investigate

4.3 Scales

Find out about pain assessment scales.

- What are the various formats?
- Why do you think they are useful?

Evidence activity

4.3 Recording and reporting the outcomes of additional support measures

While in your work setting, record and report in the required way on outcomes of an additional support measure.

LO5 Be able to contribute to reviewing support for living at home

AC 5.1 Work with the individual and others to agree methods and timescales for ongoing review

Methods

There are various methods for reviewing the support for someone living at home:

- case meetings: set at periodic times or ad hoc, where the individual and all involved can discuss support face to face
- written reports: at set periods, it may be required for careworkers to complete formal written reports on how individuals are progressing with living at home
- telephone calls: more likely to be as and when needed and may be used for more urgent issues. These always need recording somewhere
- changeover notes: to ensure consistency between staff and that everyone is fully aware and there is an overview of care.

Timescales

Support can be reviewed according to a variety of timescales:

- **Ad hoc** – situations may occur that need to be shared with all involved as they happen.
- **Periodic** – dependent on the nature or severity of the care, reviews may be weekly, monthly, quarterly, half yearly, annually, etc.
- **Final** – it may be known at the outset that the care plan will come to an end and need to be reviewed, for example if it is just to cover an individual's care while their informal carer is on holiday.
- **Urgent** – a situation may occur that is deemed an emergency if the individual is at immediate risk, in which case support may need to be reviewed straight away.

Key term

Ad hoc means as and when required.

Case study

5.1 Mr Sandhu

Mr Sandhu is a man in his fifties who has mild mental health issues. With Mr Sandhu's permission, there is a booklet in his kitchen about which all his care workers know. It is carbon copied and so allows for duplicates. Whenever a care worker has supported Mr Sandhu, they report this in the book and take a copy back to the office to put into Mr Sandhu's file. This means one copy is available to all the care workers, including the key worker, and one stays with Mr Sandhu.

The last entry states:

'Mr Sandhu seemed upset at 9 a.m. He described some nightmares he'd had the previous night, in which he was buried alive. After he'd had a cup of tea and got out of bed, he seemed calmer. Throughout the two hours I was there, however, he referred to it four times, saying "That is what you are all going to do to me!" He was not aggressive and I did not feel any threat from Mr Sandhu, but he was clearly upset by this.'

1 Why is this good practice?
2 What would you do next if you were Mr Sandhu's care worker?

Evidence activity

5.1 Agreeing methods and timescales for ongoing review

Design a role-play showing an interaction between a care worker and an individual, in which the individual is leading a discussion of the methods and timescales for reviewing their support.

Whatever methods or timescale are preferred, it is vital that the individual leads the discussions, and that final decisions are what the individual feels most comfortable with and wants.

AC 5.2 Identify any changes in an individual's circumstances that may indicate a need to adjust the type or level of support

It is hoped that the support arranged will be appropriate and meet the individual's needs to live at home. There may, however, be occasions when circumstances dictate that changes need to be made before the set review date.

Circumstances when support may need to be adjusted

- **Health** – if an individual's health improves or worsens then support will need to be adjusted to take this into account. Clearly, it is inefficient to continue to support an individual who no longer needs support.
- **Social situation** – individuals may gain, lose or rekindle friendships, so support may alter accordingly. Informal care may change as people offering informal social support change. Any other people living in the same home may change (people may move in or out), which could lead to changes to an individual's social situation.
- **Finances** – individuals' financial circumstances may change, meaning they may:
  - be able to purchase support they weren't able to before
  - have to cut back on support they were receiving before, which may mean that the plan needs to be adjusted to make up any shortfall.
- **Legal status** – there are times when an individual's legal status may change. An individual can have five potential statuses:
  1 A minor's parents or guardians hold legal guardianship over their well-being.
  2 A child with a care order may be the responsibility of the local authority, which is legally responsible for their well-being.
  3 An adult who is deemed able to do so has legal rights to decide their own well-being.
  4 Adults deemed unfit to make their own decisions may appoint, or have appointed, a legal guardian to represent them.
  5 Any individual detained under the Mental Health Act 1983 will have their legal responsibility assumed by the local authority. If they are detained in a secure hospital, treatment can be given without their consent.

AC 5.3 Work with the individual and others to agree revisions to the support provided

There is little point involving an individual from the outset in their support, only then to make revisions without their involvement or support. Individuals need to be involved at all stages (see Figure 18.4). Any revisions need to be formalised and all agencies informed of these, otherwise varying support may occur.

Working with the individual from beginning to end and allowing them to lead the process at every stage will ensure that they are able to remain living in their own home for as long as they feel it is right for them.

Figure 18.4 Discussing the options

Case study

5.3 Alison

Alison has just returned home after a long period in hospital due to being diagnosed with breast cancer. A package of support has been arranged for her, which she decided upon. This involves her staying at her mother's for a month, with the support being delivered there. She is happy with this, as she knows it is just a short-term measure. After a week, however, her mother is called into the office at work and informed that she is being made redundant. Alison's care worker hears of this from Alison's mother, and adapts the support offered to Alison to allow her mother to take a full role in her care. The care worker cancels all the support previously arranged.

When the support originally arranged doesn't turn up, Alison is confused. 'Don't worry,' her mother says, 'I'm going to sort everything out now.' Alison is furious. She doesn't always get on with her mother and if she had known this would happen, she would never have agreed to stay with her mother; she would have gone to her own house and got the support there.

1　What has the care worker failed to do?
2　How would you feel if you were Alison?

Evidence activity

5.3 Agree revisions to the support provided

Consider Alison in the case study above. Describe what best practice would have been here.

Legislation

● **Data Protection Act 1998**
● **Health and Safety at Work etc. Act 1974 (HASAWA)**

Useful resources

Websites

Benefits and allowances
www.gov.uk/browse/benefits

Citizen's Advice Bureau
www.citizensadvice.org.uk

Health and Safety Executive
www.hse.gov.uk

National Debtline
www.nationaldebtline.co.uk

StepChange Debt Charity
www.stepchange.org

This unit is worth 7 credits

What are you finding out?

In this unit you will learn about the legal and organisational requirements to protect the rights of individuals at the end of life, as well as the key factors that can affect individuals' end-of-life care. You will also find out more about the purpose and systems for advance care planning and how to provide support both to individuals and the key people involved during end-of-life care.

This unit will also equip you with the knowledge that is required to understand how to address sensitive issues that may arise in relation to end-of-life care. The role of organisations, support services and the wider team in relation to supporting individuals and key people will also be explored in more detail.

Being able to support individuals through the process of dying, knowing the actions to take following the death of individuals, as well as being able to manage your feelings in relation to the dying or death of individuals, are integral aspects of supporting end-of-life care. This chapter will provide you with the opportunity to explore these in more detail.

By the end of this unit you will:

1 Understand the requirements of legislation and agreed ways of working to protect the rights of individuals at the end of life.
2 Understand factors affecting end-of-life care.
3 Understand advance care planning in relation to end-of-life care.
4 Be able to provide support to individuals and key people during end-of-life care.
5 Understand how to address sensitive issues in relation to end-of-life care.
6 Understand the role of organisations and support services available to individuals and key people in relation to end-of-life care.
7 Be able to access support for the individual or key people from the wider team.
8 Be able to support individuals through the process of dying.
9 Be able to take action following the death of individuals.
10 Be able to manage own feelings in relation to the dying or death of individuals.

LO1 Understand the requirements of legislation and agreed ways of working to protect the rights of individuals at the end of life

AC 1.1 Outline legal requirements and agreed ways of working designed to protect the rights of individuals in end-of-life care

End-of-life care refers to the care and support provided to an individual with a life-threatening illness and to all those others involved, such as the individual's family, friends, carers and professionals. The General Medical Council defines individuals as at the end of their life when they are likely to die within the next 12 months.

The World Health Organization defines end-of-life care as follows:

- Provides relief from pain and other distressing symptoms.
- Affirms life and regards dying as a normal process.
- Intends neither to hasten nor postpone death.
- Integrates the psychological and spiritual aspects of patient care.
- Offers a support system to help patients live as actively as possible until death.
- Offers a support system to help the family cope during the patient's illness and in their own bereavement.
- Uses a team approach to address the needs of patients and their families, including bereavement counselling, if indicated.
- Will enhance quality of life, and may also positively influence the course of illness.
- Is applicable early in the course of illness, in conjunction with other therapies that are intended to prolong life, such as chemotherapy or radiation therapy, and includes those investigations needed to better understand and manage distressing clinical complications.

Legal requirements

There are a number of key pieces of legislation that can protect the rights of individuals in end-of-life care.

Equality, diversity and discrimination

- **The Equality Act 2010** applies fairness and equality in making decisions and policies, including those that relate to end-of-life care.
- **The Health and Safety at Work etc. Act 1974** sets out the responsibilities for maintaining the health, safety and welfare of everyone at work, including individuals, their families, carers, visitors and all those other professionals who work with them.
- **The Safeguarding Vulnerable Groups Act 2006** was passed to help avoid harm, or the risk of harm, by preventing people who are deemed unsuitable to work with children and vulnerable adults from gaining access to them through their work.

Data protection, recording, reporting, confidentiality and sharing information

- **The Data Protection Act 1998** was implemented in March 2000 and gives individuals a right to access information held about them by organisations such as adult social care providers. It consists of eight key principles that govern how information is recorded, reported, shared and maintained confidentially.
- **The Freedom of Information Act 2000** gives everyone a right of access to all types of recorded information held by public authorities, including publicly funded organisations, local authorities and the NHS.
- **The Human Rights Act 1998** sets out everyone's fundamental rights and freedoms in the UK. In relation to handling information in end-of-life care this includes the rights to privacy and security as well as respect for private correspondence.

The making of wills and living wills; removal of medical equipment from people is covered on page 341.

- **The Mental Capacity Act 2005** sets outs the rights of those who lack the mental capacity to make a will to have a will executed on their behalf and to apply to manage the property, money and possessions of an individual who has died.
- This Act also sets out how to make an Advanced Decision to Refuse Treatment legally binding, in

case an individual is unable to communicate the treatment they do not want to receive such as life support or CPR.

- **The Deprivation of Liberty Safeguards (DOLS)** is an amendment to this Act and provides additional rights in relation to an authority such as a hospital or care home that wishes to act on behalf of an individual that is unable to make a decision about their liberty or care.

Visitors

The Health and Safety at Work etc. Act 1974 sets out the responsibilities for maintaining the health, safety and welfare of everyone at work including individuals, their families, carers, visitors and all those other professionals who work with them.

Safeguarding of vulnerable adults

Safeguarding Vulnerable Groups Act 2006 was passed to help avoid harm, or the risk of harm, by preventing people who are deemed unsuitable to work with children and vulnerable adults from gaining access to them through their work.

Agreed ways of working

Organisations and work settings will also have agreed ways of working and policies and procedures in place to comply with these legislative requirements and protect the rights of individuals in end-of-life care.

- **Equality, diversity and discrimination** – working practices to follow for ensuring that the individual is respected and that their privacy and dignity are maintained throughout their end-of-life care including when they are deceased.
- **Data protection, recording, reporting, confidentiality and sharing information** – working practices to follow for ensuring that all verbal and written communications remain confidential and that information is only shared with those involved in the individual's end-of-life care.
- **The making of wills and living wills** – working practices to follow for ensuring that the team

are aware if an individual has made a living will and the actions to take if an individual requests that they would like to make or change their will, including what to do when an individual lacks capacity to make decisions about their care or treatment.

- **Dealing with personal property of deceased people** – working practices to follow for ensuring how the personal property of the deceased person will be kept secure, respected and to whom it may be released.
- **Removal of medical equipment from deceased people** – working practices to follow for the removal of medical equipment from deceased people, i.e. if a death is being referred to the coroner and there is any complaint about the care of the deceased then all medical equipment such as an intravenous cannula or a catheter must be left in situ so that potential evidence that may be examined at a later stage is not destroyed.
- **Visitors** – working practices to follow for maintaining the safety of all visitors including ensuring their privacy is maintained and their welfare safeguarded.
- **Safeguarding of vulnerable adults** – working practices to follow to protect the rights and safety of individuals during end-of-life care, including how to act on behalf of an individual when they lack the capacity to do so.

Agreed ways of working are also based on national guidance and frameworks:

- The government's **National End of Life Strategy**, published in 2008, provides guidance around the provision of high-quality end-of-life care, including promoting individuals' rights regarding where they would like to live and die.
- The **Six Steps Programme** (see Figure 19.1) is based on the six steps required to provide good end-of-life care as set out in the 2008 National End of Life Strategy.

- The **Supporting People to Live and Die Well (2010)** framework involves sharing best practice across services and organisations that provide end-of-life care.

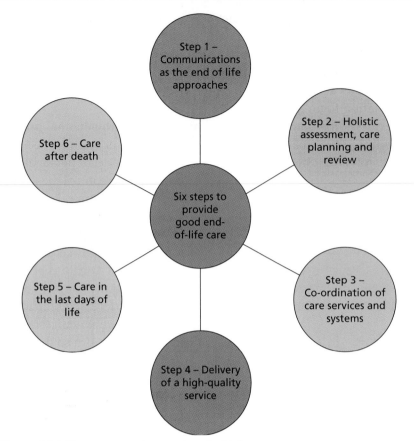

Figure 19.1 The six steps for good end-of-life care

Key term

Agreed ways of working are your work setting's policies and procedures, as well as the specific guidelines that are in place for the individuals to whom you provide care and support. They may be less formally documented with smaller employers.

Research and investigate

1.1 Protecting the rights of individuals in end-of-life care

Research the agreed ways of working for protecting the rights of individuals in end-of-life care in your local area.

AC 1.2 Explain how legislation designed to protect the rights of individuals in end-of-life care applies to own job role

The legislation that is designed to protect the rights of individuals at the end of life underpins the way organisations and work settings develop their own agreed ways of working. You and others who work in supporting end-of-life care must follow these agreed ways of working.

Table 19.1 considers how legislation designed to protect the rights of individuals in end-of-life care can apply to your job role and its associated responsibilities and working practices – can you think of any others?

Aspect of your job role	Relevant legislation	Relevance to your job role
Discussing end-of-life care with individuals and/or important others involved, such as their families	Data Protection Act 1998 Equality Act 2010 Human Rights Act 1998 Mental Capacity Act 2005	• Being open to and respecting individuals' and others' views and beliefs about end-of-life care. • Promoting an individuals' dignity and privacy. • Promoting individual's families dignity and privacy. • Providing holistic support to individuals and their families about advance planning.
Carrying out assessments, care plans and reviews	Data Protection Act 1998 Equality Act 2010 Health and Safety at Work etc. Act 1974 Human Rights Act 1998 Mental Capacity Act 2005	• The process you follow for completing an **advance care plan**. • Supporting those involved in the advance care planning process. • Carrying out care planning. • Sharing information about an individual's wishes, needs and preferences. • Recording information and maintaining records of end-of-life care.
Providing care and support to individuals' families and others, such as their carers, after the individual's death	Equality Act 2010 Human Rights Act 1998	• Knowing how to comply with your work setting's agreed ways of working. • Knowing how to comply with local and national policies. • Providing information about the support and services available to individuals' families and others. • Accessing support and services for yourself.

Table 19.1 How legislation can apply to your job role

Key term

Advance care planning is a process that enables individuals to share with others how they would like to plan for their future end-of-life care.

Time to think

1.2 How well do you know your job role?
Read through your job description.

• What does it say about protecting the rights of individuals in end-of-life care?
• How do you apply this to your working practices?

Case study

1.1, 1.2 Luciano

Luciano is a senior community carer. As part of his job role he supports a team of carers who provide end-of-life care to individuals living in their own homes. Luciano's job role includes providing information and support to individuals and their families and to the team of carers. Luciano will be meeting with and inducting three new carers who have recently been recruited to the team.

1 What legal requirements designed to protect the rights of individuals in end-of-life care must Luciano share with the team?
2 What agreed ways of working designed to protect the rights of individuals in end-of-life care must Luciano share with the team?
3 How does the relevant legislation designed to protect the rights of individuals in end-of-life care apply to Luciano's job role?

LO2 Understand factors affecting end-of-life care

AC 2.1 Outline key points of theories about the emotional and psychological processes that individuals and key people may experience with the approach of death

There are theories about the emotional and psychological processes that individuals and

key people – such as family members, friends and others who are important to the well-being of the individual – may experience with the approach of death. These theories can be useful **tools** to help you and others who support end-of-life care to gain a better insight into the thoughts and feelings of individuals and others.

A well-known theory is the **Kübler-Ross theory**, which suggests that there is a series of stages that people go through with the approach of death. It is important to remember that each person's experience with the approach of death will be unique and therefore not everyone may experience all of these stages or in the order as detailed in this theory.

Look at Figure 19.2, which provides more details about each of the stages involved in the Kübler-Ross theory.

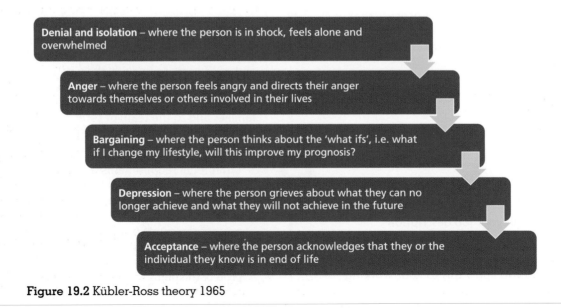

Denial and isolation – where the person is in shock, feels alone and overwhelmed

Anger – where the person feels angry and directs their anger towards themselves or others involved in their lives

Bargaining – where the person thinks about the 'what ifs', i.e. what if I change my lifestyle, will this improve my prognosis?

Depression – where the person grieves about what they can no longer achieve and what they will not achieve in the future

Acceptance – where the person acknowledges that they or the individual they know is in end of life

Figure 19.2 Kübler-Ross theory 1965

Other theories that may be useful and that include different approaches are **Corr's theory model** and **Zlatin's theory model**, as shown in Figures 19.3 and 19.4.

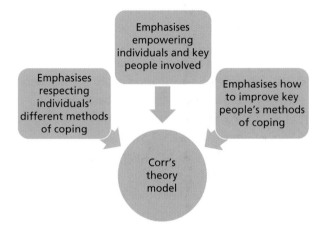

Figure 19.3 Corr's theory model 1992

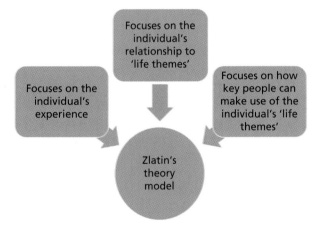

Figure 19.4 Zlatin's theory model 1995

Research and investigate

2.1 Theories of emotional and psychological processes

Research different theories about the emotional and psychological processes that individuals and key people may experience with the approach of death.

AC 2.2 Explain how the beliefs, religion and culture of individuals and key people influence end-of-life care

Individuals and key people – such as family members, friends and others who are important to the well-being of the individual – all have unique needs and preferences that are based on their personal **beliefs**, **religion** and **culture**. These will influence end-of-life care.

Respecting and following individuals' and key people's personal beliefs, religions and cultures is crucial for ensuring that the care and treatment provided are dignified and in accordance with their wishes as doing so can provide much needed comfort and strength to all those involved.

Table 19.2 includes some more information about how personal beliefs, religion and culture can impact on end-of-life care.

Personal beliefs	Religion	Culture
Rinzen is her husband's main carer. She believes in the reincarnation of her husband, who is at the end of his life. This is a great source of comfort for her.	As a Buddhist, Rinzen has asked the team to ensure that the image of Buddha is always in the view of her husband.	Rinzen has agreed with her husband that as he approaches the end of his life, he will no longer take his medication so that he can restore his inner peace in preparation for his reincarnation (see AC 4.5 for more information).
Maria is in end-of-life care and believes that it is important to continue to have **communion** every day. Maria also likes to keep her Bible close to her at all times.	As a Roman Catholic, Maria has requested a visit from a priest to administer **Holy Unction**.	Maria's family get great support from participating in regular prayers with the hospice chaplains.
Jawad, a senior home carer, believes that every person to whom he provides support will be judged in death by how they have lived their life.	As a Muslim, Jawad visits the care home's prayer room during every shift he works.	Jawad finds that reciting prayers from the **Qur'an** is a comfort to him.

Table 19.2 How personal beliefs, religion and culture can impact on end-of-life care

Key terms

Beliefs are a strong feeling that we hold as true.

Religion is a system of faith or worship.

Culture refers to the characteristics of a particular group or society.

Communion is a Christian ritual where bread and wine are made sacred and shared.

Holy Unction is a Christian ritual where the individual at the point of dying is anointed with holy oil.

The **Qur'an** is the holy book of Islam.

A **multi-disciplinary team** is a team made up of professionals from a range of different organisations and services, each of which has its own individual roles and responsibilities.

Time to think

2.2 How well do you understand the influences of end-of-life care?

Reflect on two individuals you support with end-of-life care.

- Discuss with a member of the **multi-disciplinary team** each individual's beliefs, religion and culture.
- How much did you know about each individual?
- How can you find out more about them?

AC 2.3 Explain the reasons why key people may have a distinctive role in an individual's end-of-life care

Good-quality end-of-life care involves the expertise of a range of key people, including individuals' family members, friends and others who are important to their well-being, providing physical, emotional, social and spiritual support. Figure 19.5 identifies some of the key people who may be involved in an individual's end-of-life care.

- Meeting an individual's **physical needs** will involve a range of key people – for example, a hospital consultant or other specialist such as an oncologist or urologist – who provide information about the diagnosis as well as the treatments available. Carers can provide day and night physical care and support to individuals, and specialist nurses such as Marie Curie and **Macmillan nurses** can provide information and guidance regarding pain relief and control. An individual's social worker is vital for establishing the support and services they require to meet their needs, and therapists such as occupational therapists can provide information and advice on adaptations that it

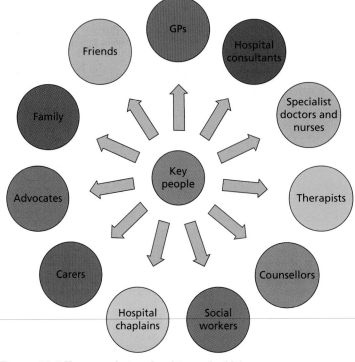

Figure 19.5 Key people involved in end-of-life care

may be beneficial to make to an individual's living environment.

- An individual's **emotional needs** can be met through their carers, family and friends, or through someone independent like an advocate or a counsellor with whom they can share their feelings and fears in confidence (see Figure 19.6).
- Volunteers in support groups play a vital role in ensuring **social needs** are met in terms of providing opportunities for the individual to meet up with others and participate in activities outside of their immediate environment. Family and friends are also important for maintaining relationships and companionship with the individual.
- **Spiritual support** can be provided by a variety of religions, groups and people such as hospital and hospice chaplains.

The support required during end-of-life care will vary for different individuals and so it is important that you are aware of the different roles key people have within a multi-disciplinary team. This will allow you to be able to draw on their areas of expertise and provide individuals with high-quality end-of-life care that meets their individual needs.

Figure 19.6 The importance of family and friends

AC 2.4 Explain why support for an individual's health and well-being may not always relate to their terminal condition

As you have learned, good-quality end-of-life care is holistic and takes account of an individual's unique needs and preferences. For this reason the support provided may not always directly relate to their terminal condition, but is still important for an individual's health and well-being.

- An individual may have concerns over their financial or housing situation and may seek support to ensure their financial affairs are in order or to find more secure and affordable housing.
- An individual may request support to remain involved in meaningful activities such as charity work or a new hobby, which will enable them to socialise with others and feel good about themselves.
- An individual may wish to address unresolved issues they have in relationships or friendships with others, and may request support to do so.
- An individual may wish to fulfil their wishes and ambitions and may request financial and/or practical support to do so.

Other areas of support that an individual may require and that are not related to their terminal condition could relate to their mental health needs, a learning difficulty or a **sensory** impairment.

Key terms

Macmillan nurses are specialist end-of-life care nurses; many have specialist knowledge in a particular type of cancer.

Sensory impairment is a loss of hearing or vision or both in an individual.

Evidence activity

2.3 Key people
- List the reasons why key people play such an important part in an individual's end-of-life care.
- Why is it important to involve family and friends in an individual's end-of-life care?

Case study

2.1, 2.2, 2.3, 2.4 Tracy

Tracy is a senior carer providing support to individuals who have been discharged from hospital and have chosen to spend their last weeks at home. As part of her senior role Tracy provides one-to-one supervision and assists with carrying out team members' initial ten-day induction and training.

1 What key points of theories about the emotional and psychological processes that individuals and key people may experience with the approach of death could Tracy include in team members' induction and training?

2 What examples could Tracy provide of how the beliefs, religion and culture of individuals and key people may influence end-of-life care?

3 What information could Tracy provide in relation to the distinctive roles that key people – such as individuals' family, friends and others who are important to the well-being of the individual – play in an individual's end-of-life care?

4 What examples could Tracy provide of why support for an individual's health and well-being may not always relate to their terminal condition?

Evidence activity

2.1, 2.2, 2.3, 2.4 Legal requirements and agreed ways of working

- Reflect on two individuals whom you support with end-of-life care. For each individual, provide brief details of the key points of theories about the emotional and psychological processes that they and the key people involved may experience with the approach of death (AC 2.1).
  Also include details with examples of how the beliefs, religion and culture of both the individuals and the key people involved influence their end-of-life care (AC 2.2).
- Reflect on both individuals and identify all the key people involved in their end-of-life care and the reasons why each has a distinctive role to play (AC 2.3).
  Then provide details with examples of why support for an individual's health and well-being may not always relate to their terminal condition (AC 2.4).

LO3 Understand advance care planning in relation to end-of-life care

AC 3.1 Describe the benefits to an individual of having as much control as possible over their end-of-life care

Person-centred approaches and ways of working involve supporting individuals to have as much control as possible over their end-of-life care. Figure 19.7 identifies some choices and decisions that an individual may wish to make with respect to their end-of-life care.

Knowing that they are in control of their own end-of-life care can be a source of great comfort to individuals, their families and any others close to them. Having their wishes respected will not only enable them to feel at peace but will also mean that they are able to die with dignity; this is sometimes referred to as 'a good death'.

Key terms

Self-worth means an individual's sense of their worth or value as a person.

Self-determination is how an individual controls their own life.

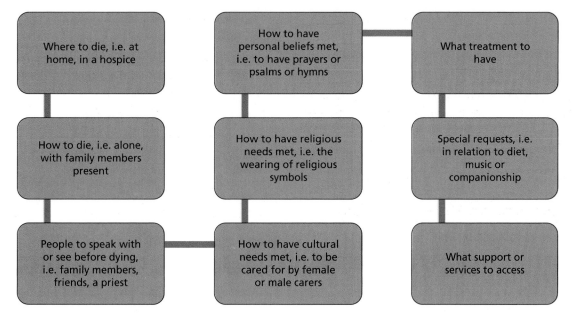

Figure 19.7 Making choices and decisions over end-of-life care

The UK government's 'End of life care strategy' for England defines 'a good death' as:

- being treated as an individual, with dignity and respect
- being without pain and other symptoms
- being in familiar surroundings
- being in the company of close family and/or friends.

Maintaining as much control as possible over end-of-life care will also provide individuals with a sense of purpose and increase their **self-worth** and **self-determination**.

AC 3.2 Explain the purpose of advance care planning in relation to end-of-life care

Advance care planning facilitates individuals' rights to have as much control as possible over their end-of-life care. It provides them with an opportunity to discuss in advance their choices, decisions and wishes with respect to their end-of-life care in case they are unable to express their preferences at a later stage. The discussions that are held are documented in full in an advance care plan.

The aims of the advance care planning process in relation to end-of-life care include:

- communicating an individual's wishes and preferences about their end-of-life care and treatment
- placing the individual at the centre of their end-of-life care
- making an individual's personal beliefs and values known to key people
- empowering an individual to make their own choices and decisions
- exploring an individual's hopes, fears and concerns
- furthering an individual's understanding of their illness and **prognosis** (see the next page for definition)
- raising an individual's awareness of the services and support available
- documenting all discussions held with an individual.

The concept of advance planning has led to the development of a number of frameworks and **tools**. These are designed for use by care providers providing end-of-life care so as to enable 'a good death'. Table 19.3 provides details of some of these.

Framework	Details

Gold Standards Framework (GSF)	• GSF involves three key steps:
	  • **Step 1:** Identifying individuals in need of care.
	  • **Step 2:** Assessing and recording individuals' needs.
	  • **Step 3:** Planning and providing individuals' care.
	• GSF involves seven key tasks known as the '7 Cs':
	  1 Communication
	  2 Co-ordination of Care
	  3 Control of symptoms and ongoing assessment
	  4 Continuing support
	  5 Continued learning
	  6 Carer and family support
	  7 Care in the final days

Preferred Priorities for Care (PPC)	• PPC involves three key steps:
	  • **Step 1:** Thinking about end-of-life care.
	  • **Step 2:** Discussing end-of-life care.
	  • **Step 3:** Recording what care an individual would like.
	• PPC involves making important decisions, such as:
	  • what an individual would like and not like as part of their care
	  • where an individual would like to receive their end-of-life care
	  • by whom an individual would like to be represented when they are unable to make their own decisions.

Improving End of Life Care (EoLC) – a toolkit for care homes	• The toolkit was designed for care home providers but is relevant also for all social care providers to help them to assess and plan for good-quality end-of-life care.
	• The toolkit consists of three steps:
	  • **Step 1:** How to provide end-of-life care as an organisation.
	  • **Step 2:** How to assess and quality-assure end-of-life care provision.
	  • **Step 3:** Practical ways to care for individuals and their families.

Table 19.3 Frameworks and tools to enable 'a good death'

Key term

Prognosis is the likely progress and life span associated with a medical condition.

Research and investigate

3.2 Systems for advance care planning
Research systems for advance care planning in your local area and in your work setting.

AC 3.3 Describe your role in supporting and recording decisions about advance care planning

Your role in supporting and recording decisions about advance care planning will vary according to your responsibilities and your work setting's agreed ways of working. There are a number of principles that should be followed for supporting and recording all decisions about advance care planning; the top ten principles are detailed below.

Top ten principles for supporting decisions about advance care planning

- Support individuals to make their own decisions about their end-of-life care and treatment.
- Support key people to understand the individual's decisions about advance care planning.
- Support individuals to review and update their advance care plan regularly.
- Ensure you communicate the individual's advance care plan to other members of the multi-disciplinary team only with the individual's permission; the same goes for aspects of discussions with the individual and/or revisions made. If the individual lacks **capacity**, share aspects of the plan only when it is in their **best interests** to do so.
- Support individuals through the process of making **advance statements**; these will inform best interests decisions made at a later stage.
- Support individuals through the process of making advance decisions to refuse treatment.
- Support individuals through the process of appointing **lasting powers of attorney**.

Key terms

Capacity is the ability to understand information provided to make a decision.

Best interests – The Mental Capacity Act 2005 requires that any decision made or action done for or on behalf of a person who lacks capacity must be done or made in their best interests.

An **advance statement** is a written statement (either written down by an individual or written down for them with their agreement) made by an individual before losing capacity. It details their wishes and preferences in case of future loss of capacity, such as how they wish to be cared for.

Lasting powers of attorney is when a person is appointed to represent an individual who is unable to make their own decisions, such as in relation to their property, financial affairs and/or personal welfare.

- Report concerns over any inaccurate information immediately.
- Ensure you are trained and competent to discuss end-of-life care with individuals and their families.
- Know the roles of all those in the multi-disciplinary team in which you work, and how to access them.

Top ten principles for recording decisions about advance care planning

- All entries made must be signed, dated and timed.
- All entries made must be legible.
- All entries made must contain accurate and up-to-date information.
- Confidentiality must be maintained for all information recorded.
- Confidentiality must be maintained for all information shared.
- Support an individual who has capacity to check the content of the advance care plan.
- Ask the individual to sign the advance care plan if they are in agreement.
- Have a clear understanding of the information to be collated and how to do so.
- Have a clear understanding of the documents to be completed and how to do so.
- Ensure you know which advance care plan tools are used in your work setting.

AC 3.4 Outline ethical and legal issues that may arise in relation to advance care planning

As you will have learned advance care planning involves discussing and listening to sensitive and personal information about an individual's wishes and preferences for end-of-life care. It is not surprising therefore that a number of ethical and legal issues can arise during the advance care planning process.

- **Ethical issues** – an individual may express a wish to make an advanced decision to refuse treatments, such as resuscitation or **artificial feeding**, and may decide that they do not wish to seek the advice of a healthcare professional. An individual may share with you whom they wish to inform of and involve in their end-of-life care; this might not be their family or those people who are emotionally attached to the individual, it might be you or another carer. Conflicts may arise among those involved in the individual's multi-disciplinary team in relation to what type of care should be provided; conflicts over how an individual's end-of-life care or treatment should be provided may also arise among the individual's family.
- **Legal issues** – withdrawing and withholding **life-sustaining treatments** for an individual is one example of a legal issue that can arise in relation to advance care planning. The appointment of lasting powers of attorney to make decisions on an individual's behalf and determining whether an individual has capacity are examples of other legal issues that can arise as well as where and who you want to be with when you receive care and treatment.

Key terms

Artificial feeding involves the feeding of an individual via a tube or drip that enters the body.

Life-sustaining treatments are treatments that prolong life, such as artificial feeding, ventilation or dialysis.

Case study

3.1, 3.2, 3.3, 3.4 Dechen

Dechen is a senior carer and an end-of-life care lead. As part of her role Dechen provides guidance to carers delivering end-of-life care, raises awareness of end-of-life issues and provides end-of-life care training to carers and to other professionals working in different multi-disciplinary teams.

1 How can Dechen communicate the benefits to an individual of having as much control as possible over their end-of-life care?
2 What information and examples can Dechen provide in terms of the purpose of advance care planning in relation to end-of-life care?
3 What tools can Dechen use to detail the different roles in supporting and recording decisions about advance care planning?
4 About what examples of ethical and legal issues that can arise during advance care planning could Dechen provide more information?

Evidence activity

3.1, 3.2, 3.3, 3.4 Do you understand advance care planning?

Reflect on an individual you know has completed an advance care plan in relation to their end-of-life care.

● Provide details of the benefits to this individual of having as much control as possible over their end-of-life care. Explain with examples the purpose of this individual's advance care plan in relation to end-of-life care.
● Provide details of your role in supporting and recording decisions about advance care planning, and briefly detail the ethical and legal issues that may arise in relation to advance care planning.

Time to think

3.4 What are your ethics?

Reflect on an ethical issue that arose during the advance care planning process with an individual.

● How did you feel about it? Why?
● What did you do?

LO4 Be able to provide support to individuals and key people during end-of-life care

AC 4.1 Support the individual and key people to explore their thoughts and feelings about death and dying

Being able to support individuals and key people to explore their thoughts and feelings about death and dying can be very difficult for some carers. They may feel that they will not know what to say, or may find the thought of doing this too upsetting or uncomfortable, or may be afraid of becoming upset in front of the individual and their family, friends or others.

Providing supportive end-of-life care involves having the skills and confidence to support not only the individual but also their families, friends and other carers in the team to explore their thoughts and feelings about death and dying. Before doing so it is important that you have had the relevant training from your work setting, which will have enabled you also to explore your own thoughts and feelings about death and dying. There must also be relevant support systems in place that you can access.

There is a range of different ways to support individuals and key people to explore their thoughts and feelings about death and dying. Having open and honest discussions with the individual is one way of doing this. For example, you could empower the individual by asking them how they would like you to support them – some individuals may have specific questions that they want to ask you, other individuals may say nothing but may want to explore their thoughts and feelings by doing an activity with you, such as painting or writing. It is important for you to be honest with the individual when you feel uncomfortable or upset about any aspect of your discussion with them; it is better for you to tell the individual how you are feeling, as if you don't they will still be able to sense that something is wrong through your body language and tone of voice and thus they may mistakenly think that you are not interested in what they are saying or that you are angry or upset with them.

Support for families

Supporting individuals' families to explore their thoughts and feelings about death and dying will involve not only providing sufficient time and opportunity for them to do so but also being flexible over when they can do so. Each family member may prefer to speak with you on their own, or the family may decide that they would like to speak with you and have the discussions together. You may come across some family members who find it difficult to think about the topic of death; providing these family members instead with supportive information about death and dying, or referring them to a counsellor or specialist nurse, may be more appropriate.

Support for your team

The team that is caring for the individual will also need to be provided with the opportunity to explore their thoughts and feelings about death and dying. One-to-one discussions and forums for the team to listen to each other and explore their thoughts and feelings are important, particularly during the provision of an individual's care and after they have died. You may decide also to arrange for a professional or specialist to facilitate the discussions with the team, or you may decide to undertake a course and support the team to do this yourself.

AC 4.2 Provide support for the individual and key people that respects their beliefs, religion and culture

As you learned in AC 2.2, individuals and key people such as family members, friends and others all have unique needs and preferences based on their personal beliefs, religion and culture. Supportive end-of-life care involves therefore being respectful of individuals' and key people's unique beliefs, religion and culture and any associated practices and rituals.

Figure 19.8 identifies some of the ways in which you can do this; what other ways do you use?

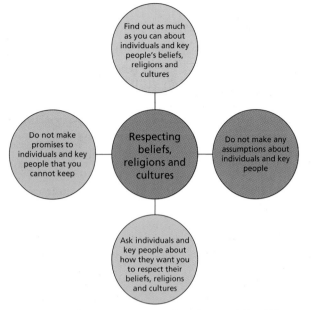

Figure 19.8 Ways of respecting individuals' and key people's beliefs, religions and cultures

Research and investigate

4.1, 4.2 Agreed ways of working

Find out your work setting's agreed ways of working with individuals and key people in end-of-life care.

AC 4.3 Demonstrate ways to help the individual feel respected and valued throughout the end-of-life period

An individual's end-of-life period could be a year or a few months, weeks or days. Throughout this period – however long or short it may be – it can be very comforting for an individual to know that their wishes and preferences, as discussed with them and documented in their **advance directives**, are being followed by you; it is also a way of showing your utmost respect.

Key term

An **advance directive** is documented information agreed with an individual, which lets others know an individual's wishes and preferences for their end-of-life care.

Ask questions

Other ways of assisting an individual to feel respected and valued can involve you asking them questions. For example, you might ask whether they require anything else, such as additional support from a professional to speak to them or to their family. Or you might ask whether they want to do anything else, such as request a visit from someone or have a particular type of spiritual or religious practice carried out, or have a change made to their environment.

Listen attentively

Attentively listening to an individual and observing what they are expressing is a way of acknowledging their feelings and thoughts; the individual will feel listened to, respected and valued. Understanding more about what an individual is experiencing will enable you to access any additional support or services that they may require. This may, for example, be in relation to supporting an individual to manage their physical well-being; the individual may require advice from their GP or a specialist nurse such as a Macmillan nurse on how to alleviate any physical pain they may be experiencing or how to change their nutrition as their appetite decreases.

Adapt to individuals' needs

Helping an individual to feel valued and respected will also involve you and others being able to adapt to the individual's changing needs. For example, respecting an individual's decision if they decide during the end-of-life period that they no longer want a treatment, and ensuring this is documented clearly. Or for example when an individual is no longer able to communicate with you verbally it will be important for you to develop other methods of communication so that they can continue to be informed and understood, as well as to understand what others are communicating.

AC 4.4 Provide information to the individual and/or key people about the individual's illness and the support available

Providing high-quality end-of-life care involves promoting not only an individual's physical well-being but also their emotional, social and spiritual well-being. Providing information to the individual and/or key people about the individual's illness and the support available to meet their physical, emotional, social or spiritual needs is crucial to supporting them effectively and professionally through end-of-life care. Information may be provided through discussions with you or other professionals, or through group and individual forums such as support groups and counselling sessions, or may consist of literature such as leaflets and books that can be provided in a variety of formats: digitally recorded, in writing including in large print, using pictures, in different languages. Figure 19.9 identifies sources of information that may be useful for communicating to an individual and/or key people about the individual's illness and the support available.

Figure 19.9 Sources of information

AC 4.5 Give examples of how an individual's well-being can be enhanced by environmental factors, non-medical interventions, use of equipment and aids, and alternative therapies

Supportive end-of-life care involves being aware of how an individual's environment and other factors can play an important role in their physical, emotional, social and spiritual well-being.

- **Environmental factors** – as mentioned in AC 3.2, ensuring an individual has control over where they receive their end-of-life care is important to them being valued and respected. For some this may be at home surrounded by their family, or for others in a hospice where they feel they can relieve their family of the burden of their care. The people who are present in an individual's environment can also make the individual feel like they belong and feel confident that their wishes and preferences will be respected, for instance a carer who spends time with an individual attentively listening to their fears and wishes. An individual's well-being will also be enhanced if they feel comfortable in their environment, e.g. by it being neither too hot nor too cold, by it being private, by it having background noise in it such as a radio, or by it being quiet and peaceful.
- **Non-medical interventions** – interventions such as counselling can enhance an individual's physical, emotional and spiritual well-being because listening with **empathy** can enable the individual to express their innermost thoughts and feelings. Supporting the individual to engage in activities such as music or the arts can enable them to meet with others and provide them with a sense of fulfilment and enjoyment.
- **Use of equipment and aids** – using equipment and aids that can promote an individual's independence or maintain their comfort is important for an individual to have a 'good death' and can therefore enhance their physical and emotional well-being. For example, a pressure-relieving mattress for an individual who is unable to move independently, or a hoist for an individual who wishes to change

Key terms

Empathy is the ability to understand how an individual feels and thinks.

Aromatherapy is an alternative therapy that involves the use of plant extracts and essential oils to manage physical and emotional well-being.

Reflexology is an alternative therapy that involves the application of pressure to different reflex points on the body to manage physical and emotional well-being.

Inner peace means mental, emotional and spiritual well-being.

position, e.g. from their bed to a chair, or hand rails for an individual who wishes to have a bath in the mornings.
- **Alternative therapies** – alternative therapies, for example **aromatherapy**, **reflexology** and relaxation techniques, are useful for relieving and controlling an individual's symptoms and improving their sense of '**inner peace**'.

AC 4.6 Contribute to partnership working with key people to support the individual's well-being

Supportive, good-quality end-of-life care that enhances an individual's well-being involves actively **working in partnership** with their family, friends and others, such as carers, advocates and professionals from a range of services, by:

- **finding out their individual needs**, e.g. by listening to the support or services they require to effectively support an individual's well-being
- **having open discussions**, e.g. by being approachable so as to ensure issues of concern or aspects of an individual's end-of-life care can be discussed honestly
- **working flexibly**, e.g. by being responsive to key people's needs for information or support so that they can provide the best possible support to the individual
- **providing clear information**, e.g. by having one person key people can approach with questions or for advice on how to support an individual's well-being, and providing

clear information about everyone's roles and responsibilities.

- **Providing training and support**, e.g. by providing a range of different types of training and support based on key people's individual requirements, and that can be easily accessed.
- **Valuing contributions**, e.g. by actively recognising the valuable roles key people play

in supporting an individual's well-being in terms of their experience and knowledge of the individual.

Working in partnership involves different people working towards the same objectives. For this to be effective there must be good communication, effective co-operation and clear co-ordination between all the different partners.

Case study

4.1, 4.2, 4.3, 4.4, 4.5, 4.6 Joshua

Joshua has a learning disability and lives in supported living. He has recently been diagnosed with terminal cancer. This has come as a shock to him, his team of carers and his family and friends, as up until now he has never experienced any problems with his physical or mental health and has always maintained a healthy lifestyle.

1 How can Joshua and the key people involved be supported to explore their thoughts and feelings about death and dying?

2 How can the support provided respect the beliefs, religions and cultures of Joshua and the key people involved?

3 What methods can be used to enable Joshua to feel respected and valued throughout the end-of-life period?

4 What information about Joshua's illness and the support available can be provided to Joshua and/or the key people involved?

5 How can Joshua's well-being be enhanced by his environment, by non-medical interventions, use of equipment and aids, and alternative therapies?

6 What methods of partnership working with key people could support Joshua's well-being?

Evidence activities

4.1, 4.2, 4.3, 4.4, 4.5 Supporting individuals during end-of-life care

Reflect on two individuals you have supported during end-of-life care. For each individual detail:

- how you supported them to explore their thoughts and feelings about death and dying
- how the support you provided respected their beliefs, religion and culture, and helped the individual to feel respected and valued.

Include in your accounts the information you provided to each individual about their illness and the support available, and provide examples of how each individual's well-being was enhanced by environmental factors, non-medical interventions, use of equipment and aids, and alternative therapies.

4.1, 4.2, 4.4, 4.6 Supporting key people during end-of-life care

Reflect on two key people you have supported during end-of-life care. For each key person detail how you supported them to explore their thoughts

and feelings about death and dying, and how the support you provided respected their beliefs, religion and culture (AC 4.1).

- Include in your accounts the information you provided to each key person about the individual's illness and the support available (AC 4.2), and your contributions to partnership working with each key person to support the individual's well-being (AC 4.6).
- You will also need to be observed by your assessor or an expert witness supporting individuals and key people during end-of-life care to explore their thoughts and feelings about death and dying (AC 4.1), respecting their beliefs, religion and culture, and providing information about the individual's illness and the support available (AC 4.2). You must also demonstrate ways to help individuals feel respected and valued throughout the end-of-life period (AC 4.3) and your contribution to partnership working with key people to support the individual's well-being (AC 4.6).

LO5 Understand how to address sensitive issues in relation to end-of-life care

AC 5.1 Explain the importance of recording significant conversations during end-of-life care

The UK government's 'End of life care strategy' (2008) states that:

'all people approaching the end of life, and their carers, should be entitled to know that systems are in place to ensure that information about their needs and preferences can be accessed by all relevant health and social care staff, with their permission.'

Recording significant conversations during end-of-life care – which could involve, for example, a request for additional support or a preference for who should be present in the individual's last hours – is important for the following reasons:

- It ensures that the information recorded can be accessed by key people involved in the individual's end-of-life care so that they can provide high-quality care that meets the individual's wishes and preferences.

- It encourages communication (with the individual's permission) between different members of the multi-disciplinary team to ensure consistent working approaches.
- It avoids key people providing care that does not respect the individual's personal beliefs or preferences.
- It is a way of ensuring that the individual's plan of care remains up to date throughout their end-of-life care.
- It is a way of maintaining the individual's 'best interests' if they lose capacity to make their own decisions at a later stage.

AC 5.2 Explain factors that influence who should give significant news to an individual or key people

Giving significant news to an individual or key people in relation to end-of-life care is a sensitive issue that requires skill and empathy. There are a number of factors that influence who should give significant news:

- **The individual's preferences** – some individuals or key people may prefer to receive significant news from someone they know well or have a close relationship with; others may prefer to receive it from a trained professional.
- **The individual's capacity** – some individuals may lack capacity and therefore an independent person such as an advocate or a family member may act as their representative in deciding who should give significant news, and how.
- **The type of significant news** – depending on what the significant news is, the knowledge and expertise of the person giving it will be important, as the individual and key people will require as much information as possible and may at this point raise questions and concerns with the person providing the news.
- **Relationships with individuals or key people** – giving significant news may provoke a range of different reactions from individuals and/or key people, such as denial, anger, fear

and/or shock, and therefore it is important that the person giving the news feels able to manage these emotions in a supportive way. In some cases it may be more appropriate to ensure different people are involved in giving significant news to individuals and key people, for example a **key worker** who knows the individual well could provide the news to the individual, while a manager could provide the news to the individual's family and members of the team.

AC 5.3 Describe conflicts and legal or ethical issues that may arise in relation to death, dying or end-of-life care

Building relationships with different individuals and key people, and working as part of a multi-disciplinary team where each person has their own personal beliefs, religion and culture, can mean that from time to time **conflicts**, legal and ethical issues can arise. These may arise in relation to death, dying or end-of-life care between professionals, individuals and their families and friends. Look at Figure 19.10, which includes some examples of these; have you come across any others? You may also find it useful to revisit AC 3.4, which detailed legal and ethical issues that may arise in advance care planning.

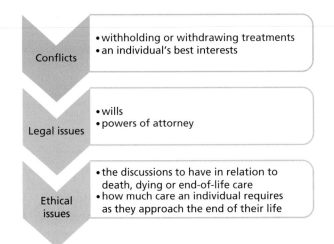

Conflicts	• withholding or withdrawing treatments • an individual's best interests
Legal issues	• wills • powers of attorney
Ethical issues	• the discussions to have in relation to death, dying or end-of-life care • how much care an individual requires as they approach the end of their life

Figure 19.10 Conflicts, legal and ethical issues

AC 5.4 Analyse ways to address such conflicts

Conflicts may arise in relation to death, dying or end-of-life care between professionals, individuals and their families and friends. How you and others address these conflicts will depend on the nature and extent of the conflicts and your work setting's agreed ways of working, as well as your role and responsibilities. Below is a list of five top tips for addressing such conflicts:

1 Use different communication methods to explain more about the care provided, the treatments available and agreed ways of working, e.g. verbally and in writing.
2 Use negotiation strategies to enable different perspectives and opinions to be considered.
3 Provide more information on, for example, treatments and the well-being of the individual, as this will improve key people's

understanding of what treatments are available and of the current physical and emotional well-being of the individual.

4 Seek advice from others, such as specialists and other professionals.

5 Provide opportunities to meet with others to talk about and reflect on such conflicts.

Case study

5.1, 5.2, 5.3, 5.4 Lynn

Lynn is a senior home carer and leads a team of ten carers who provide live-in care and support to individuals who require end-of-life care and to their families. As part of her role Lynn works closely with the local hospice and the hospital palliative care team to provide regular training and mentoring.

1 What explanation could Lynn provide to her team about the importance of recording significant conversations during end-of-life care?

2 What explanation could Lynn provide to her team about the factors that influence who should give significant news to an individual or key people?

3 What examples could Lynn provide to the team regarding conflicts and legal or ethical issues that may arise in relation to death, dying or end-of-life care?

4 What different strategies could Lynn and her team use to address such conflicts?

Evidence activity

5.1, 5.2, 5.3, 5.4 Addressing sensitive issues

Reflect on two occasions where you had to address sensitive issues in relation to end-of-life care.

- Provide details with examples of the importance of recording significant conversations during end-of-life care, and the factors that influence

who should give significant news to an individual or key people.

- Detail examples of conflicts and legal or ethical issues that may arise in relation to death, dying or end-of-life care, and examine in detail the different ways to address such conflicts. Did you use different methods for different conflicts? Why?

LO6 Understand the role of organisations and support services available to individuals and key people in relation to end-of-life care

AC 6.1 Describe the role of support organisations and specialist services that may contribute to end-of-life care

Being able to seek advice, support and information from support organisations and specialist services

is integral to providing high-quality end-of-life care that meets an individual's needs, wishes and preferences. Such support organisations and specialist services include nursing and care homes, specialist palliative care services, domiciliary, respite and day services, as well as funeral directors.

Table 19.4 provides some more information about the role of each of these support organisations and specialist services in relation to end-of-life care.

Support organisation or specialist service	Role in relation to contributing to end-of-life care
Nursing homes	Provide individuals with a home. Provide nursing care to individuals and support to their families and friends.
Care homes	Provide individuals with a home. Provide care to individuals and support to their families and friends.
Specialist palliative care services, e.g. those based in hospitals, hospices	Provide individuals and key people with information, advice and support on end-of-life care, such as pain control and emotional support.
Domiciliary services	Provide individuals and key people with additional support at home with tasks such as personal care, household tasks and shopping that may be difficult to do when providing end-of-life care to an individual.
Respite services, e.g. Marie Curie nursing service	Provide nurses that enable individuals' families and friends to have respite from caring during the day or at night time.
Day services	Provide individuals and/or their families and friends with opportunities to meet with others, engage in meaningful activities and share their feelings and thoughts in relation to end-of-life care.
Funeral directors	Look after and wash the individual's body after death in accordance with the individual's and their family's beliefs, religion and culture. Can also provide support with arranging a funeral and a burial or cremation.

Table 19.4 The role of support organisations and specialist services

AC 6.2 Analyse the role and value of an advocate in relation to end-of-life care

The role of an **advocate** is to represent or speak up for an individual. The end-of-life care advocate can be involved in:

A **A**ssisting the individual to have control over their life.
D **D**ecisions about end-of-life care in line with an individual's wishes and preferences.
V **V**aluing an individual's beliefs, religion and culture.
O **O**pen conversations with the individual and others.
C **C**hoices about end-of-life care.
A **A**ssisting the individual to access services and facilities available.
T **T**rust building.
E **E**nsuring the individual is listened to.

Key term

Advocates represent individuals or speak on their behalf to ensure their rights are supported.

Having an end-of-life care advocate can be a very effective way of ensuring that the individual remains at the centre of the end-of-life care being provided and that their views, wishes, preferences and rights continue to be listened to, respected and upheld.

AC 6.3 Explain how to establish when an advocate may be beneficial

An end-of-life care advocate is independent. Their sole role is to support an individual to make their own choices and decisions about their end-of-life care and to communicate these to others.

An end-of-life care advocate may be requested by an individual as they may prefer to discuss their concerns and/or anxieties with an independent person than with someone who knows them well, who may get upset by discussing this with them.

When an individual wishes to make plans for their end-of-life care an advocate can be beneficial in preparing advance directives with an individual. Discussions with an advocate can also be a source of comfort to the individual and provide them with reassurance that their wishes and preferences are not only being listened to but will also be acted on.

An individual may also seek help from an advocate when meeting with others, such as their family, carers and other professionals, to discuss plans for end-of-life care.

AC 6.4 Explain why support for spiritual needs may be especially important at the end of life

As individuals near the end of their lives they may develop a desire for self-worth or meaning and this may involve talking through their feelings and beliefs with someone else or taking part in prayers or other rituals to meet their spiritual needs.

Support for spiritual needs is particularly important at the end of life for the following reasons:

- It can be how the individual achieves their 'inner peace', i.e. by resolving issues or conflicts they have with key people.
- It can be comforting for the individual to take part in prayers, or to speak with someone about their spirituality.
- It can be comforting for the individual's family, friends and others involved in their life to know that their relative is at peace at the end of life.

Time to think

6.4 Do you understand spirituality?

Reflect on an occasion when you supported an individual and their key people through end-of-life care.

- What agreed ways of working did you follow?
- How did these address spiritual needs?
- Why was this important?

- It can be a way of reflecting on an individual's achievements in life.
- It can be a way of providing the individual with companionship.

AC 6.5 Describe a range of sources of support to address spiritual needs

Meeting an individual's spiritual needs is crucial to providing good-quality end-of-life care. This involves being able to empathise with an individual. It is important that you are aware of your own limitations in this and when to refer to others for support.

A range of sources of support is available within your own work setting, including your manager and other members of staff who may be more experienced than you. The individual's family and friends can also be involved as they will know the individual well and may be able to talk through with the individual their innermost thoughts and feelings, for example.

Case study

6.1, 6.2, 6.3, 6.4, 6.5 Shoi-ming

Shoi-ming is meeting with his manager today to talk through how he has found his first week in his new role as an end-of-life enabler. Shoi-ming's role involves supporting a team of carers to provide high-quality end-of-life care that involves meeting individuals' physical, mental, emotional, social and spiritual needs. Shoi-ming has drawn up a list of questions to ask his manager in relation to the role of organisations and support services available to the individuals and key people who use the service.

1 What details could Shoi-ming's manager provide him with about the role of support organisations and specialist services that may contribute to end-of-life care?

2 What details could Shoi-ming's manager provide him with about the role and value of an advocate in relation to end-of-life care, and how to establish when an advocate may be beneficial?

3 What explanation could Shoi-ming's manager provide him with about why support with spiritual needs may be especially important at the end of life?

4 What details could Shoi-ming's manager provide him with about the range of sources of support to address spiritual needs?

Other sources of support can include professionals who work in specialist services such as counsellors, psychologists and chaplains, all of whom can provide specialist support in addressing an individual's spiritual needs. Volunteers from support groups can also play a vital role in visiting individuals to address their spiritual needs. It is important to remember that some individuals may also find solace in reading about spirituality.

Research and investigate

LO6 Find out about your team's understanding of spirituality.

Evidence activity

6.1, 6.2, 6.3, 6.4, 6.5 Support organisations and specialist services

- Provide details of the roles of three support organisations and three specialist services that are available in relation to end-of-life care for the individuals and key people with whom you work.
- Examine in detail the role and value of an advocate for the individuals and key people with whom you work in relation to end-of-life care; include details and examples of how to establish when an advocate may be beneficial.
- Detail the range of support services available to the individuals and key people with whom you work in relation to addressing spiritual needs; include details and examples of why support with spiritual needs may be especially important at the end of life.

LO7 Be able to access support for the individual or key people from the wider team

AC 7.1 Identify when support would best be offered by other members of the team

As you learned in AC 2.3, support for individuals and key people can be accessed from other members of the multi-disciplinary team, including your line manager, individuals' family and friends, religious

representatives, social workers, psychologists and other professionals such as specialist doctors and nurses, occupational therapists, physiotherapists and complementary therapists.

When support would best be offered by other members of the team will depend on a number of factors:

- The individual's or key person's needs, e.g. a deterioration in an individual's physical or emotional condition may result in a referral to a specialist.
- The individual's or key person's preferences, e.g. whether they would like support early on or not.
- The individual's or key person's personal coping strategies, e.g. this may affect when support is required.

Research and investigate

7.1 Members of your wider team

Find out who the members of your wider team are and what support they offer.

AC 7.2 Liaise with other members of the team to provide identified support for the individual or key people

Your role in end-of-life care will involve working closely with other members of the multi-disciplinary team to provide the support required for the individual or key people. Effective liaison with other members of the team in relation to end-of-life care involves:

- understanding all team members' roles and responsibilities
- sharing agreed ways of working for making decisions and communicating decisions made to individuals and key people
- supporting each other
- listening to each other
- valuing each other
- respecting each other
- developing shared principles and goals
- being open and honest
- being able to work constructively through conflicts or other issues that arise.

Case study

7.1, 7.2 Aishita

Aishita is supporting her team of residential carers to provide support to an individual who has had a stroke and who has recently developed difficulties with breathing, as well as kidney disease. Aishita has noted that this individual is visited regularly by her son and husband, and that – although the individual is very accepting of her condition – her husband and one of her carers who knows her well are finding it difficult and upsetting.

1   When would support best be offered by other members of the team to the individual, her husband and the carer?
2   How could Aishita liaise with other members of the team to provide identified support for the individual, her husband and the carer?

Evidence activity

7.1, 7.2 Accessing support from the wider team

● Reflect on an occasion when you accessed support from the wider team for an individual or key people in relation to end-of-life care.
● Discuss with your manager when and why you accessed support, and the type of support that was offered by other members of the team. Discuss how you liaised with other members of the team to provide the identified support.
● You will also need to be observed by your assessor or an expert witness supporting individuals and key people through end-of-life care, identifying when support would best be offered by other members of the team and liaising with other members of the team to provide identified support for the individual or key people.

Time to think

7.2 Can you liaise effectively?

Reflect on an occasion when you liaised with other members of the team to provide identified end-of-life care support to an individual or key people.

● On a scale of 0 to 10, rate yourself on how effective you were.
● What were your strengths?
● What were your areas for development?
● How can you develop these?

LO8 Be able to support individuals through the process of dying

AC 8.1 Carry out own role in an individual's care

Your role in an individual's care when they are going through the process of dying will involve providing holistic support in relation to an individual's physical, mental, emotional and spiritual needs. The process of dying will be experienced differently by each individual, and may happen slowly or quickly. When supporting individuals through the process of dying it is important that you follow the agreed ways of working of your work setting and are able to meet individuals' unique and varying needs. Below are some examples of the different ways you may provide support to individuals through the process of dying.

● **Physical care and support** – an individual may become incontinent and you will need to support them to manage their incontinence and ensure that they remain dry and comfortable. As an individual becomes weaker they may no longer be able to eat and drink independently; you may be required to assist them.
● **Mental care and support** – an individual's mental well-being may decline as they approach death. Answering an individual's questions and talking through their fears, anxieties and concerns can play a crucial role in restoring their mental health.
● **Emotional care and support** – as an individual approaches death they may become more drowsy. You may be required to sit with an individual and talk to them, as although the individual may not be able to engage with you they may get comfort from hearing you talk to them.
● **Spiritual care and support** – an individual may show anxious or restless behaviour, which may be due to the treatments they are receiving. Reading with an individual during these times or simply placing your hand on theirs can restore their sense of 'inner peace'. Similarly, ensuring you support individuals with any religious or **spiritual practices** may also be of great comfort.

Your role will also involve reporting and recording the support you have provided and any concerns that have arisen, as well as any referrals you have made to other members of the multi-disciplinary team.

AC 8.2 Contribute to addressing any distress experienced by the individual promptly and in agreed ways

Fear of the unknown, pain and the reactions of key people can underlie individuals' **distress** as they approach the end of their lives. Read through Table 19.5, which provides details of how you can address different types of distress that individuals may experience. Your job role and your work setting's agreed ways of working will determine the actions you must follow so it is important that you are familiar with these and understand how to comply with them.

Area of distress	Actions to take
An individual develops a fear of the unknown and becomes increasingly anxious	<ul><li>Reassure the individual immediately.</li><li>Listen to the individual's fears and anxieties.</li><li>Ask the individual how you can help.</li><li>Ask the individual if they want to talk to someone else or have someone else present, such as a chaplain or another member of the team.</li><li>Record your observations and agreed actions promptly.</li><li>Report your observations and agreed actions promptly.</li></ul>
An individual is in pain	<ul><li>Seek advice immediately from the doctor, nurse or **palliative care team**, providing them with as much information as possible.</li><li>Reassure the individual and tell them what actions you have taken.</li><li>Ask the individual if there is anything else they would like.</li><li>Support the individual to communicate with key people.</li><li>Monitor the individual's condition.</li><li>Record your observations and agreed actions promptly.</li><li>Report your observations and agreed actions promptly.</li></ul>
An individual is distressed by the reactions of key people	<ul><li>Reassure the individual immediately.</li><li>Ask the individual how you can help.</li><li>Be sensitive when speaking with key people; they may be upset, angry or in denial about the imminent death of the individual.</li><li>Ask key people whether they would like to talk to someone else about how they are feeling.</li><li>Record your observations and agreed actions promptly.</li><li>Report your observations and agreed actions promptly.</li></ul>

Table 19.5 Different types of distress

AC 8.3 Adapt support to reflect the individual's changing needs or responses

The support you provide to individuals through the process of dying must also be flexible so as to reflect the individual's changing physical, mental, emotional or spiritual needs or responses during their last days or hours. You can adapt your support in different ways; Figure 19.11 provides some examples of how you can do this.

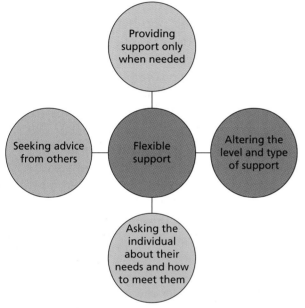

Figure 19.11 Ways of adapting support

AC 8.4 Assess when an individual and key people need to be alone

Although communication and support are important in supporting individuals through the dying process, it is also important to remember that there may be times when an individual and key people need to have some time alone. Respecting their privacy during these times is crucial. There is no definitive way to tell when an individual and key people need to be alone, as all people are different, but the five key questions provided below may be useful to consider, as these can be indicators that there is a need for time alone.

1 Do the individual and key people stop communicating when you enter the room?
2 Are the individual and key people sharing private feelings and/or memories?
3 Do key people leave the room when you enter?
4 Have the individual or key people received significant news?
5 Do you sense you are in the way?

Case study

8.1, 8.2, 8.3, 8.4 Vanessa

Vanessa is being shadowed by a new member of staff who has never supported individuals through the process of dying. As a carer, Vanessa will be mentoring her and supporting her.

1 How could Vanessa explain to the new member of staff what her role in an individual's care will involve?
2 What agreed ways of working will Vanessa need to explain in relation to addressing any distress experienced by an individual?
3 What ways of adapting the support provided to meet individuals' changing needs or responses will Vanessa need to explain?
4 What tools could Vanessa use to explain to the new member of staff how to assess when an individual and key people need to be alone?

Evidence activity

8.1, 8.2, 8.3, 8.4 Supporting an individual through the dying process

Reflect on an occasion when you supported an individual through the dying process.

- Provide details of your role in the individual's care, including how you addressed any distress experienced by the individual, how you adapted your support to reflect the individual's changing needs or responses, and how you assessed when the individual and key people needed time to be alone.
- You will also need to be observed by your assessor or an expert witness supporting individuals and key people during end-of-life care to demonstrate how you carried out your role, contributed to alleviating any distress experienced by the individual promptly and in agreed ways, adapted support to reflect the individual's changing needs or responses, and assessed when an individual and key people needed to be alone.

LO9 Be able to take action following the death of individuals

AC 9.1 Explain why it is important to know about an individual's wishes for their after-death care

You will need to know also about your role in **after-death care**, once an individual has died. Knowing an individual's wishes for their after-death care is very important for a number of reasons:

- To ensure compliance with an individual's advance directives.
- To show respect for an individual.
- To show respect for an individual's family and friends.
- To find out more about how to follow practices and rituals in line with an individual's wishes.
- To be able to be involved in saying 'goodbye' to the individual.
- To provide comfort from the knowledge that the individual's wishes were met.

AC 9.2 Carry out actions immediately following a death that respect the individual's wishes and follow agreed ways of working

Following an individual's death there are a number of actions that must be taken. It is important that these respect an individual's wishes and follow your work setting's agreed ways of working:

- **Attending to the body of the deceased** – your role will vary depending on the preferences and personal beliefs of individuals and their families in relation to after-death care. For example, some individuals may have agreed with their family in advance for their body to remain at home before the funeral; others may have agreed for it to be taken to a chapel of rest. Some individuals may want their families involved in washing and dressing their body after their death; others may not and may prefer you and your team to do it.
- **Reporting the death through agreed channels** – an individual's death must be reported promptly to the GP or the out-of-hours doctor service promptly, i.e. within a few hours. Who does this will depend on your job role and responsibilities in line with the agreed ways of working of your work setting. Once a medical death certificate has been issued by the individual's GP (this may take longer if the GP requests that a **post mortem** be carried out), this must be taken to the local registrar who will register the death; again, who does this will depend on your job role and responsibilities in line with your work setting's agreed ways of working.
- **Informing key people** – once a death has occurred all relevant key people can be informed. Who is informed first and how will depend on the individual's wishes as set out in their advance directives and also on advance discussions held with family members. Similarly, when informing members of the team it will be important to respect an individual's and their family's wishes and privacy; careful consideration

should be given to when team members are informed and how they can maintain confidentiality.

All actions taken must be documented fully in line with your work setting's agreed ways of working.

Key term

A **post mortem** is the examination of a body to establish the cause of death.

AC 9.3 Describe ways to support key people immediately following an individual's death

In the immediate moments following an individuals' death support will need to be made available to key people, such as the individual's family, friends and others who are important to their well-being. Figure 19.11 identifies some of the ways support can be provided.

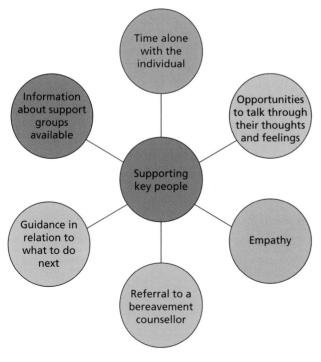

Figure 19.12 Ways of supporting key people

Case study

9.1, 9.2, 9.3 Ben

Ben is a senior support worker and is discussing with his manager in supervision the advance care plan in place for an individual who lives in supported living and is approaching death.

1 Why is it important for Ben and his manager to know about the individual's wishes for after-death care?
2 How can Ben and his manager ensure that the individual's wishes are respected after their death and that they follow agreed ways of working?
3 How can Ben and his manager support members of the team and the individual's family and friends following the individual's death?

Evidence activity

9.1, 9.2, 9.3 After-death care

Reflect on an occasion when you were involved in an individual's after-death care.

- Provide details and examples of:
  - the importance of knowing about an individual's wishes for their after-death care
  - the actions taken immediately following an individual's death, including how these respected an individual's wishes and agreed ways of working
  - the support provided to key people immediately following the individual's death.
- You will also need to be observed by your assessor or an expert witness carrying out actions immediately following an individual's death that respect the individual's wishes and follow agreed ways of working.

Time to think

9.3 Providing support

Reflect on an occasion when you provided support to key people immediately following an individual's death.

- How effective was your support?
- Why?

LO10 Be able to manage own feelings in relation to the dying or death of individuals

AC 10.1 Identify ways to manage own feelings in relation to an individual's dying or death

Managing your feelings in relation to an individual's dying or death forms part of the **grieving process**. How you grieve will be unique to you as it will depend on your relationship with the individual and how you found the experience of supporting them, as well as your personal beliefs, religion and culture. It is difficult to prescribe, therefore, how to manage your feelings in relation to an individual's dying or death. Feelings may vary from being upset, to being in shock, angry or relieved. Below are examples of different ways of managing your feelings in relation to an individual's dying or death; have you used any of these strategies or are there any others that you find useful for you?

- Talking openly and honestly with others about how you feel can help you to acknowledge and manage your feelings.
- Resting and having sufficient sleep will help you to think more clearly.
- Eating healthy and nutritious meals will help to maintain your physical health and strength.
- Asking for support and help from others can provide reassurance and comfort. This could be from family or friends, or professionals such as bereavement counsellors.
- Saying 'goodbye' to the individual can help with acknowledging your feelings and sharing how you feel with others.
- Favourite pieces of music, looking at photos – can help you with making sense of what has happened.

> ### Key term
>
> The **grieving process** is the stages and emotions an individual experiences when another individual dies.

> ### Research and investigate
>
> **10.1** The grieving process
> Research different models of the grieving process.

AC 10.2 Utilise support systems to deal with own feelings in relation to an individual's dying or death

There are many different support systems available to help you deal with your feelings in relation to an individual's dying or death. These may include formal and informal sources of support available from your work setting and externally. Figure 19.13 below identifies some of these.

It is not always easy to ask for help from others, for fear of being a burden or feeling inadequate or not wishing to face talking through your emotions and the causes of these. Avoiding doing so will only prolong the grieving process, however; it cannot be avoided. It is vital therefore that you are able to make use of the support systems that are available and that you feel comfortable using, to deal with your feelings so that you can maintain your physical, mental, emotional and spiritual health and well-being, and enable others to do the same.

Figure 19.13 Support systems to deal with your feelings

Case study

10.1, 10.2 Laila

Laila is a senior residential carer and has supported three individuals through the dying process this week. Laila has also provided support to their families and friends and to different members of the team who were involved.

1 How can Laila manage her feelings in relation to supporting these individuals through the dying process?
2 What support systems can Laila make use of to deal with her feelings in relation to supporting individuals through the dying process?

Evidence activity

10.1, 10.2 Managing your feelings

Reflect on an occasion when you supported an individual through the dying process.

- Identify how you managed your feelings in doing so, and provide details of the support systems you used to deal with your feelings in relation to the individual's dying or death.
- You will also need to be observed by your assessor or an expert witness utilising support systems to deal with your feelings in relation to an individual's dying or death.

Time to think

10.2 Do you know the support systems available to you?

Reflect on what support is available in your work setting for dealing with your feelings in relation to an individual's dying or death.

- Identify an occasion you used the support available.
- How did it help you?

Legislation

- Data Protection Act 1998
- Equality Act 2010
- Freedom of Information Act 2000
- Health and Safety at Work etc. Act 1974
- Human Rights Act 1998
- Mental Capacity Act 2005
- Mental Health Act 1983 (amended 2007)
- Safeguarding Vulnerable Groups Act 2006

Useful resources

Websites

Centre for Spirituality, Health and Disability
www.abdn.ac.uk/cshad/

Dying Matters
http://dyingmatters.org

Mental Health Foundation
http://mentalhealth.org.uk

National Council for Palliative Care
http://ncpc.org.uk

National End of Life Care Intelligence Network
http://endoflifecare-intelligence.org.uk

National Institute for Health & Clinical Excellence
www.nice.org.uk

Social Care Institute for Excellence
www.scie.org.uk

Skills for Care
www.skillsforcare.org.uk

Skills for Health
http://skillsforhealth.org.uk

Publications

Corr, C., Corr, M. and Nabbe, C. (2002) *Death and Dying, Life and Living*. Boston: Wadsworth Publishing Company.

Kübler-Ross, E. (1969) *On Death and Dying*. New York: Macmillan.

Kübler-Ross, E. (1997) *The Wheel of Life: A memoir of living and dying*. New York: Scribner.

Reports

Department of Health (2008) 'End of life care strategy: promoting high quality care for adults at the end of their life'

Macmillan Cancer Support and Marie Curie Cancer Care (2011) 'End of life: the facts, a booklet for people in the final stages of life and their carers'

NEoLCP (2012) 'Capacity, care planning and advance care planning in life-limiting illness: a guide for health and social care staff'

National Institute for Health and Care Excellence (2011) 'The NICE quality standard for end of life care for adults'

Glossary

Abuse is cruel or inhumane treatment that ignores an individual's human and civil rights.

Actions to take constitute the learner's responsibilities in responding to allegations or suspicions of abuse.

Active listening requires the listener to feed back, acknowledging they have understood what is being said.

Active participation is a way of working that recognises an individual's right to participate in the activities and relationships of everyday life as independently as possible; the individual is regarded as an active partner in their own care or support, rather than a passive recipient.

Active partners is a way of working that recognises an individual's right to participate in the activities and relationships of everyday life as independently as possible.

Advance care planning is a way of working that improves the planning and provision of care for an individual and recognises the individual's right to live their life as they wish.

Advocates represent individuals or speak on their behalf to ensure their rights are supported.

Agreed ways of working are your work setting's policies and procedures, as well as the specific guidelines that are in place for the individuals to whom you provide care and support. They may be less formally documented with smaller employers.

Allegations of abuse are when it is reported that abuse has happened or is happening.

Allied health professionals are clinical healthcare professionals, distinct from medicine, dentistry and nursing, who work in a healthcare team to make the healthcare system function.

Assistive technologies are electronic and physical items, devices or systems that enable individuals to maintain and develop their independence and skills for everyday life.

An **audiologist** is a healthcare professional who specialises in the ears and hearing. **Audiology** is the branch of medicine concerned with the sense of hearing.

Behavioural therapy is a way of working that involves finding out the reasons for difficult behaviours, e.g. individuals who have dementia may display behaviours such as wandering, repetitive actions and questions, or inappropriate sexual behaviours.

Braille is a system of writing and printing for blind or visually impaired people. Varied arrangements of raised dots representing letters and numerals are identified by touch.

British Sign Language is a visual form of communicating that involves hand signs and facial expressions.

The **bronchi** are the large airways that carry air from the trachea into the lungs.

An individual's **care plan** is the document where day-to-day requirements and preferences for care and support are detailed. It may be known by other names, e.g. support plan, individual plan or care delivery plan.

A **catheter** is a plastic tube inserted into the body to drain fluid.

Closed questions are questions that encourage a 'yes'/'no' or 'true'/'false' response.

A **code of practice** is a set of written rules explaining how workers should carry out their job role.

Cognitive abilities are abilities to learn, remember, problem solve, and pay attention.

Communication guides are trained professionals who support deaf blind individuals to participate in day-to-day activities.

Communication style is an individual's preferred way of communicating with others, e.g. by using big gestures, a calm manner.

Communication system means the unique methods used by an individual to communicate, i.e. can include words, sounds, pictures, signs.

Competence is the ability to do something (e.g. your job) successfully due to having the right knowledge, understanding and capabilities.

Confidential information is given in private and intended to be kept secret. You must restrict access to this information and respect its privacy.

Consent is a person giving permission for something to be carried out.

Cross infection is the spread of pathogens from one person, object, place or part of the body to another.

Demographic factors are the characteristics of a population, e.g. in terms of its size, growth, distribution.

Disclosures of abuse are when an individual tells you that abuse has happened or is happening to them.

Discrimination is the acting out of negative prejudices.

Domiciliary carers, sometimes referred to as **home carers**, are carers who provide support in an individual's own home.

Duty of care is a professional's ethical and legal responsibility to safeguard and protect the well-being of others.

Electrochemical signals are chemical signals that are sent from one nerve cell to another.

An **episode of care** is one of a series of care tasks in the course of a continuous care activity.

Equality relates to being equal, especially to having the same political, social and economic rights.

Evaluation is a process used to assess the effectiveness of an activity, approach, system or piece of work.

Evidence-based policies are policies that have been proven to work.

Flash cards are cards that contain key information and that aid communication and learning.

Haptic communication is a tactile form of communicating that involves making signs on a part of the body, such as on the individual's back or shoulder, which describe what is happening visually.

Hazardous materials are materials that have the potential to cause harm and illness.

A **hazard** is a danger that exists and has the potential to cause harm.

The **Health and Safety Executive (HSE)** is the regulator or official supervisory body for the health, safety and welfare of people in work settings in the UK.

Health and safety legislation is laws relevant to health and safety.

Health and safety policies and procedures are an employer's agreed ways of working relevant to health and safety.

Hearing loops provide information on an induction loop system, to assist the hearing impaired by transmitting sound from a sound system, microphone, television or other source, directly to a hearing aid.

Holistic means acknowledging the person as a 'whole' and not just focusing on one aspect of their health and well-being.

Homely remedies are treatments for minor ailments that can be bought over the counter, such as paracetamol for headaches or indigestion remedies.

An **in-dwelling device** is a device that is inserted into the body, such as a catheter.

Infection is the process of contamination.

Informed choices and decisions are the processes of choosing from options and making decisions based on accurate information and knowledge that is understood by an individual.

Intensive interactions are practical communication approaches used to engage and involve individuals who are congenitally deaf blind.

An **interpreter** is a person who translates orally or into sign language.

Intervenors are trained professionals who support deaf blind individuals to experience the world around them.

Isolation nursing is the physical separation of an infected patient from others.

A **label** is a 'tag' that we use to describe someone and is usually based on their appearance or behaviour.

Lip reading is a visual form of communication that involves observing a person's lip shapes, gestures and facial movements.

Local systems may include employer/organisational policies and procedures and multi-agency adult protection arrangements for a locality.

Logistics refers to the full management of a task or procedure, from beginning to end.

Makaton is a visual form of communication for individuals who have learning disabilities and communication difficulties, in which gestures are used in combination with pictures and symbols to communicate messages.

Manual alphabets are a tactile form of communicating that involve spelling out words on individuals' hands.

The **medical model** of disability views disability as a 'problem' that belongs to the disabled individual.

Memory impairment is memory loss caused by damage to the brain.

Mencap is the leading UK charity for people who have a learning disability and their families.

Meniere's disease is a disease that affects the inner ear and causes hearing loss.

Micro-organisms are organisms such as bacteria, parasites and fungi that can only be seen with the use of a microscope.

Mini Mental State Examination (MMSE) is a tool comprising a series of questions and tests, used by health professionals to diagnose and assess dementia.

A **multi-disciplinary team** is a team made up of professionals from a range of different organisations and services, each of which has its own individual roles and responsibilities.

Need-to-know basis means secure information that must be made available only to those who need to know it to carry out their job role.

A **needle stick injury** is a skin puncture by a hypodermic needle or other sharp object.

Negligence means a failure to carry out your duty of care that results in individuals being placed at risk of danger, harm or abuse.

Neurological disorders are disorders of the brain.

Non-verbal communication is ways of communicating using body language, facial expression, eye contact, touch, behaviour, gestures and visual aids.

Objects of reference are objects that are used to communicate by them representing actions and activities, such as an individual using a cup to indicate that they are thirsty or a key to indicate that they would like to go out.

Occupational therapists are professionals who support individuals to engage in daily activities.

Open questions can, in theory, result in any answer and can be better for getting people's opinions than closed questions.

Ophthalmologists are professionals who support individuals affected by eye diseases.

Ophthalmology is the branch of medicine concerned with the anatomy, physiology and diseases of the eye.

An **optometrist** is a healthcare professional who specialises in the eyes and vision. **Optometry** is the branch of medicine concerned with vision.

An **organic action plan** is a plan of action that is updated regularly to meet an individual's changing needs or preferences.

A **pathogen** is a disease-producing bacterium, fungus, virus, infestation or prion.

Being on the **periphery** means being on the edge, or having only minor involvement in something.

A **perpetrator** is someone who does something wrong.

Person-centred planning is a process of life planning for individuals, based around the principles of inclusion and the social model of disability.

Person-centred values are principles on which care and support are based, such as respecting individuality, rights, choice, privacy, independence, dignity, respect, partnership.

Person-centred working is a way of working that recognises what is important to individuals and helps them to live the life they choose.

Person-identifiable information is information that identifies a person, such as their name, address, date of birth, National Insurance number or photograph.

Person specification is a description of the qualities required in a person to carry out a job role.

Personal development is a process used to increase your self-awareness and achieve your goals.

Personal development plan (PDP) is a way of recording your past achievements and future learning objectives.

The **personalisation agenda** promotes individual choice and control over the shape of client support in all care settings.

Photosymbols is a collection of pictures for making EasyRead information, they are designed to be placed alongside words to make information easier to understand.

Physiology means the functions of different parts of the human body.

Physiotherapists are professionals who support individuals affected by injury, illness or disability through using movement and exercises.

A **pill box** is a box for holding tablets that is divided into the days of the week.

An individual's **plan of care** is the document where day-to-day requirements and preferences for care and support are detailed. It may be known by other names, e.g. support plan, individual plan or care delivery plan.

Policies are rules and guidelines about how something is carried out.

Power of attorney is when you give someone you trust the power to make decisions about you if you are unable to.

Precautions are measures taken in advance to prevent infections from occurring.

Preferences means liking some things more than other things.

A **prejudice** is an attitude or way of thinking based on an unfair pre-judgement of a person, rather than on a factual assessment.

Prevalence is the proportion of individuals in a population having a disease.

Principles of care underpin practice and include privacy, dignity and choice.

Procedures state how each policy will be actioned in the organisation.

Professional development refers to the skills and knowledge necessary to develop your work practices and understanding.

Qualitative information is descriptive and subjective information on progress made towards identified short-, medium- or long-term goals.

Quantitative information is measurable and factual statistics or information on progress made towards identified short-, medium- or long-term goals.

Reading aids are items that enable individuals who have a visual impairment to see small print, e.g. a hands-free magnifier.

Reflective practice is an approach used to think about and improve your knowledge, understanding and skills.

A **reflective practitioner** is someone who looks back over the work they do on a regular basis and spends time thinking about and making improvements to their working practices.

Regulators are organisations responsible for monitoring health and social care professionals.

Reminiscence is an approach used to recall memories from the past, e.g. through talking about past events or looking at old family photographs.

Risk is the likelihood of harm occurring as a result of a hazard.

Risk assessments are in place to allow individuals to carry out their normal day-to-day duties safely, rather than restrict or stop them.

The **Royal College of Nursing (RCN)** represents nurses and nursing, promotes excellence in practice and shapes health policies.

Safeguarding means ensuring that vulnerable adults are kept safe from danger, harm and abuse.

Safeguarding policies are the safeguarding principles and guidelines adopted by organisations that influence how they keep individuals safe from danger, harm and abuse.

Safeguarding systems are the detailed methods of keeping individuals safe from danger, harm and abuse.

Sector skills councils are employer-led, independent organisations that aim to improve people's skills at work.

Self-esteem is the value an individual puts on him/herself.

Sensitive information is information about, for example, a person's physical or mental health.

Sensitive personal information is information about, for example, a person's race, ethnicity, religious beliefs, physical or mental health.

Sensor mats are items that are used to make others aware of when an individual who may be unsteady on their feet gets out of bed in the middle of the night or stands up or leaves a room.

Sexual orientation means sexual preference, for someone of the same or the opposite sex or both.

Signs of abuse are visible indications of abuse, such as bruises, cuts.

Single Assessment Process is the process that should be followed by health and social services staff when assessing the needs of older people.

Single-use equipment is items that can be used only once.

Social exclusion means exclusion from the mainstream of society.

Societal attitudes are society's positive and negative views towards, for example, the needs of individuals who have sensory loss.

Societal beliefs are society's positive and negative assumptions about, for example, the abilities of individuals who have sensory loss.

Sock and stocking aids are items that enable individuals with limited flexibility to put on their socks and stockings.

Speech-to-text reporters are a communication aid that listens to what is said and then converts this into a format that can be used.

A **spore** is a temporary, dormant structure into which a bacterium changes when conditions for its survival become hazardous.

Standard precautions are based on a set of principles designed to minimise exposure to and transmission of a wide variety of micro-organisms.

A **standing frame** is an aid that enables individuals who use wheelchairs to stand safely.

Strategies are ways to manage stress.

Stress is the result of pressures and tensions, which can have both positive and negative effects.

Support or information is people and resources that can provide guidance and information in relation to health and safety.

Suspicions of abuse are when you witness either abuse or signs that make you suspect it is happening.

Symptoms of abuse are what an individual experiences and feels as a result of abuse, such as fear, sadness.

Syndromes are groups of symptoms that usually occur together in a condition.

Talking books are audio recordings of books.

Total communication approaches are practical communication approaches used with individuals who have a sensory loss. They involve the use of a mixture of different communication methods suitable for the individual.

Toxoplasmosis is a disease caused by parasites, found for example in undercooked meat.

Triggers are the causes of stress.

Unsafe practices are poor working practices, resource difficulties, operational difficulties that place individuals in danger or at risk of harm and abuse.

Usher syndrome is a syndrome that causes vision, hearing and balance loss.

Validation therapy is a way of working that involves acknowledging how an individual who has dementia thinks and feels.

Verbal communication methods are ways of communicating using speech, tone and pitch.

Whistle-blowing is reporting concerns about unsafe practices or abuse to management and/or other authorities.

Work settings may include one specific location or a range of locations, depending on the context of a particular work role.

Index